SM358
Science: Level 3



# The Quantum World

## Book 2

# Quantum mechanics and its interpretation

Edited by John Bolton and Ray Mackintosh

# SM358 Course Team

**Course Team Chair**
John Bolton

**Academic Editors**
John Bolton, Stuart Freake, Robert Lambourne, Raymond Mackintosh

**Authors**
Silvia Bergamini, John Bolton, Mark Bowden, David Broadhurst, Jimena Gorfinkiel, Robert Lambourne, Raymond Mackintosh, Nigel Mason, Elaine Moore, Jonathan Underwood

**Other Course Team Members**
Robert Hasson, Mike Thorpe

**Consultant**
Derek Capper

**Course Manager**
Gillian Knight

**Course Team Assistant**
Yvonne McKay

**LTS, Project Manager**
Rafael Hidalgo

**Editors**
Peter Twomey, Alison Cadle

**TeX Specialist**
Jonathan Fine

**Graphic Design Advisors**
Mandy Anton, Chris Hough

**Graphic Artist**
Roger Courthold

**Picture Researcher/Copyrights**
Lydia Eaton

**Software Designers**
Fiona Thomson, Will Rawes

**Video Producers**
Owen Horn, Martin Chiverton

**External Assessor**
Charles Adams (Durham University)

This publication forms part of an Open University course SM358 The Quantum World. The complete list of texts which make up this course can be found at the back. Details of this and other Open University courses can be obtained from the Student Registration and Enquiry Service, The Open University, PO Box 197, Milton Keynes, MK7 6BJ, United Kingdom: tel. +44 (0)870 333 4340, email general-enquiries@open.ac.uk

Alternatively, you may visit the Open University website at http://www.open.ac.uk where you can learn more about the wide range of courses and packs offered at all levels by The Open University.

To purchase a selection of Open University course materials visit http://www.ouw.co.uk or contact Open University Worldwide, Michael Young Building, Walton Hall, Milton Keynes MK7 6AA, United Kingdom for a brochure. tel. +44 (0)1908 858785; fax +44 (0)1908 858787; email ouwenq@open.ac.uk

The Open University
Walton Hall, Milton Keynes
MK7 6AA



Edited and designed by The Open University.

Typeset at The Open University.

Printed and bound in the United Kingdom at the University Press, Cambridge.

ISBN 978 07492 2516 2

**2.1**

# QUANTUM MECHANICS AND ITS INTERPRETATION

# Introduction

The first book in this course focused on *wave mechanics*, a way of thinking about quantum mechanics in terms of wave functions and wave equations. This book presents a more general and powerful approach to quantum theory, which encompasses wave mechanics, but extends it in new directions. This new approach is properly called *quantum mechanics*. Towards the end of the book, we will also raise some issues related to the meaning and interpretation of quantum theory, emphasizing the evidence provided by modern experiments.

Quantum mechanics is hugely successful in its predictions. Some of this success is apparent from the wave mechanics you studied in Book 1; you will meet further successes in this book, and even more in Book 3, which uses quantum mechanics to explain the properties of atoms, molecules and solids. The successes are precise and quantitative. Equally important, quantum-mechanical concepts such as quantization and tunnelling have given us fresh ways of interpreting the world, leading to new scientific explanations and major advances in technology, including transistors and lasers.

But the undoubted success of quantum mechanics does not lessen the shock of its claims, including the idea that fundamental laws of physics are probabilistic. Even the scientists who created quantum theory struggled to come to terms with it and Einstein believed that the probabilities of quantum mechanics only betray our ignorance of the real states of systems. In 1935, Einstein, Podolsky and Rosen proposed a thought experiment which they claimed demonstrated that quantum mechanics was incomplete; otherwise, the outcomes of the experiment would be contrary to common sense. But, many years later, such experiments have been performed and quantum mechanics stands vindicated. Far from undermining quantum mechanics, Einstein's thought experiment only shows us how extraordinary the world is.

Erwin Schrödinger gave the name '*entanglement*' to the key feature of quantum mechanics exposed by Einstein's argument. Entanglement is also the key to some truly remarkable applications that are just beginning to be developed. These modern applications are known collectively as *quantum information*. One of the most advanced areas of quantum information is *quantum cryptography*, which lies at the heart of protocols that allow encrypted information to be sent from one person to another with absolutely no fear of eavesdropping. Internet shopping companies and banks are, of course, very interested. Astonishingly, it is also possible to teleport the unmeasured state of a photon from one place to another — not quite the 'beaming-up' of people, but an impressive feat nonetheless. The greatest prize for physicists working in the field of quantum information would be to construct practical computers whose logical processes are based on quantum-mechanical principles, including the principle of superposition. Again, this subject is still in its infancy, but intensive effort is currently being devoted to making *quantum computing* a reality.

These applications will be discussed towards the end of this book but, before we can describe them, we need to go deeper into the theory of quantum mechanics itself. This theory is, of course, the central theme of this course, and is the foundation upon which all applications rely.

Chapter 1 presents a fresh way of thinking about quantum mechanics — one that shifts attention away from wave functions and towards basic notions about vectors and operators. This change in emphasis is accompanied by a notation invented by Dirac which will be a valuable ally throughout this book. Because it deals with notation and the rules for manipulating symbols, Chapter 1 may seem rather formal, but it will give you the chance to master techniques that will be useful later on. Chapter 1 also shows where Heisenberg's uncertainty principle and Ehrenfest's theorem come from, and how conservation laws arise in the world of atoms.

Book 1 was largely devoted to one-dimensional systems. It will not have escaped your notice that most interesting things around us are not one-dimensional. A key concept needed in descriptions of real systems in more than one dimension is *angular momentum*. Chapter 2 shows how angular momentum is represented in quantum mechanics; you will see that the route to the operators that describe angular momentum is similar to the route that led to Schrödinger's equation in Book 1. You will also see that molecules have quantized energies associated with their rotational motion, and the extent to which atomic states can be labelled by quantum numbers for angular momentum.

Nature has a huge surprise for us: there is also a purely quantum-mechanical form of angular momentum called *spin*, a property of electrons and many other fundamental particles of which matter is composed. The quantum formalism for spin is the subject of Chapter 3, and the concept of spin will be exploited in almost every chapter that follows.

The phrase 'a property of electrons' suggests that all electrons have the exactly the same properties, and indeed they do. All electrons are absolutely identical, as are all protons, all neutrons, and so on. Such *identity* of particles has no parallel in the world of everyday objects. Yet, at the same time, it has a profound significance for what we see in the everyday world. One consequence of particle identity is the *Pauli exclusion principle*, which has a decisive influence on the physical and chemical properties of matter. This reminds us that real systems, like atoms or solids, consist of more than one particle. The way quantum mechanics handles systems of more than one particle, whether identical or nor, is the subject of Chapter 4.

There follows a relatively short Chapter 5 that will give you the opportunity to pause and take stock. This chapter summarizes the formalism developed in the first four chapters and clarifies some issues associated with the process of measurement in quantum mechanics and with the description of quantities that have a continuum of possible values. The chapter closes by updating the *preliminary principles of wave mechanics* given in Chapter 2 of Book 1, presenting a revised list of the *principles of quantum mechanics* that encapsulates the key ideas on which the whole subject is based.

The last two physics chapters, Chapters 6 and 7, are devoted to the subject of entanglement and its applications. Chapter 8 is a *Mathematical toolkit*, which covers the mathematics of vectors, vector spaces and matrices. This chapter is designed to support the physics chapters, especially Chapters 1 and 3, so do not delay your reading of it until the end.

# Chapter 1 A new language for quantum mechanics

## Introduction

> 'By relieving the brain of all unnecessary work, a good notation sets it free to concentrate on more advanced problems . . . '
>
> A.N. Whitehead

The wave mechanics in the first book of this course was presented in the language of calculus. Energy eigenfunctions were obtained by solving differential equations, and expectation values and uncertainties were found by evaluating integrals. This chapter will introduce an alternative notation for quantum mechanics — one that emphasizes different aspects of the subject.

Notation is not a trivial issue. Many breakthroughs owe their existence to the invention of friendly notation. Roman accountants, for example, must have found it exhausting to multiply or divide two long numbers; nowadays, we have a much better way of writing numbers, with different columns for units, tens and hundreds, and a special symbol for zero, so basic arithmetic is far easier for us. The notation used for calculus is another case in point. Newton used dots to indicate differentiation while his rival, Leibniz, used the $\mathrm{d}x/\mathrm{d}t$ notation. It has been said that the refusal of English mathematicians to adopt Leibniz's notation inhibited the development of mathematics in England for more than a century.

This chapter presents a famous notation that was developed for quantum mechanics by the Nobel prize-winning physicist Paul Dirac. Behind Dirac's notation, there is a striking insight — that the state of a system can be represented by a vector in an abstract space. This allows us to think about quantum mechanics in geometric terms. Dirac's notation has other advantages as well. Later in this book, you will see that it can be used to describe the quantum property of spin, something that is beyond the scope of ordinary wave mechanics.

A second theme of this chapter is based on the fact that measurements give real, rather than complex, values. When you measure the energy of an electron, for example, you might get $6.8\,\mathrm{eV}$, but you will never get $(6.8 - 3.7\mathrm{i})\,\mathrm{eV}$. This fact is so obvious that you might not give it a second thought, but it turns out to have profound consequences. It implies that the operators used to represent observable quantities in quantum mechanics must be of a special kind; they are called *Hermitian operators*. When this fact is combined with Dirac notation, we obtain a powerful set of tools that can be used to prove many important results in quantum mechanics, including Ehrenfest's theorem and the uncertainty principle.

The chapter is organized as follows. Section 1.1 introduces the idea that quantum states can be represented by vectors in an abstract space, and Section 1.2 then goes on to develop Dirac's notation. Section 1.3 introduces the concept of a Hermitian operator, based on the fact that observable quantities have real values. The methods developed in the first half of the chapter are then used in Sections 1.4 and 1.5 to establish two results which were stated without proof in the first book of this course: Ehrenfest's theorem and the Heisenberg uncertainty principle. In both cases, we shall derive results more general than those discussed in Book 1 and, in the case of Ehrenfest's theorem, we shall discuss the profound relationship between conservation laws and symmetries.

You may find the chapter rather abstract. This is because we are laying down the 'rules of the game' of quantum mechanics and exploring their general consequences. Later chapters will build on the rules introduced here, and use them to describe the behaviour of specific physical systems.

References to the *Mathematical toolkit* mean the last chapter of *this* book, unless stated otherwise.

One of the themes in this chapter is the use of vectors in an abstract vector space. It is therefore advisable to refresh your memory of ordinary vectors in three-dimensional space by reading Section 8.1 of the *Mathematical toolkit* now.

# 1.1 A geometric view of quantum mechanics

## 1.1.1 Quantum states as vectors

Figure 1.1 shows an example of quantum-mechanical interference. A beam of helium atoms is sent through the slits shown in Figure 1.1a, and the interference pattern shown in Figure 1.1b is produced. At first sight, this is an example of atoms behaving as waves, but there is more to it than this; the interference pattern appears spot-by-spot as each atom is detected on the screen, so the experiment shows that atoms can exhibit the properties of both particles and waves.

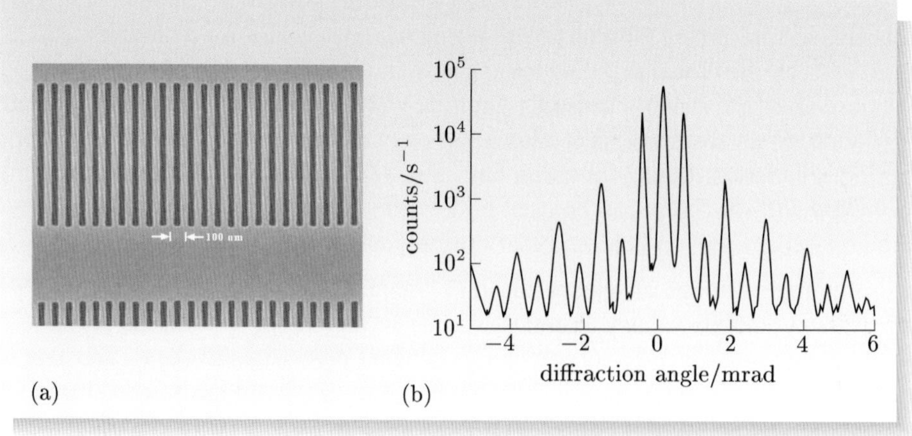


**Figure 1.1** (a) A silicon nitride diffraction grating fabricated so that its slits have a spacing of 100 nm. (b) An interference pattern formed by a beam of helium atoms passing through the grating in (a).

The underlying reason for quantum interference is the *principle of superposition*. This tells us that, if $\Psi_1(x,t)$, $\Psi_2(x,t)$, $\Psi_3(x,t)$, ... are possible wave functions of a system, then the linear combination

$$\Psi(x,t) = a_1\Psi_1(x,t) + a_2\Psi_2(x,t) + a_3\Psi_3(x,t) + \cdots \qquad (1.1)$$

is also a possible wave function of the system, provided that $\Psi(x,t)$ is normalized. This can always be achieved by multiplying the right-hand side of Equation 1.1 by a suitable constant.

In the case of the interference pattern in Figure 1.1b, $\Psi_i(x,t)$ corresponds to a wave emerging from the $i$th slit in Figure 1.1a. Usually, no information is available about which slit the particle passed through. In such a case, we must suppose that the wave function is a linear combination of contributions associated with passage through different slits. These contributions interfere with one another and produce an interference pattern on the detecting screen. The twist is that $\Psi_1(x,t)$, $\Psi_2(x,t)$, $\Psi_3(x,t), \ldots$ describe different ways in which a *single* particle can propagate from the slits to the detecting screen. The propagating particle interferes with itself.

The principle of superposition tells us that any normalized linear combination of wave functions yields another wave function. Conversely, we can also regard a given wave function as being a linear combination of parts.

For example, when studying wave packets in Book 1, you saw that the harmonic oscillator energy eigenfunctions form a **complete set**. This important property means that any reasonable function can be expanded as a linear combination of these eigenfunctions. So, if a harmonic oscillator is described by the wave function $\Psi(x,0)$ at time $t=0$, we can always write

This sum starts from zero because the lowest quantum number for a harmonic oscillator is $n=0$.

$$\Psi(x,0)=\sum_{i=0}^{\infty} c_i\,\psi_i(x), \tag{1.2}$$

where the functions $\psi_i(x)$ are energy eigenfunctions of the harmonic oscillator, the coefficients $c_i$ are complex constants, and the sum may contain infinitely many terms.

The harmonic oscillator eigenfunctions obey the condition

$$\int_{-\infty}^{\infty}\psi_i^*(x)\,\psi_j(x)\,\mathrm{d}x=\delta_{ij}=\begin{cases}1 & \text{if } i=j,\\ 0 & \text{if } i\neq j.\end{cases} \tag{1.3}$$

We say that they are *normalized* and *mutually orthogonal* or, equivalently, that they are *orthonormal*. Because the energy eigenfunctions are orthonormal, we can find each unknown coefficient $c_j$ in the wave packet as follows. We multiply both sides of Equation 1.2 by $\psi_j^*(x)$, and integrate over all $x$ to obtain

$$\int_{-\infty}^{\infty}\psi_j^*(x)\,\Psi(x,0)\,\mathrm{d}x=\sum_{i=0}^{\infty}c_i\int_{-\infty}^{\infty}\psi_j^*(x)\,\psi_i(x)\,\mathrm{d}x. \tag{1.4}$$

The orthonormality property (Equation 1.3) then gives

$$\int_{-\infty}^{\infty}\psi_j^*(x)\,\Psi(x,0)\,\mathrm{d}x=\sum_{i=0}^{\infty}c_i\delta_{ji}=c_j, \tag{1.5}$$

The Kronecker delta symbol kills off all terms in the sum except for that with $i=j$.

so each coefficient can be found by evaluating the integral on the left-hand side of Equation 1.5; this was called an **overlap integral** in Book 1.

- Do Equations 1.1–1.5 remind you of anything else in mathematics?

- If you have read Section 8.1 of the *Mathematical toolkit*, you might have sensed that there is an analogy with the mathematics of vectors.

We shall now examine this analogy in detail. There are four points of comparison.

1. Given any set of vectors $\mathbf{v}_1, \mathbf{v}_2, \mathbf{v}_3, \ldots$ in ordinary three-dimensional space, and any set of real constants $a_1, a_2, a_3, \ldots$, we can form the linear combination

$$\mathbf{v}=a_1\mathbf{v}_1+a_2\mathbf{v}_2+a_3\mathbf{v}_3+\cdots, \tag{1.6}$$

and this is also a vector in ordinary space. *Equation 1.1 can be regarded as the quantum-mechanical analogue of this result.*

2. In ordinary three-dimensional space, we can choose a set of three normalized and mutually orthogonal **basis vectors**, which we have labelled $\mathbf{e}_1$, $\mathbf{e}_2$ and $\mathbf{e}_3$ in Figure 1.2. Because this set of vectors is orthonormal, we can write

$$\mathbf{e}_i \cdot \mathbf{e}_j = \delta_{ij}. \tag{1.7}$$

*Equation 1.3 is the quantum-mechanical analogue of this property.*

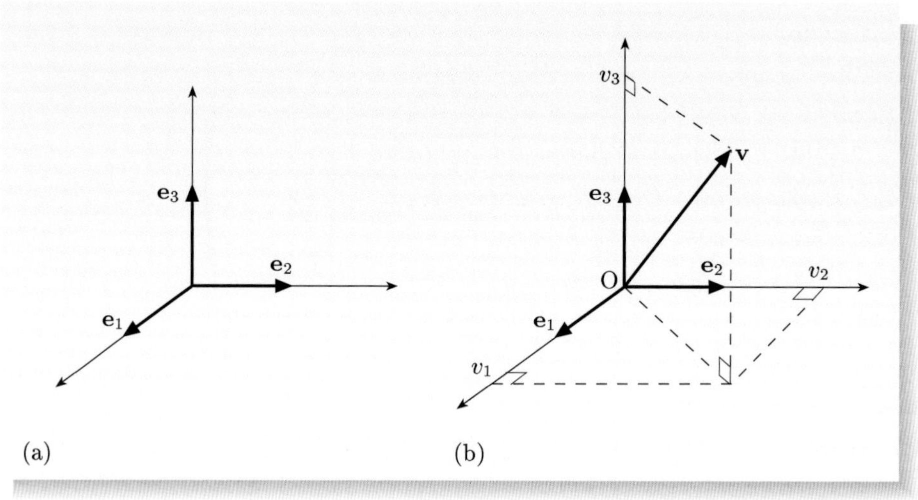


**Figure 1.2** (a) Three basis vectors in ordinary three-dimensional space. Because we are interested in generalizing to many dimensions, we have labelled these vectors $\mathbf{e}_1$, $\mathbf{e}_2$ and $\mathbf{e}_3$ rather than $\mathbf{e}_x$, $\mathbf{e}_y$ and $\mathbf{e}_z$. (b) The components $v_1$, $v_2$ and $v_3$ of a vector $\mathbf{v}$ are found by projecting onto axes defined by the three basis vectors.

3. The three basis vectors form a complete set, and are said to provide a **basis** for ordinary three-dimensional space; they are also said to **span** this space. This means that any vector $\mathbf{v}$ can be written as a linear combination of the basis vectors:

$$\mathbf{v} = v_1\mathbf{e}_1 + v_2\mathbf{e}_2 + v_3\mathbf{e}_3 = \sum_{i=1}^{3} v_i\,\mathbf{e}_i. \tag{1.8}$$

*Equation 1.2 is the quantum-mechanical analogue of this expansion.* The coefficients $v_i$ are called the **components** of the vector $\mathbf{v}$, and their geometric significance is shown in Figure 1.2b.

4. Because the basis vectors are orthonormal, we can find the $j$th component of the vector $\mathbf{v}$ by taking its **scalar product** with the basis vector $\mathbf{e}_j$. Using Equation 1.8, we obtain

$$\mathbf{e}_j \cdot \mathbf{v} = \sum_{i=1}^{3} v_i\,(\mathbf{e}_j \cdot \mathbf{e}_i), \tag{1.9}$$

and the orthonormality of the basis vectors then gives

$$\mathbf{e}_j \cdot \mathbf{v} = \sum_{i=1}^{3} v_i\delta_{ji} = v_j. \tag{1.10}$$

*Equations 1.4 and 1.5 are the quantum-mechanical analogues of these last two results.*

To summarize, the analogy between wave functions and vectors is based on the following comparisons.

**Equations 1.1 and 1.6:** A linear combination of wave functions is analogous to a linear combination of vectors.

**Equations 1.2 and 1.8:** Any wave function can be written as a linear combination of eigenfunctions from a complete set, just as any vector can be written as a linear combination of basis vectors. The complete set of eigenfunctions is analogous to the complete set of basis vectors.

**Equations 1.3 and 1.7:** A set of orthonormal eigenfunctions $\psi_i(x)$ is analogous to a set of orthonormal basis vectors $\mathbf{e}_i$.

**Equations 1.4 and 1.9:** An overlap integral is analogous to a scalar product.

**Equations 1.5 and 1.10:** A coefficient $c_j$ in a wave packet can be found by evaluating an overlap integral, just as a component $v_j$ in a vector can be found by evaluating a scalar product.

This chapter will build on this analogy. First, we shall think of functions as being 'vectors' in an abstract **vector space**. For example, we shall think of $\mathrm{e}^{-x^2} \cos x$ as pointing in one direction, and $\mathrm{e}^{-x^2} \sin x$ as pointing in another direction, in a space that represents all functions.

The general mathematical concept of a vector space is discussed in Section 8.2 of the *Mathematical toolkit*. This is background material, which you may read at any time.

In fact, quantum mechanics restricts attention to complex-valued functions that can be normalized, that is, functions $\psi(x)$ for which

$$\int_{-\infty}^{\infty} |\psi(x)|^2 \, \mathrm{d}x \quad \text{is finite.}$$

The vector space used to represent normalizable functions is called **function space**. Wave functions and eigenfunctions are normalizable functions, so we say that *they correspond to vectors in function space*. This is just a description — a choice of words — but it is one that emphasizes the close analogies between wave functions and vectors that were outlined above.

### 1.1.2 Dirac notation

Many physicists appreciated the analogy between wave functions and vectors, but it was Paul Dirac (Figure 1.3) who invented a notation that fully captures the spirit of this analogy. Although Dirac was one of the pioneers of quantum mechanics, making fundamental contributions from 1925 onwards, he only developed his notation in 1939. The notation rapidly caught on and is now a favorite choice of physicists.

Ordinary vectors are usually printed in bold type (e.g. **r**), but it would be confusing to use the same convention for vectors in function space. Dirac therefore devised a new and distinctive notation: to denote a particular vector in function space, he used an angled bracket $|\ \rangle$, which he called a **ket vector**. The contents of the angled bracket indicate the function under discussion. For example, we can write $|f\rangle$ to denote the ket vector for the function $f(x)$.

**Figure 1.3** Paul Dirac (1902–1984) was one of the pioneers of quantum mechanics. He shared the 1933 Nobel prize for physics with Erwin Schrödinger.

However, one advantage of **Dirac notation** is that the contents of the angled bracket can be anything that sensibly labels the function. For example, the harmonic oscillator energy eigenfunction $\psi_n(x)$, with eigenvalue $E_n$ and quantum number $n$, could be written as

$$|\psi_n\rangle, \quad |E_n\rangle \quad \text{or} \quad |n\rangle.$$

We can even put words or numbers inside the angled bracket, as in

$$|\text{ground state}\rangle, \quad |0\rangle \quad \text{or} \quad |n=0\rangle.$$

Note, however, that function arguments are always omitted: we can write $|\psi_n\rangle$, but we *never* write $|\psi_n(x)\rangle$.

In wave mechanics, the state of the system at a given time $t$ is described by the wave function $\Psi(x,t)$. The ket vector corresponding to the wave function is called the **state vector**, and can be denoted by a symbol such as $|\Psi\rangle$. As time passes, the wave function changes, so the state vector continuously changes its direction in function space. By contrast, the energy eigenfunctions $\psi_n(x)$ are time-independent, and are represented by static vectors in function space. Usually, we do not bother to show the time-dependence of the state vector in our notation, but interpret the symbol $|\Psi\rangle$ as meaning the state vector *at the time of interest*; if necessary we can always indicate the time concerned by something like $|\Psi\rangle_{\text{initial}}$.

We can now begin to write some equations using Dirac notation. An example is given by Equation 1.1, which we now write in the form

$$|\Psi\rangle = a_1\,|\Psi_1\rangle + a_2\,|\Psi_2\rangle + a_3\,|\Psi_3\rangle + \ldots,$$

obtained simply by replacing functions by the corresponding ket vectors.

A crucial part of Dirac notation is the way it deals with overlap integrals. We have already seen that the overlap integral in Equation 1.5 is analogous to the scalar product in Equation 1.10. When we go beyond ordinary space, the term 'scalar product' is usually replaced by the more general term 'inner product'. We are therefore led to think of an overlap integral as an *inner product* between vectors in function space.

Dirac denoted the **inner product** of two ket vectors $|f\rangle$ and $|g\rangle$ by the symbol $\langle f|g\rangle$, and he identified this with the overlap integral of the corresponding functions $f(x)$ and $g(x)$. In other words, he defined

$$\text{inner product of } |f\rangle \text{and } |g\rangle = \langle f|g\rangle = \int_{-\infty}^{\infty} f^*(x)\,g(x)\,\mathrm{d}x. \tag{1.11}$$

The symbol $\langle f|g\rangle$ can be thought of as a shorthand for the overlap integral that appears on the right-hand side of Equation 1.11. We shall call it the **Dirac bracket** of the functions $f(x)$ and $g(x)$. It is important to note that the function $f(x)$ in the left-hand slot of a Dirac bracket is complex-conjugated in the overlap integral. In general, the two functions $f(x)$ and $g(x)$ have complex values, and the Dirac bracket $\langle f|g\rangle$ is a complex number.

Equation 1.11 applies to functions of a single variable. When describing a particle in three dimensions, the wave function depends on three spatial coordinates. Under these circumstances, the Dirac bracket of $|f\rangle$ and $|g\rangle$, corresponding to the functions $f(x, y, z)$ and $g(x, y, z)$, is defined by

$$\langle f|g\rangle = \int_{-\infty}^{\infty}\int_{-\infty}^{\infty}\int_{-\infty}^{\infty} f^*(x, y, z)\, g(x, y, z)\, \mathrm{d}x\, \mathrm{d}y\, \mathrm{d}z. \qquad (1.12)$$

For simplicity, we will discuss the one-dimensional case here, but the extension to three dimensions is straightforward. In any case, Dirac notation is unaffected by the number of dimensions, and this is one of its advantages.

To illustrate Dirac notation in action, let's rewrite Equations 1.2–1.5 using vectors and Dirac brackets.

Equation 1.2 is written as

$$|\Psi\rangle = \sum_{i=0}^{\infty} c_i|\psi_i\rangle. \qquad (1.13)$$

Equation 1.3 takes the form

$$\langle\psi_i|\psi_j\rangle = \delta_{ij}. \qquad (1.14)$$

Equation 1.4 then becomes

$$\langle\psi_j|\Psi\rangle = \sum_{i=0}^{\infty} c_i\,\langle\psi_j|\psi_i\rangle. \qquad (1.15)$$

Finally, Equation 1.5 is written as

$$\langle\psi_j|\Psi\rangle = \sum_{i=0}^{\infty} c_i\delta_{ji} = c_j. \qquad (1.16)$$

Turning this last equation around, we see that the coefficient $c_j$ is given by

$$c_j = \langle\psi_j|\Psi\rangle \equiv \int_{-\infty}^{\infty} \psi_j^*(x)\,\Psi(x, 0)\,\mathrm{d}x. \qquad (1.17)$$

All we have done to convert Equations 1.2–1.5 into Equations 1.13–1.16 is to replace functions by vectors and overlap integrals by Dirac brackets. *You are strongly advised to check how this works in each case.*

Dirac notation is a sort of shorthand. Rather than writing down a cumbersome overlap integral, we simply write down the corresponding Dirac bracket. If we need to *evaluate* an overlap integral, we usually have to write it out in full so that we can use the techniques of calculus. However, there are many occasions when we do not need to do this, and it is here that Dirac notation is invaluable — offering us reductions in time, effort and clutter on the page.

Yet Dirac notation is more than a shorthand. It also emphasizes the close analogy between ket vectors and ordinary vectors, and you have seen that the Dirac bracket $\langle f|g\rangle$ can be thought of as an inner product, analogous to the scalar product $\mathbf{a} \cdot \mathbf{b}$ between ordinary vectors. The next subsection will discuss the extent to which ordinary geometric language and pictures can be used in function space.

**Exercise 1.1** Use Dirac notation to write down: (a) the normalization condition for a wave function $\Psi$; (b) the probability that an energy measurement on a system in a state $\Psi$ will yield the discrete energy eigenvalue $E_i$ corresponding to the energy eigenfunction $\psi_i(x)$. ■

### 1.1.3 Picturing vectors in function space

At first sight, there are some major differences between ordinary three-dimensional space and function space. For example, the scalar product $\mathbf{a} \cdot \mathbf{b}$ in ordinary space is a real quantity, but the inner product in function space is given by the Dirac bracket

$$\langle f|g\rangle = \int_{-\infty}^{\infty} f^*(x)\, g(x)\, \mathrm{d}x,$$

which involves complex functions, and is therefore complex in general.

Three-dimensional space has a set of three basis vectors $\mathbf{e}_1$, $\mathbf{e}_2$ and $\mathbf{e}_3$, which means that any vector $\mathbf{a}$ can be expressed as a sum

$$\mathbf{a} = \sum_{i=1}^{3} a_i\, \mathbf{e}_i.$$

Although a vector $|\Psi\rangle$ in function space can also be expressed as a sum

$$|\Psi\rangle = \sum_{i=0}^{\infty} c_i\, |\psi_i\rangle,$$

in this case the sum may involve an infinite number of terms; in this sense, function space has an infinite number of dimensions.

In spite of these differences, a close analogy remains. The analogy is strengthened by the fact that we can extend the concept of the *magnitude of a vector* into function space. In ordinary three-dimensional space, the **magnitude** of the vector $\mathbf{a}$ is given by

$$a = |\mathbf{a}| = \sqrt{\mathbf{a} \cdot \mathbf{a}},$$

where the positive square root is taken. There is no difficulty in doing this because $\mathbf{a} \cdot \mathbf{a} = a_1^2 + a_2^2 + a_3^2$ is real and non-negative. The magnitude of $\mathbf{a}$ is therefore real and non-negative too. In function space, the inner product $\langle f|g\rangle$ is complex, but putting $g(x) = f(x)$ gives

$$\langle f|f\rangle = \int_{-\infty}^{\infty} f^*(x)\, f(x)\, \mathrm{d}x = \int_{-\infty}^{\infty} \left|f(x)\right|^2 \mathrm{d}x.$$

The integrand is real and non-negative everywhere, so $\langle f|f\rangle$ is also real and non-negative. We can therefore take the positive square root to obtain a real, non-negative quantity $\sqrt{\langle f|f\rangle}$ which is interpreted as the magnitude of $|f\rangle$. In practice, we generally use the word **norm** instead of magnitude when dealing with vectors in function space, and therefore say that

$$\text{norm of } |f\rangle = \sqrt{\langle f|f\rangle} \geq 0. \tag{1.18}$$

A vector with zero norm is called the **zero vector**, while a vector with unit norm is said to be **normalized**.

Ordinary vectors in three-dimensional space also obey the inequality

$$(\mathbf{a} \cdot \mathbf{a})(\mathbf{b} \cdot \mathbf{b}) \geq (\mathbf{a} \cdot \mathbf{b})^2,$$

which follows from the identity

$$a^2b^2 \geq \left(ab\cos\theta\right)^2 = a^2b^2\cos^2\theta = (\mathbf{a}\cdot\mathbf{b})^2.$$

Remember that $\mathbf{a}\cdot\mathbf{b} = ab\cos\theta$, where $\theta$ is the angle between the directions of $\mathbf{a}$ and $\mathbf{b}$.

It is interesting to note that vectors in function space satisfy a similar inequality:

$$\langle f|f\rangle\langle g|g\rangle \geq \left|\langle f|g\rangle\right|^2. \tag{1.19}$$

This is known as the **Cauchy–Schwarz inequality**; later in the chapter, you will see that it is a key ingredient in proving the uncertainty principle.

These analogies suggest that it is reasonable to use basic geometric notions in function space. In particular, we shall say that $|f\rangle$ is **orthogonal** to $|g\rangle$ if $\langle f|g\rangle = 0$. Here, the phrase 'orthogonal to' is used in analogy to its ordinary geometric sense: 'at right angles to'. Of course, we anticipated this terminology much earlier in the course when we described two functions $f(x)$ and $g(x)$ with a vanishing overlap integral $\langle f|g\rangle$ as being *orthogonal* to one another.

We have seen that a harmonic oscillator has an infinite set of energy eigenfunctions $\psi_1(x), \psi_2(x), \ldots$, with a corresponding set of ket vectors $|\psi_1\rangle, |\psi_2\rangle, \ldots$. These vectors are normalized and orthogonal, and are therefore said to be **orthonormal**. We also know that the harmonic oscillator energy eigenfunctions are a *complete* set, so that any vector $|\Psi\rangle$ in function space can be expressed as

$$|\Psi\rangle = \sum_{i=0}^{\infty} c_i\,|\psi_i\rangle, \tag{1.20}$$

where the $c_i$ are complex scalars. We shall describe this fact using the same language as for ordinary vectors. The vectors $|\psi_1\rangle, |\psi_2\rangle, \ldots$ will be called **basis vectors**. We shall say that these basis vectors form a **complete set** or a **basis** in function space, or equivalently, that they **span** function space. All of these statements express the fact that any vector in function space can be expressed as a linear combination of the basis vectors $|\psi_i\rangle$. However, it is worth noting that the harmonic oscillator energy eigenfunctions are not unique in this respect. They provide one example of a basis in function space, but many other sets of functions provide alternative bases.

By analogy with ordinary vectors, the coefficient $c_i$ in Equation 1.20 can be called the (scalar) **component** of the vector $|\Psi\rangle$ in the direction of the basis vector $|\psi_i\rangle$. Because the sum in Equation 1.20 involves an infinite number of orthogonal basis vectors, function space has an infinite number of dimensions, and vectors within it have an infinite number of complex components. It is not possible to visualize this situation in any realistic way. Even so, it is helpful to draw some 'cartoons', which should not be taken too literally but still capture the essence of the situation.

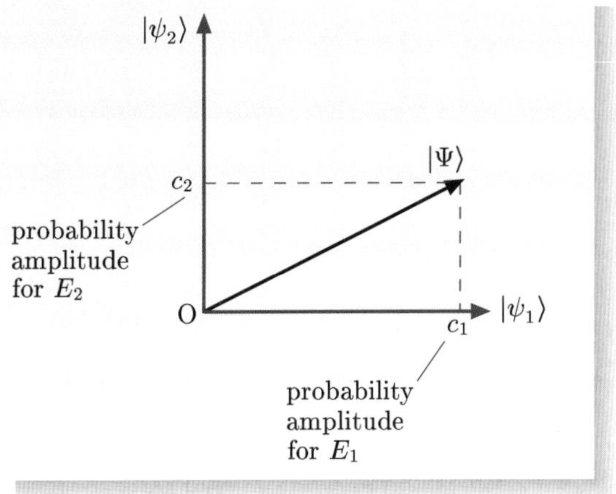


**Figure 1.4** A sketch indicating the relationship between a state vector $|\Psi\rangle$ and a basis of energy eigenvectors $|\psi_1\rangle, |\psi_2\rangle, \ldots$.

Figure 1.4 is a 'cartoon' representing the expansion of a state vector $|\Psi\rangle$ in terms of the basis vectors $|\psi_i\rangle$. Compromises have been made in order to draw this sketch: we show only two of the basis vectors, $|\psi_1\rangle$ and $|\psi_2\rangle$, and the components $c_1$ and $c_2$ are represented by real (rather than complex) numbers. In spite of these deficiencies, the figure illustrates some important points:

1. The basis vectors $|\psi_1\rangle$ and $|\psi_2\rangle$ both have the same (unit) length and are drawn perpendicular to one another. This is because they are normalized and mutually orthogonal. The state vector $|\Psi\rangle$ describes the state of a system at a given time. It has the same length as the basis vectors because it is normalized too.
2. The components $c_1$ and $c_2$ are found by a process of *projection*, dropping perpendiculars onto the directions of the basis vectors. This is similar to the picture for ordinary vectors given in Figure 1.2b.
3. The components $c_1$ and $c_2$ are also the coefficients of the energy eigenfunctions $\psi_1(x)$ and $\psi_2(x)$ in the wave function. They are therefore interpreted as the *probability amplitudes* for getting the energy eigenvalues $E_1$ and $E_2$ in an energy measurement. The corresponding probabilities are $|c_1|^2$ and $|c_2|^2$. In the situation shown in Figure 1.4, both $E_1$ and $E_2$ are possible values, but $E_1$ is more likely than $E_2$ because $|c_1|^2 > |c_2|^2$.

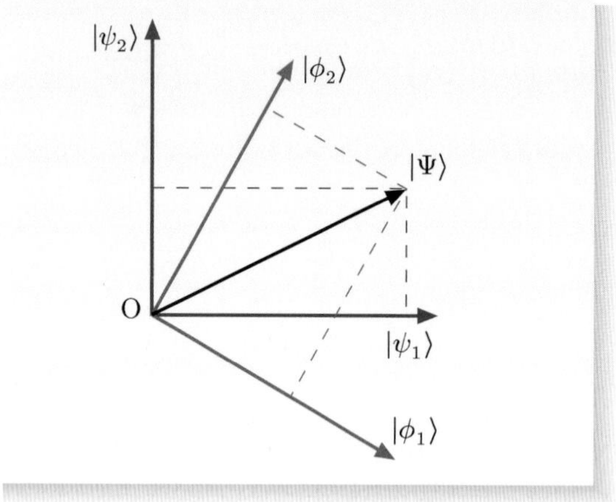


**Figure 1.5** A sketch showing a state vector $|\Psi\rangle$ and two sets of basis vectors, $(|\psi_1\rangle, |\psi_2\rangle)$ and $(|\phi_1\rangle, |\phi_2\rangle)$.

Another important point is illustrated in Figure 1.5. Many different sets of basis vectors span function space, and the components of a given state vector depend on the choice of basis. What is the physical significance of this geometric fact? In quantum mechanics, different bases correspond to different measurable quantities. By projecting the state vector onto the red set of basis vectors, we get the probability amplitudes for one set of quantities. By projecting the state vector onto the blue set of basis vectors, we get the probability amplitudes for a different set of quantities. This helps us visualize the fact that the state vector (or equivalently the wave function) is a complete description of the state of the system; by projecting the state vector onto an appropriate basis, we can find the probability of any given experimental outcome.

It is worth saying once more that the sketches in this subsection have their limitations; we cannot hope to give faithful pictures of vectors with many complex components. Nevertheless, the simple sketches given here illustrate the sort of image most physicists carry in their heads when they talk of projecting a state vector onto a basis. Dirac was known for being terse and literal-minded, and his famous book on quantum mechanics contained no diagrams; however, it is interesting to learn that his personal notebooks were full of them, and he declared a personal preference for 'relationships which I can visualize in geometric terms'.

# 1.2 Using Dirac notation

## 1.2.1 Manipulating Dirac brackets

We would like to carry out calculations using vectors and Dirac brackets without having to justify each step by referring back to functions and overlap integrals. To make this possible, you need to know some rules that apply to all Dirac brackets, so that you can manipulate them routinely. This section will state and derive the few rules that are required.

### 1. Complex conjugation

An overlap integral is a complex number, so we can take its complex conjugate:

$$\left[\int_{-\infty}^{\infty} f^*(x)\, g(x)\, \mathrm{d}x\right]^* = \int_{-\infty}^{\infty} f(x)\, g^*(x)\, \mathrm{d}x$$
$$= \int_{-\infty}^{\infty} g^*(x)\, f(x)\, \mathrm{d}x.$$

Remember that $(f^*)^* = f$.

In terms of Dirac brackets, this result can be expressed as

$$\langle f|g\rangle^* = \langle g|f\rangle. \tag{1.21}$$

We must therefore be careful about the order of terms in a Dirac bracket: $\langle f|g\rangle$ is generally different from $\langle g|f\rangle$.

**Exercise 1.2** Use Equation 1.21 to show that $\langle f|f\rangle$, $\langle f|g\rangle\langle g|f\rangle$ and $\langle f|g\rangle + \langle g|f\rangle$ are all real quantities. ■

Remember that an expression is real if it is equal to its own complex conjugate.

### 2. Taking constants outside Dirac brackets

Any multiplicative constant $c$ can be taken outside an integral, so we have

$$\int_{-\infty}^{\infty} f^*(x)\big[cg(x)\big]\, \mathrm{d}x = c\int_{-\infty}^{\infty} f^*(x)\, g(x)\, \mathrm{d}x$$

and

$$\int_{-\infty}^{\infty} \big[cg(x)\big]^* f(x)\, \mathrm{d}x = c^*\int_{-\infty}^{\infty} g^*(x)\, f(x)\, \mathrm{d}x.$$

In terms of Dirac brackets, these results can be expressed as

$$\langle f|cg\rangle = c\,\langle f|g\rangle, \tag{1.22}$$
$$\langle cg|f\rangle = c^*\langle g|f\rangle. \tag{1.23}$$

Notice the star in Equation 1.23. A constant in the right-hand slot of a Dirac bracket can be extracted from the bracket without change, but a constant in the left-hand slot must be complex-conjugated when it is extracted. This rule will be used throughout this chapter; do not get caught out by forgetting it!

**Exercise 1.3** Simplify $\langle f|f\rangle$, where $f(x) = \mathrm{e}^{\mathrm{i}\alpha} g(x)$ and $\alpha$ is a real constant. ■

### 3. Dirac brackets of linear combinations of functions

The integral of any sum of functions is a sum of integrals, so it immediately follows that

$$\langle f|g+h\rangle = \langle f|g\rangle + \langle f|h\rangle \tag{1.24}$$

and

$$\langle g+h|f\rangle = \langle g|f\rangle + \langle h|f\rangle. \tag{1.25}$$

Combining these results with Equations 1.22 and 1.23, we see that:

If $g(x) = \sum_i c_i\, g_i(x)$, then

$$\langle f|g\rangle = \sum_i c_i\, \langle f|g_i\rangle, \tag{1.26}$$

$$\langle g|f\rangle = \sum_i c_i^*\, \langle g_i|f\rangle. \tag{1.27}$$

So the Dirac bracket of a linear combination of functions can be expanded as a linear combination of Dirac brackets; however, any constants extracted from the *left-hand slots* of the brackets must be complex-conjugated.

**Exercise 1.4** Simplify $\langle f|f+\mathrm{i}g\rangle - \langle g-\mathrm{i}f|g\rangle$, given that $\langle f|f\rangle = \langle g|g\rangle$. ■

## 1.2.2 Bra and ket vectors

It is sometimes convenient to think of $\langle f|g\rangle$ as being formed from two separate entities, $\langle f|$ and $|g\rangle$, which are joined together. Dirac called $\langle f|$ a **bra vector** and $|g\rangle$ a **ket vector** — simply so that he could say that a bra and a ket join up to give a bra-ket (a bracket)!

We can obtain valid equations for bra and ket vectors by looking at our results for Dirac brackets. For example, if we strip away $\langle f|$ from Equation 1.22 and strip away $|f\rangle$ from Equation 1.23, we get

$$|cg\rangle = c\,|g\rangle \quad \text{and} \quad \langle cg| = c^*\,\langle g|. \tag{1.28}$$

More generally, if we strip away $\langle f|$ from Equation 1.26 and strip away $|f\rangle$ from Equation 1.27, we get

$$|g\rangle = \sum_i c_i\,|g_i\rangle \quad \text{and} \quad \langle g| = \sum_i c_i^*\,\langle g_i|. \tag{1.29}$$

This gives us the following rule:

To convert a ket vector $|g\rangle = \sum_i c_i\,|g_i\rangle$ into the corresponding bra vector $\langle g| = \sum_i c_i^*\,\langle g_i|$, we replace all the ket vectors by their corresponding bra vectors, and all the coefficients by their complex conjugates.

The following example will show how this rule is used.

### Worked Example 1.1

Given two vectors

$$|f\rangle = \sum_{i=0}^{\infty} a_i \, |\psi_i\rangle \quad \text{and} \quad |g\rangle = \sum_{i=0}^{\infty} b_i \, |\psi_i\rangle,$$

where the vectors $|\psi_i\rangle$ are a complete orthonormal set of energy eigenfunctions, express the Dirac bracket $\langle f|g\rangle$ in terms of the coefficients $a_i$ and $b_i$.

#### Solution

Given that $|f\rangle = \sum_{i=0}^{\infty} a_i \, |\psi_i\rangle$, we use Equation 1.29 to write

$$\langle f| = \sum_{i=0}^{\infty} a_i^* \, \langle\psi_i|, \quad \text{which must be joined to} \quad |g\rangle = \sum_{i=0}^{\infty} b_i \, |\psi_i\rangle.$$

To avoid omitting 'cross-product' terms, we take the precaution of using different indices in the two sums. Changing the dummy index in the sum for $|g\rangle$ from $i$ to $j$, we obtain

$$\langle f|g\rangle = \Big(\sum_{i=0}^{\infty} a_i^* \, \langle\psi_i|\Big)\Big(\sum_{j=0}^{\infty} b_j \, |\psi_j\rangle\Big).$$

Regrouping terms, and noting that each $\langle\psi_i|$ on the left can join up with each $|\psi_j\rangle$ on the right to give $\langle\psi_i|\psi_j\rangle$, we obtain

$$\langle f|g\rangle = \sum_{i=0}^{\infty}\sum_{j=0}^{\infty} a_i^* b_j \, \langle\psi_i|\psi_j\rangle.$$

The energy eigenfunctions are orthonormal, so $\langle\psi_i|\psi_j\rangle = \delta_{ij}$ giving

$$\langle f|g\rangle = \sum_{i=0}^{\infty}\sum_{j=0}^{\infty} a_i^* b_j \delta_{ij}.$$

Finally, the Kronecker delta symbol kills off all terms in the double sum except those with $j = i$, so we are left with the single sum

$$\langle f|g\rangle = \sum_{i=0}^{\infty} a_i^* b_i. \qquad (1.30)$$

**Essential skill**

Using bra and ket notation and dummy indices

Equation 1.30 provides another analogy with ordinary vectors in three-dimensional space. You will recall that the scalar product of two ordinary vectors is given by

$$\mathbf{a} \cdot \mathbf{b} = a_1 b_1 + a_2 b_2 + a_3 b_3,$$

which is a sum of products of components. Equation 1.30 is the natural extension of this formula to function space; it further supports our interpretation of Dirac brackets as inner products in function space.

It is also interesting to interpret Equation 1.30 when $|f\rangle = |g\rangle = |\Psi\rangle$, a state vector. In this special case, it becomes

$$\langle\Psi|\Psi\rangle = \sum_{i=0}^{\infty} a_i^* a_i = \sum_{i=0}^{\infty} |a_i|^2. \tag{1.31}$$

The left-hand side can be recognized as the norm of $|\Psi\rangle$, which is equal to 1. On the right-hand side, $|a_i|^2$ is the probability of measuring the $i$th energy eigenvalue. The sum extends over all possible values, so the right-hand side is the probability of measuring *one or another* of the allowed energies, which must also be equal to 1.

**Exercise 1.5** Two vectors $|a\rangle$ and $|b\rangle$ in function space are *not* orthogonal to one another. What value of the constant $\beta$ must be chosen to ensure that the vector $|c\rangle = |a\rangle + \beta\,|b\rangle$ is orthogonal to $|a\rangle$?

**Exercise 1.6** If $|u\rangle$ and $|v\rangle$ are orthonormal vectors, show that:

(a) $|a\rangle = |u\rangle + |v\rangle$ is orthogonal to $|b\rangle = |u\rangle - |v\rangle$;

(b) $|c\rangle = |u\rangle + \mathrm{i}\,|v\rangle$ is orthogonal to $|d\rangle = \mathrm{i}\,|u\rangle + |v\rangle$.

**Exercise 1.7** Given two vectors $|a\rangle$ and $|b\rangle$, we can construct the vector

$$|c\rangle = \langle b|b\rangle\,|a\rangle - \langle b|a\rangle\,|b\rangle.$$

Show that

$$\langle c|c\rangle = \langle b|b\rangle\Big(\langle a|a\rangle\langle b|b\rangle - \big|\langle a|b\rangle\big|^2\Big),$$

and hence prove the Cauchy–Schwarz inequality (Equation 1.19). ■

## 1.3 Real values and Hermitian operators

In quantum mechanics, we make a distinction between entities like wave functions or state vectors that cannot be observed directly, and quantities like energy or momentum that can be measured by suitable equipment. Quantities that can be measured are called **observables**.

Obviously, the results of measurements are described by *real* numbers, rather than complex numbers. This fact usually goes unnoticed in classical physics, which deals exclusively with real-valued variables, but it becomes more significant in quantum mechanics, since Schrödinger's equation includes $\mathrm{i} = \sqrt{-1}$ and wave functions are generally complex. In spite of this use of complex numbers, the formalism of quantum mechanics must ensure that observable quantities have real values. In quantum mechanics, each observable $A$ is represented by a linear operator $\widehat{\mathrm{A}}$. The requirement that $A$ has only real values imposes an additional constraint on this operator. We shall now see what this is.

### 1.3.1 Hermitian operators

To clarify our notation, it is helpful to picture the action of an operator $\widehat{\mathrm{A}}$ in quantum mechanics. Figure 1.6 is drawn in a similar spirit to the diagrams of

Section 1.1.3. It shows a vector $|f\rangle$ that represents a function $f(x)$. The effect of the operator $\widehat{A}$ is to change this vector into a new vector, $\widehat{A}\,|f\rangle$, representing a new function, $\widehat{A}f(x)$. We can therefore write

$$\widehat{A}\,|f\rangle = |\widehat{A}f\rangle. \tag{1.32}$$

Both these expressions mean the same thing; the first treats the operator as acting directly on the vector, while the second treats the operator as acting on the function $f(x)$, which is then represented by the vector $|\widehat{A}f\rangle$.

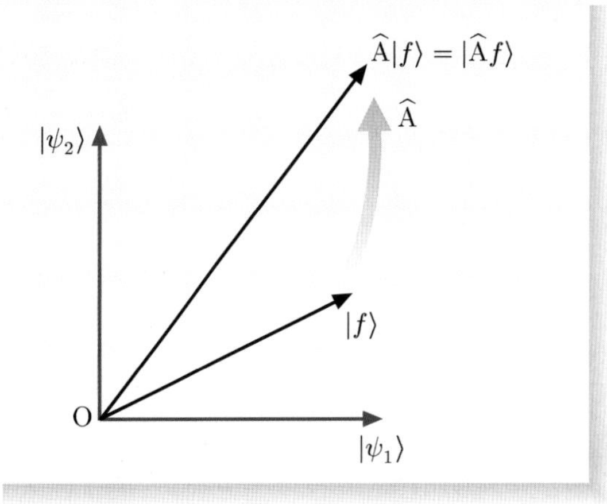


**Figure 1.6** A cartoon indicating the effect of an operator $\widehat{A}$ on a vector $|f\rangle$ in function space.

We shall assume that the observable $A$ has only real values, which implies that the expectation value of $A$ is always real in any state. From Book 1, we know that the expectation value of $A$ is given by the sandwich integral

$$\langle A\rangle = \int_{-\infty}^{\infty} \Psi^*(x,t)\,\widehat{A}\,\Psi(x,t)\,\mathrm{d}x,$$

where the wave function $\Psi(x,t)$ describes the state of the system at the time of measurement. This expectation value can be expressed more compactly using Dirac notation, either as

$$\langle A\rangle = \langle\Psi|\widehat{A}\Psi\rangle \tag{1.33}$$

or, using Equation 1.32, as

$$\langle A\rangle = \langle\Psi|\,\widehat{A}\,|\Psi\rangle. \tag{1.34}$$

The important point is that $\langle A\rangle$ must be real. In general, a complex number $z$ is real if and only if $z = z^*$, so we must have $\langle A\rangle = \langle A\rangle^*$, and Equation 1.33 then gives

$$\langle\Psi|\widehat{A}\Psi\rangle = \langle\Psi|\widehat{A}\Psi\rangle^*.$$

Hence, recalling that $\langle g|f\rangle^* = \langle f|g\rangle$, we conclude that

$$\langle\Psi|\widehat{A}\Psi\rangle = \langle\widehat{A}\Psi|\Psi\rangle \tag{1.35}$$

for any state $\Psi$.

- Write out Equation 1.35 in full, using an integral sign.
- Explicitly,

$$\int_{-\infty}^{\infty} \Psi^*(x,t)\big(\widehat{A}\Psi(x,t)\big)\,\mathrm{d}x = \int_{-\infty}^{\infty} \big(\widehat{A}\Psi(x,t)\big)^*\,\Psi(x,t)\,\mathrm{d}x.$$

In other words, it does not matter whether the operator $\widehat{A}$ acts on the left-hand $\Psi(x,t)$ in the sandwich integral, and the result is then complex-conjugated, or whether it acts on the right-hand $\Psi(x,t)$, which is not complex-conjugated.

Because it originates from an expectation value, Equation 1.35 involves $\Psi$ in both slots of the Dirac bracket. However, it is generally assumed that all operators representing observable quantities obey an even stronger condition. First, we shall make a mathematical definition:

The restriction to normalizable functions is a natural one to make in quantum mechanics, which deals with normalized wave functions and eigenfunctions.

### Hermitian operators

If an operator $\widehat{\mathrm{A}}$ satisfies the condition

$$\langle f|\widehat{\mathrm{A}}g\rangle = \langle \widehat{\mathrm{A}}f|g\rangle \tag{1.36}$$

for *any* normalizable functions $f(x)$ and $g(x)$, the operator is said to be **Hermitian**.

Then we make a sweeping physical assumption:

### Operators that represent observables

In quantum mechanics, any observable quantity $A$ is represented by a linear *Hermitian* operator $\widehat{\mathrm{A}}$.

Equation 1.36 is very important. From a physical point of view, it embodies the fact that measured values are real for, if we set $f = g = \Psi$, we recover Equation 1.35 — Hermitian operators have real expectation values. From a mathematical point of view, it completes the repertoire of operations that can be carried out with Dirac brackets. You will see that many things follow from this, including Ehrenfest's theorem and the uncertainty principle.

**Exercise 1.8** Write out Equation 1.36 in full, using integral signs. ■

Let us check that some familiar operators, used to represent observables, are indeed Hermitian. First, consider the position operator $\widehat{\mathrm{x}}$, which tells us to multiply functions by $x$. Because $x$ is real, we can write

$$\int_{-\infty}^{\infty} f^*(x)\big(x\,g(x)\big)\,\mathrm{d}x = \int_{-\infty}^{\infty} \big(x f(x)\big)^* g(x)\,\mathrm{d}x.$$

This means that

$$\langle f|\widehat{\mathrm{x}}\,g\rangle = \langle \widehat{\mathrm{x}}f|g\rangle,$$

so the position operator $\widehat{\mathrm{x}}$ is Hermitian. The same conclusion applies to any real-valued function of $\widehat{\mathrm{x}}$, so the potential energy operator $\widehat{\mathrm{V}}$, which tells us to multiply functions by $V(x)$, is also Hermitian.

Now consider the momentum operator $\widehat{\mathrm{p}}_x = -\mathrm{i}\hbar\,\partial/\partial x$. This operator includes a factor of i, so it will be interesting to see whether it satisfies the Hermitian condition (which, remember, delivers *real* expectation values). In this case,

$$\langle \widehat{\mathrm{p}}_x f|g\rangle = \int_{-\infty}^{\infty} \left(-\mathrm{i}\hbar\,\frac{\partial f}{\partial x}\right)^* g(x)\,\mathrm{d}x,$$

$$\langle f|\widehat{\mathrm{p}}_x g\rangle = \int_{-\infty}^{\infty} f^*(x)\left(-\mathrm{i}\hbar\,\frac{\partial g}{\partial x}\right)\mathrm{d}x.$$

So

$$\begin{aligned}\langle \widehat{\mathrm{p}}_x f|g\rangle - \langle f|\widehat{\mathrm{p}}_x g\rangle &= \mathrm{i}\hbar \int_{-\infty}^{\infty} \left( \frac{\partial f^*}{\partial x}\, g(x) + f^*(x)\, \frac{\partial g}{\partial x} \right) \mathrm{d}x \\ &= \mathrm{i}\hbar \int_{-\infty}^{\infty} \frac{\partial (f^* g)}{\partial x}\, \mathrm{d}x \\ &= \mathrm{i}\hbar \Big[ f^*(x)\, g(x) \Big]_{-\infty}^{\infty} = 0, \end{aligned} \tag{1.37}$$

where the last step follows because normalizable functions must tend to zero at $\pm\infty$. We therefore conclude that the momentum operator obeys $\langle \widehat{\mathrm{p}}_x f|g\rangle = \langle f|\widehat{\mathrm{p}}_x g\rangle$, and so is Hermitian.

Surprisingly, perhaps, it is the presence of the imaginary factor, $-\mathrm{i}\hbar$, that allows the momentum operator to be Hermitian. The derivative operator $\partial/\partial x$, with no imaginary factor, is *not* Hermitian.

If you ever found the presence of i in the momentum operator surprising, here is a good reason for it.

**Exercise 1.9** Show that

$$\left\langle \frac{\partial f}{\partial x} \Big| g \right\rangle + \left\langle f \Big| \frac{\partial g}{\partial x} \right\rangle = 0$$

for all normalizable functions $f(x)$ and $g(x)$. Hence show that the derivative operator $\partial/\partial x$ is *not* Hermitian. ■

## 1.3.2 Eigenvalues and measured values

We have seen that observables, represented by linear Hermitian operators, have real expectation values. Now we shall examine a more detailed point: *every measured value* of an observable $A$ must be real.

As a general rule, the allowed values of an observable $A$ are found by solving an eigenvalue equation for the operator $\widehat{\mathrm{A}}$. For example, the eigenvalue equation for energy is the time-independent Schrödinger equation

$$\widehat{\mathrm{H}}\, \psi_i(x) = E_i\, \psi_i(x),$$

and the eigenvalues $E_i$ are the possible energies of the system.

More generally, we can write the eigenvalue equation for any observable $A$ in the form

$$\widehat{\mathrm{A}}\, \phi_i(x) = a_i\, \phi_i(x),$$

or, in the language of ket vectors,

$$\widehat{\mathrm{A}}\, |\phi_i\rangle = a_i\, |\phi_i\rangle.$$

The functions $\phi_i(x)$ are called the *eigenfunctions* of $\widehat{\mathrm{A}}$, and the corresponding vectors $|\phi_i\rangle$ are called **eigenvectors**. The numbers $a_i$ are the *eigenvalues*, and these are interpreted as the possible values of $A$. Since $A$ is an observable, $\widehat{\mathrm{A}}$ is Hermitian. Let us see what effect this has on the eigenvalues and eigenvectors.

We write down the Hermitian condition for $\widehat{\mathrm{A}}$, using a pair of its own eigenfunctions, $\phi_i(x)$ and $\phi_j(x)$:

$$\langle \phi_j|\widehat{\mathrm{A}}\phi_i\rangle = \langle \widehat{\mathrm{A}}\phi_j|\phi_i\rangle.$$

Then, applying the eigenvalue equation on both sides,

$$\langle \phi_j | a_i \phi_i \rangle = \langle a_j \phi_j | \phi_i \rangle.$$

Pulling out the constants $a_i$ and $a_j$ from the Dirac brackets, we get

$$a_i \langle \phi_j | \phi_i \rangle = a_j^* \langle \phi_j | \phi_i \rangle,$$

which can be rearranged to give

$$(a_i - a_j^*) \langle \phi_j | \phi_i \rangle = 0. \tag{1.38}$$

One or other of the factors $(a_i - a_j^*)$ and $\langle \phi_j | \phi_i \rangle$ must be equal to zero. If we take $j = i$, we know that $\langle \phi_i | \phi_i \rangle \neq 0$, so we conclude that $a_i = a_i^*$:

The eigenvalues of a Hermitian operator are real.

Using this fact, Equation 1.38 becomes

$$(a_i - a_j)\langle \phi_j | \phi_i \rangle = 0,$$

and it immediately follows that

$$\langle \phi_j | \phi_i \rangle = 0 \quad \text{for } a_i \neq a_j.$$

We therefore conclude that:

Different eigenfunctions (or eigenvectors) of a Hermitian operator, corresponding to different eigenvalues, are orthogonal.

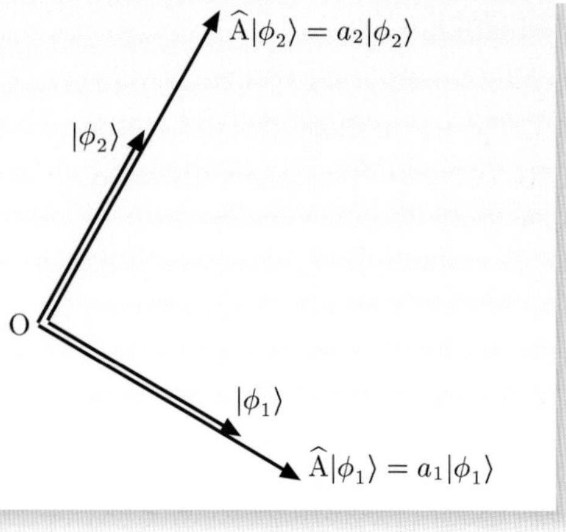


**Figure 1.7** A cartoon indicating the effect of an operator $\widehat{A}$ on two of its eigenvectors, $|\phi_1\rangle$ and $|\phi_2\rangle$.

Both these results make good sense. The eigenvalues of a Hermitian operator $\widehat{A}$ are the possible values of the observable $A$, and this whole section has been based on the premise that these are real. Moreover, we know from Book 1 that $\langle \psi_i | \psi_j \rangle$ is the probability amplitude of getting the eigenvalue $a_i$ when the system is in a state $\psi_j$ in which we are certain to get the eigenvalue $a_j$. If $a_i$ and $a_j$ are different, this probability amplitude is clearly equal to zero.

Finally, we draw another cartoon, which summarizes our results. Figure 1.7 shows two of the eigenvectors $|\phi_1\rangle$ and $|\phi_2\rangle$ of a Hermitian operator $\widehat{A}$. The operator $\widehat{A}$ does not change the directions of the eigenvectors, but just stretches (or contracts) them by the real factors $a_1$ and $a_2$. This is quite different from the effect of $\widehat{A}$ on a general vector (Figure 1.6). The sketch also shows that the eigenvectors are orthogonal.

### 1.3.3 Combining Hermitian operators

Operators can be combined in various ways. For example, the Hamiltonian operator of a free particle is $\widehat{H} = \widehat{p}_x^2/2m$, which is the square of the momentum operator, multiplied by the real constant $1/2m$. More generally, we are interested in combinations such as $\widehat{\mathrm{A}} + \widehat{\mathrm{B}}$ or $\widehat{\mathrm{A}}\widehat{\mathrm{B}}$. The issue is: if $\widehat{\mathrm{A}}$ and $\widehat{\mathrm{B}}$ are both Hermitian, are particular combinations of $\widehat{\mathrm{A}}$ and $\widehat{\mathrm{B}}$ also Hermitian?

We can always test whether a given operator $\widehat{\mathrm{O}}$ is Hermitian by checking whether

$$\langle f|\widehat{\mathrm{O}}g\rangle = \langle \widehat{\mathrm{O}}f|g\rangle$$

for all normalizable functions $f(x)$ and $g(x)$. For example, if $\widehat{\mathrm{A}}$ is Hermitian and $\lambda$ is a *real* constant, we have

$$\begin{aligned}\langle f|\lambda\widehat{\mathrm{A}}g\rangle &= \lambda\langle f|\widehat{\mathrm{A}}g\rangle, &&\text{because } \lambda \text{ is a constant,}\\ &= \lambda\langle \widehat{\mathrm{A}}f|g\rangle, &&\text{because } \widehat{\mathrm{A}} \text{ is Hermitian,}\\ &= \langle \lambda\widehat{\mathrm{A}}f|g\rangle, &&\text{because } \lambda \text{ is real.}\end{aligned}$$

We can therefore conclude that $\lambda\widehat{\mathrm{A}}$ is a Hermitian operator. Without going into the details, we can state the following rules of thumb:

### Rules for Hermitian operators

If $\widehat{\mathrm{A}}$ and $\widehat{\mathrm{B}}$ are both Hermitian and $\lambda$ is a *real* constant, it can be shown that:

- $\lambda\widehat{\mathrm{A}}$ is Hermitian;
- any power of $\widehat{\mathrm{A}}$ is Hermitian;
- $\widehat{\mathrm{A}} + \widehat{\mathrm{B}}$ is Hermitian.

Using these rules, and starting from the knowledge that $\widehat{\mathrm{x}}$ and $\widehat{\mathrm{p}}_x$ are Hermitian, we can see that $\widehat{\mathrm{H}} = \widehat{\mathrm{p}}_x^2/2m + \frac{1}{2}C\,\widehat{\mathrm{x}}^2$ is Hermitian, provided that $m$ and $C$ are real constants. This is just as well, of course, because $\widehat{\mathrm{H}}$ is the Hamiltonian operator of a harmonic oscillator.

However, not all combinations of Hermitian operators are Hermitian. To illustrate this point, we shall consider the product of two Hermitian operators, $\widehat{\mathrm{A}}$ and $\widehat{\mathrm{B}}$. Operators act on functions placed to their right, so the meaning of the product $\widehat{\mathrm{A}}\widehat{\mathrm{B}}f(x)$ is that we first let $\widehat{\mathrm{B}}$ act on $f(x)$, to give $\widehat{\mathrm{B}}f(x)$, and then let $\widehat{\mathrm{A}}$ act on the result. Taking $\widehat{\mathrm{A}}$ and $\widehat{\mathrm{B}}$ to be Hermitian, we therefore have

$$\langle f|\widehat{\mathrm{A}}\widehat{\mathrm{B}}g\rangle = \langle f|\widehat{\mathrm{A}}(\widehat{\mathrm{B}}g)\rangle = \langle \widehat{\mathrm{A}}f|\widehat{\mathrm{B}}g\rangle = \langle \widehat{\mathrm{B}}\widehat{\mathrm{A}}f|g\rangle. \tag{1.39}$$

This equation shows that $\widehat{\mathrm{A}}\widehat{\mathrm{B}}$ would be Hermitian if we could take one extra step and write $\langle \widehat{\mathrm{B}}\widehat{\mathrm{A}}f|g\rangle = \langle \widehat{\mathrm{A}}\widehat{\mathrm{B}}f|g\rangle$ for all normalizable functions $f(x)$ and $g(x)$. In effect, this means that:

If $\widehat{\mathrm{A}}$ and $\widehat{\mathrm{B}}$ are Hermitian, the product $\widehat{\mathrm{A}}\widehat{\mathrm{B}}$ is Hermitian if and only if

$$\widehat{\mathrm{A}}\widehat{\mathrm{B}} - \widehat{\mathrm{B}}\widehat{\mathrm{A}} = 0. \tag{1.40}$$

The expression on the left-hand side of Equation 1.40 is called the **commutator** of $\widehat{\mathrm{A}}$ and $\widehat{\mathrm{B}}$. When this vanishes, we say that the two operators **commute** with one another. This means that their ordering does not matter: $\widehat{\mathrm{A}}\widehat{\mathrm{B}}$ has the same effect as $\widehat{\mathrm{B}}\widehat{\mathrm{A}}$.

In practice, the ordering of operators often does matter. For example, if we let $\widehat{\mathrm{x}}\,\widehat{\mathrm{p}}_x$ act on an arbitrary function $f(x)$, we get

$$\widehat{\mathrm{x}}\,\widehat{\mathrm{p}}_x f(x) = -\mathrm{i}\hbar x\,\frac{\partial f}{\partial x}.$$

But if we let $\widehat{\mathrm{p}}_x\widehat{\mathrm{x}}$ act on the same function, we get something different:

$$\widehat{\mathrm{p}}_x\widehat{\mathrm{x}} f(x) = -\mathrm{i}\hbar\,\frac{\partial}{\partial x}(xf(x)) = -\mathrm{i}\hbar\left(x\,\frac{\partial f}{\partial x} + f(x)\right).$$

Subtracting these two equations and omitting the arbitrary function $f(x)$ on which the operators act, we obtain the following **commutation relation** between the operators $\widehat{\mathrm{x}}$ and $\widehat{\mathrm{p}}_x$:

This equation is of fundamental importance; you will meet it again later in this chapter.

$$\widehat{\mathrm{x}}\,\widehat{\mathrm{p}}_x - \widehat{\mathrm{p}}_x\widehat{\mathrm{x}} = \mathrm{i}\hbar. \tag{1.41}$$

This commutation relation shows that $\widehat{\mathrm{x}}\,\widehat{\mathrm{p}}_x$ and $\widehat{\mathrm{p}}_x\widehat{\mathrm{x}}$ do not commute with one another: ordering is important in this case.

This leaves us with a puzzle: in classical physics, $xp_x$ is a perfectly good dynamical variable, so we should be able to ask what is the corresponding operator in quantum mechanics. Neither $\widehat{\mathrm{x}}\,\widehat{\mathrm{p}}_x$ nor $\widehat{\mathrm{p}}_x\widehat{\mathrm{x}}$ will do, because they are not Hermitian. The correct choice turns out to be $\frac{1}{2}(\widehat{\mathrm{x}}\,\widehat{\mathrm{p}}_x + \widehat{\mathrm{p}}_x\widehat{\mathrm{x}})$, which is Hermitian, as you can show in Exercise 1.11 below. This example shows that it is not always obvious how to make the transition from classical variables to quantum-mechanical operators; ultimately, a choice must be made that is justified by experimental results.

**Exercise 1.10** Demonstrate that $\widehat{\mathrm{A}} + \widehat{\mathrm{B}}$ is Hermitian provided that $\widehat{\mathrm{A}}$ and $\widehat{\mathrm{B}}$ are both Hermitian.

**Exercise 1.11** Show that $\widehat{\mathrm{A}}\widehat{\mathrm{B}} + \widehat{\mathrm{B}}\widehat{\mathrm{A}}$ is Hermitian whenever $\widehat{\mathrm{A}}$ and $\widehat{\mathrm{B}}$ are Hermitian. Hence confirm that $\frac{1}{2}(\widehat{\mathrm{x}}\,\widehat{\mathrm{p}}_x + \widehat{\mathrm{p}}_x\widehat{\mathrm{x}})$ is Hermitian. ■

## 1.4 The generalized Ehrenfest theorem

Book 1 introduced Ehrenfest's theorem:

$$\frac{\mathrm{d}\langle x\rangle}{\mathrm{d}t} = \frac{\langle p_x\rangle}{m}, \tag{1.42}$$

$$\frac{\mathrm{d}\langle p_x\rangle}{\mathrm{d}t} = -\left\langle\frac{\partial V}{\partial x}\right\rangle, \tag{1.43}$$

and gave examples of its use. Ehrenfest's theorem is of considerable interest because it provides a link between quantum and classical mechanics. A simple example is provided by a free particle, for which $V(x) = 0$. In this special case, Equation 1.43 shows that $\langle p_x\rangle$ is a constant, and Equation 1.42 then shows that $\mathrm{d}\langle x\rangle/\mathrm{d}t$ is a constant. These are the quantum-mechanical versions of the law of conservation of momentum for a free particle and Newton's first law.

This section will show where Ehrenfest's theorem comes from. In fact, we will go further and derive a generalized version of Ehrenfest's theorem, a formula for the rate of change of *any* expectation value. The main principle we shall use is Schrödinger's equation, which determines the rate of change of the wave function, but a vital part of the argument hinges on the fact that the Hamiltonian operator is Hermitian.

The expectation value of any observable $A$ is given by

$$\langle A\rangle = \int_{-\infty}^{\infty} \Psi^*(x,t)\,\widehat{\mathrm{A}}\,\Psi(x,t)\,\mathrm{d}x. \tag{1.44}$$

We shall assume that the operator $\widehat{\mathrm{A}}$ does not depend on time, so that there is no '$t$' in the expression for $\widehat{\mathrm{A}}$. This is true for operators such as $\widehat{\mathrm{x}}$ and $\widehat{\mathrm{p}}_x$, and it is also true for the Hamiltonian operator $\widehat{\mathrm{H}}$ in an isolated system. Taking the derivative of Equation 1.44 with respect to time, the rate of change of $\langle A\rangle$ is

$$\frac{\mathrm{d}\langle A\rangle}{\mathrm{d}t} = \int_{-\infty}^{\infty} \frac{\partial\Psi^*}{\partial t}\,\widehat{\mathrm{A}}\,\Psi(x,t)\,\mathrm{d}x + \int_{-\infty}^{\infty} \Psi^*(x,t)\,\widehat{\mathrm{A}}\,\frac{\partial\Psi}{\partial t}\,\mathrm{d}x.$$

The left-hand side of this equation is written with an ordinary derivative, $\mathrm{d}/\mathrm{d}t$, while the rest of the equation uses partial derivatives, $\partial/\partial t$. This is appropriate because $\langle A\rangle$ depends only on one variable, $t$, while the wave function in the integrand depends on both $x$ and $t$. We shall now use Dirac brackets to write the right-hand side in a more compact form:

$$\frac{\mathrm{d}\langle A\rangle}{\mathrm{d}t} = \left\langle\frac{\partial\Psi}{\partial t}\middle|\widehat{\mathrm{A}}\Psi\right\rangle + \left\langle\Psi\middle|\widehat{\mathrm{A}}\frac{\partial\Psi}{\partial t}\right\rangle. \tag{1.45}$$

From Schrödinger's equation, the rate of change of the wave function is

$$\frac{\partial\Psi}{\partial t} = \frac{1}{\mathrm{i}\hbar}\widehat{\mathrm{H}}\Psi,$$

so we have

$$\frac{\mathrm{d}\langle A\rangle}{\mathrm{d}t} = \left\langle\frac{1}{\mathrm{i}\hbar}\widehat{\mathrm{H}}\Psi\middle|\widehat{\mathrm{A}}\Psi\right\rangle + \left\langle\Psi\middle|\widehat{\mathrm{A}}\frac{1}{\mathrm{i}\hbar}\widehat{\mathrm{H}}\Psi\right\rangle.$$

In the second term on the right-hand side, we have placed the Hamiltonian operator immediately next to $\Psi$ because this is what Schrödinger's equation tells us to do. The operator $\widehat{\mathrm{A}}$ then appears to the left of $\widehat{\mathrm{H}}$, and we must take care to preserve this ordering because $\widehat{\mathrm{A}}$ does not necessarily commute with $\widehat{\mathrm{H}}$.

Taking constant factors outside the Dirac brackets, we have

$$\frac{\mathrm{d}\langle A\rangle}{\mathrm{d}t} = -\frac{1}{\mathrm{i}\hbar}\langle\widehat{\mathrm{H}}\Psi|\widehat{\mathrm{A}}\Psi\rangle + \frac{1}{\mathrm{i}\hbar}\langle\Psi|\widehat{\mathrm{A}}\widehat{\mathrm{H}}\Psi\rangle.$$

Remember that constants extracted from the left-hand slot of a Dirac bracket must be complex-conjugated.

Finally, we use the key fact that $\widehat{\mathrm{H}}$ is Hermitian to obtain

$$\frac{\mathrm{d}\langle A\rangle}{\mathrm{d}t} = -\frac{1}{\mathrm{i}\hbar}\langle\Psi|\widehat{\mathrm{H}}\widehat{\mathrm{A}}\Psi\rangle + \frac{1}{\mathrm{i}\hbar}\langle\Psi|\widehat{\mathrm{A}}\widehat{\mathrm{H}}\Psi\rangle,$$

which can be rewritten as

$$\frac{\mathrm{d}\langle A\rangle}{\mathrm{d}t} = \frac{1}{\mathrm{i}\hbar}\langle\Psi|(\widehat{\mathrm{A}}\widehat{\mathrm{H}} - \widehat{\mathrm{H}}\widehat{\mathrm{A}})\Psi\rangle \equiv \frac{1}{\mathrm{i}\hbar}\langle\Psi|\left(\widehat{\mathrm{A}}\widehat{\mathrm{H}} - \widehat{\mathrm{H}}\widehat{\mathrm{A}}\right)|\Psi\rangle.$$

The combination of operators $\widehat{\mathrm{A}}\widehat{\mathrm{H}} - \widehat{\mathrm{H}}\widehat{\mathrm{A}}$ is the commutator of $\widehat{\mathrm{A}}$ and $\widehat{\mathrm{H}}$. In general, we shall use the widely-adopted shorthand notation

$$[\widehat{\mathrm{A}}, \widehat{\mathrm{B}}] = \widehat{\mathrm{A}}\widehat{\mathrm{B}} - \widehat{\mathrm{B}}\widehat{\mathrm{A}}$$

for the commutator of any $\widehat{A}$ and $\widehat{B}$. Using this notation, we conclude that

$$\frac{d\langle A\rangle}{dt} = \frac{1}{i\hbar}\left\langle[\widehat{A},\widehat{H}]\right\rangle, \tag{1.46}$$

where the expectation values on both sides are calculated using the wave function $\Psi$ that describes the state of the system at the time of interest.

We shall call Equation 1.46 the **generalized Ehrenfest theorem**. This important result tells us that:

> In any system, the rate of change of the expectation value of a quantity $A$ is determined by the expectation value of the commutator of $\widehat{A}$ with the Hamiltonian operator $\widehat{H}$ of the system.

The generalized Ehrenfest theorem applies to any observable $A$ whose operator does not depend on time. Going back over the derivation, you can see we did not even use the fact that $\widehat{A}$ is Hermitian, although a crucial step relied on the Hermitian character of $\widehat{H}$.

The **identity operator** $\widehat{I}$ leaves all functions unchanged: that is, $\widehat{I}f(x) = f(x)$.

**Exercise 1.12** An important result follows from the generalized Ehrenfest theorem in the special case where $\widehat{A} = \widehat{I}$, the identity operator. What is this result?

**Exercise 1.13** Show that $\left[\widehat{A},\widehat{B}+\widehat{C}\right] = \left[\widehat{A},\widehat{B}\right]$ if $\left[\widehat{A},\widehat{C}\right] = 0$. ■

### 1.4.1 Ehrenfest's equations

#### Ehrenfest's first equation

Before looking at the full implications of the generalized Ehrenfest theorem, we shall return to the unfinished business of justifying Equations 1.42 and 1.43.

First, for Equation 1.42, we put $\widehat{A} = \widehat{x}$ in Equation 1.46 to obtain

$$\frac{d\langle x\rangle}{dt} = \frac{1}{i\hbar}\left\langle[\widehat{x},\widehat{H}]\right\rangle. \tag{1.47}$$

So we need to evaluate the commutator of $\widehat{x}$ with $\widehat{H}$. We shall assume that the Hamiltonian operator takes the usual form

$$\widehat{H} = \frac{\widehat{p}_x^2}{2m} + \widehat{V}(x).$$

Then

$$\left[\widehat{x},\widehat{H}\right] = \widehat{x}\left(\frac{\widehat{p}_x^2}{2m} + \widehat{V}(x)\right) - \left(\frac{\widehat{p}_x^2}{2m} + \widehat{V}(x)\right)\widehat{x}.$$

The operator $\widehat{x}$ commutes with $\widehat{V}(x)$, so we have

The result of Exercise 1.13 is being used here.

$$\left[\widehat{x},\widehat{H}\right] = \widehat{x}\frac{\widehat{p}_x^2}{2m} - \frac{\widehat{p}_x^2}{2m}\widehat{x} = \frac{1}{2m}\left[\widehat{x},\widehat{p}_x^2\right]. \tag{1.48}$$

The details of working out the remaining commutator are discussed in the following worked example.

**Essential skill**

Evaluating a commutator

### Worked Example 1.2

Simplify the commutator $[\widehat{\mathrm{x}}, \widehat{\mathrm{p}}_x^2]$.

**Solution**

There are two different ways of answering this question.

**General method:** We can always write the commutator in terms of explicit operators, let it act on an arbitrary function $f(x)$, and simplify the result. In the present case, $\widehat{\mathrm{x}} = x$ and $\widehat{\mathrm{p}}_x^2 = -\hbar^2\,\partial^2/\partial x^2$, so we obtain

$$[\widehat{\mathrm{x}}, \widehat{\mathrm{p}}_x^2]\,f(x) = -\hbar^2\left(x\,\frac{\partial^2}{\partial x^2}f(x) - \frac{\partial^2}{\partial x^2}(xf(x))\right).$$

The derivative in the second term on the right-hand side is

$$\frac{\partial}{\partial x}\left(\frac{\partial}{\partial x}(xf(x))\right) = \frac{\partial}{\partial x}\left(x\,\frac{\partial f}{\partial x} + f(x)\right) = x\,\frac{\partial^2 f}{\partial x^2} + 2\,\frac{\partial f}{\partial x},$$

so

$$[\widehat{\mathrm{x}}, \widehat{\mathrm{p}}_x^2]\,f(x) = 2\hbar^2\frac{\partial f}{\partial x}.$$

Since this equation is true for all $f(x)$, we can write it as a relationship between operators:

$$[\widehat{\mathrm{x}}, \widehat{\mathrm{p}}_x^2] = 2\hbar^2\frac{\partial}{\partial x} = 2\mathrm{i}\hbar\left(-\mathrm{i}\hbar\,\frac{\partial}{\partial x}\right) = 2\mathrm{i}\hbar\,\widehat{\mathrm{p}}_x. \tag{1.49}$$

**Alternative method:** An alternative method can be used for any commutator involving powers of $\widehat{\mathrm{x}}$ and powers of $\widehat{\mathrm{p}}_x$. The idea is to write out the commutator in full,

$$[\widehat{\mathrm{x}}, \widehat{\mathrm{p}}_x^2] = \widehat{\mathrm{x}}\,\widehat{\mathrm{p}}_x\widehat{\mathrm{p}}_x - \widehat{\mathrm{p}}_x\widehat{\mathrm{p}}_x\widehat{\mathrm{x}},$$

and then use the known commutation relation $\widehat{\mathrm{x}}\,\widehat{\mathrm{p}}_x - \widehat{\mathrm{p}}_x\widehat{\mathrm{x}} = \mathrm{i}\hbar$ (Equation 1.41) to achieve the same ordering in both terms. This gives

$$[\widehat{\mathrm{x}}, \widehat{\mathrm{p}}_x^2] = (\widehat{\mathrm{p}}_x\widehat{\mathrm{x}} + \mathrm{i}\hbar)\widehat{\mathrm{p}}_x - \widehat{\mathrm{p}}_x(\widehat{\mathrm{x}}\,\widehat{\mathrm{p}}_x - \mathrm{i}\hbar) = 2\mathrm{i}\hbar\,\widehat{\mathrm{p}}_x, \tag{1.50}$$

as before.

Combining the result of this worked example with Equations 1.47 and 1.48, we conclude that

$$\frac{\mathrm{d}\langle x\rangle}{\mathrm{d}t} = \frac{1}{\mathrm{i}\hbar}\left\langle[\widehat{\mathrm{x}}, \widehat{\mathrm{H}}]\right\rangle = \frac{1}{\mathrm{i}\hbar}\,\frac{2\mathrm{i}\hbar\langle p_x\rangle}{2m} = \frac{\langle p_x\rangle}{m},$$

which confirms Ehrenfest's first equation (Equation 1.42).

#### Ehrenfest's second equation

Ehrenfest's second equation can be derived in a similar way. Putting $\widehat{\mathrm{A}} = \widehat{\mathrm{p}}_x$ in Equation 1.46 and noting that the momentum operator $\widehat{\mathrm{p}}_x$ commutes with the kinetic energy operator $\widehat{\mathrm{p}}_x^2/2m$, we have

$$\frac{\mathrm{d}\langle p_x\rangle}{\mathrm{d}t} = \frac{1}{\mathrm{i}\hbar}\left\langle\left[\widehat{\mathrm{p}}_x, \widehat{\mathrm{H}}\right]\right\rangle = \frac{1}{\mathrm{i}\hbar}\left\langle\left[\widehat{\mathrm{p}}_x, \widehat{\mathrm{V}}(x)\right]\right\rangle. \tag{1.51}$$

The following exercise asks you to fill in the remaining details.

**Exercise 1.14** Show that

$$\left[\widehat{\mathrm{p}}_x, \widehat{\mathrm{V}}(x)\right] = -\mathrm{i}\hbar\,\frac{\partial V}{\partial x}, \tag{1.52}$$

and hence derive Ehrenfest's second equation (Equation 1.43),

$$\frac{\mathrm{d}\langle p_x\rangle}{\mathrm{d}t} = -\left\langle\frac{\partial V}{\partial x}\right\rangle.$$

■

## 1.4.2 Conservation laws

The generalized Ehrenfest theorem links the rate of change of $\langle A\rangle$ to the commutator of $\widehat{\mathrm{A}}$ with $\widehat{\mathrm{H}}$. The simplest possibility is for $\widehat{\mathrm{A}}$ to commute with $\widehat{\mathrm{H}}$, so that the commutator $\left[\widehat{\mathrm{A}}, \widehat{\mathrm{H}}\right]$ is equal to zero. In this case,

$$\frac{\mathrm{d}\langle A\rangle}{\mathrm{d}t} = 0,$$

and $\langle A\rangle$ remains constant in time, *no matter what state the system is in*. We shall now consider some examples of this behaviour.

### Conservation of energy

The Hamiltonian operator obviously commutes with itself: $\widehat{\mathrm{H}}\widehat{\mathrm{H}} - \widehat{\mathrm{H}}\widehat{\mathrm{H}} = 0$. So we have

$$\frac{\mathrm{d}\langle H\rangle}{\mathrm{d}t} = 0. \tag{1.53}$$

The observable corresponding to the Hamiltonian operator is the energy of the system, so Equation 1.53 tells us that the expectation value of the energy remains constant in time. This conclusion is based on the generalized Ehrenfest theorem, which assumes that the operator under discussion ($\widehat{\mathrm{H}}$ in this case) does not depend on time. This is a reasonable assumption, provided that the system is isolated, so that it is not subject to time-dependent influences. We are therefore led to the following quantum-mechanical version of the conservation of energy:

> The expectation value of the energy of any isolated system remains constant in time.

**Exercise 1.15** Does the uncertainty in energy depend on time in an isolated system? *Hint*: Does $\widehat{\mathrm{H}}^2$ commute with $\widehat{\mathrm{H}}$? ■

### Conservation of momentum

We now consider an isolated system of two interacting particles. In classical mechanics, we would expect the total momentum of such a system to remain fixed. Let us see what happens in quantum mechanics.

As usual, we simplify the analysis by restricting to one dimension (the $x$-direction). We assume that the Hamiltonian operator of the isolated two-particle system takes the form

$$\widehat{\mathrm{H}} = \frac{\widehat{\mathrm{p}}_1^2}{2m_1} + \frac{\widehat{\mathrm{p}}_2^2}{2m_2} + \widehat{\mathrm{V}}(x_1 - x_2), \tag{1.54}$$

where the subscripts 1 and 2 label the two particles. For clarity, we have dropped the subscript $x$ from the momentum operators, but it is understood that these operators refer to momenta in the $x$-direction. Thus,

$$\widehat{\mathrm{p}}_1 = -\mathrm{i}\hbar\frac{\partial}{\partial x_1} \quad \text{and} \quad \widehat{\mathrm{p}}_2 = -\mathrm{i}\hbar\frac{\partial}{\partial x_2}.$$

The total momentum of the two-particle system is represented by the operator $\widehat{\mathrm{p}}_1 + \widehat{\mathrm{p}}_2$, and the rate of change of the expectation value of the total momentum is

$$\frac{\mathrm{d}}{\mathrm{d}t}\langle p_1 + p_2\rangle = \frac{1}{\mathrm{i}\hbar}\left\langle[\widehat{\mathrm{p}}_1 + \widehat{\mathrm{p}}_2, \widehat{\mathrm{H}}]\right\rangle = \frac{1}{\mathrm{i}\hbar}\left\langle[\widehat{\mathrm{p}}_1, \widehat{\mathrm{H}}] + [\widehat{\mathrm{p}}_2, \widehat{\mathrm{H}}]\right\rangle.$$

The momentum operators $\widehat{\mathrm{p}}_1$ and $\widehat{\mathrm{p}}_2$ commute with both of the kinetic energy operators $\widehat{\mathrm{p}}_1^2/2m_1$ and $\widehat{\mathrm{p}}_2^2/2m_2$ (because the ordering of different partial differentiations does not matter). So we have

$$\frac{\mathrm{d}}{\mathrm{d}t}\langle p_1 + p_2\rangle = \frac{1}{\mathrm{i}\hbar}\left\langle[\widehat{\mathrm{p}}_1, \widehat{\mathrm{V}}] + [\widehat{\mathrm{p}}_2, \widehat{\mathrm{V}}]\right\rangle,$$

and Equation 1.52 gives

$$\frac{\mathrm{d}}{\mathrm{d}t}\langle p_1 + p_2\rangle = -\left\langle\frac{\partial V}{\partial x_1} + \frac{\partial V}{\partial x_2}\right\rangle.$$

The potential energy function can be regarded as a function of the single variable $z = x_1 - x_2$, so

$$\frac{\partial V}{\partial x_1} = \frac{\mathrm{d}V}{\mathrm{d}z} \times \frac{\partial}{\partial x_1}(x_1 - x_2) = \frac{\mathrm{d}V}{\mathrm{d}z} \times (+1),$$
$$\frac{\partial V}{\partial x_2} = \frac{\mathrm{d}V}{\mathrm{d}z} \times \frac{\partial}{\partial x_2}(x_1 - x_2) = \frac{\mathrm{d}V}{\mathrm{d}z} \times (-1).$$

Hence we conclude that

$$\frac{\mathrm{d}}{\mathrm{d}t}\langle p_1 + p_2\rangle = 0. \tag{1.55}$$

This is the quantum-mechanical version of the law of conservation of momentum. The conclusion relies heavily on our assumption that the potential energy function takes the form $V(x_1 - x_2)$. This assumption makes good sense for an *isolated* system because it means that the potential energy of the system depends only on the *relative* positions of its particles, not on their positions with respect to anything else.

**Figure 1.8** Emmy Noether (1882–1935) proved theorems that established a link between symmetries and conservation laws.

**Figure 1.9** Murray Gell-Mann (1929–) proposed the existence of quarks on the basis of symmetry arguments. Gell-Mann won the 1969 Nobel prize for physics.

### Conservation laws and symmetry

The above examples give a glimpse into a powerful way of thinking about conservation laws. We know that the expectation value of any observable $A$ is conserved if the operator $\widehat{\mathrm{A}}$ commutes with $\widehat{\mathrm{H}}$ for the system under discussion. When thinking about conservation laws, our attention therefore turns to the form of the Hamiltonian operator.

To derive the quantum-mechanical version of energy conservation, we assumed that the Hamiltonian of an isolated system is independent of time. To derive the quantum-mechanical version of momentum conservation, we assumed that the Hamiltonian of an isolated two-particle system depends only on the *relative* coordinates of the particles; this implies that it does not depend on the centre-of-mass coordinate, which tells us where the system is in space.

These assumptions can be expressed in terms of symmetry. We say that there is a symmetry if a given action does not change things. The fact that the Hamiltonian operator is independent of time means that it is symmetric under translations in time. The fact that it is independent of the centre-of-mass coordinate means that it is symmetric under translations in space. In general, wherever there is a symmetry in physics, there is a corresponding conservation law. In the next chapter you will see that the lack of a special direction in space leads to the law of conservation of angular momentum. Even the conservation of charge is related to a symmetry (known as *gauge invariance*).

The link between symmetries and conservation laws pervades both classical and quantum physics. In classical physics, this link was explored extensively by Emmy Noether in 1918 (Figure 1.8). Noether was one of the first women to make an indelible mark on physics. This is not surprising, given the prejudices of her day; Noether faced considerable opposition, and had to overcome rules preventing women from enrolling on courses or giving lectures. Later generations of physicists exploited Noether's ideas in the context of quantum physics, and especially particle physics. For example, Murray Gell-Mann (Figure 1.9) used symmetry arguments to predict the existence and mass of a new particle, and to inspire the idea that protons and neutrons contain quarks.

# 1.5 The generalized uncertainty principle

## 1.5.1 A more general uncertainty principle

In Book 1 you met the Heisenberg uncertainty principle, which tells us that the product of the uncertainties in $x$ and $p_x$ in any state must be at least as large as $\hbar/2$:

$$\Delta x\,\Delta p_x \geq \frac{\hbar}{2}. \tag{1.56}$$

This principle denies us the possibility of knowing both the position and momentum of a particle. It forces us to abandon the idea that particles move along definite trajectories, and so finally demolishes old models of atoms in which electrons orbit the nucleus like planets going around the Sun.

Heisenberg proposed his uncertainty principle in 1927, but gave no rigorous proof. Over the next year or so, other physicists filled in the gaps in Heisenberg's reasoning. Then, in 1929, Howard Robertson realized that the Heisenberg uncertainty principle is a special case of a more general inequality that applies to all observables. This **generalized uncertainty principle** states that

$$\Delta A\,\Delta B \geq \tfrac{1}{2}\left|\left\langle[\widehat{\mathrm{A}},\widehat{\mathrm{B}}]\right\rangle\right|, \tag{1.57}$$

where $\Delta A$ and $\Delta B$ are the uncertainties of *any* observables $A$ and $B$ in a given state, and the right-hand side involves the expectation value of the commutator of $\widehat{\mathrm{A}}$ and $\widehat{\mathrm{B}}$ in the same state.

It is easy to see that the generalized uncertainty principle reduces to the Heisenberg uncertainty principle when $A = x$ and $B = p_x$, for we then have

$$\left[\widehat{\mathrm{x}},\widehat{\mathrm{p}}_x\right] = \mathrm{i}\hbar, \qquad \text{(Eqn 1.41)}$$

which, when used in Equation 1.57, leads back to Equation 1.56.

**Exercise 1.16** What restriction does the generalized uncertainty principle place on the 'mixed' uncertainty product $\Delta x\,\Delta p_y$?

**Exercise 1.17** Combine the generalized uncertainty principle with the generalized Ehrenfest theorem to show that the rate of change of the expectation value of any observable $A$ must obey the inequality

$$\left|\frac{\mathrm{d}\langle A\rangle}{\mathrm{d}t}\right| \leq \frac{2}{\hbar}\,\Delta A\,\Delta E, \tag{1.58}$$

where $E$ is the energy of the system. ■

In a stationary state, the energy has a definite value, so $\Delta E = 0$. Equation 1.58 then shows that $|\mathrm{d}\langle A\rangle/\mathrm{d}t| = 0$. So the expectation value of *any* observable remains constant in a stationary state. This is a result you met in Book 1, and is a good reason to call these states *stationary*.

However, the static character of stationary states should not be confused with the conservation laws we described earlier. Conservation laws apply to observables whose operators commute with the Hamiltonian operator. If this occurs for an observable $A$ in a given system, the expectation value of $A$ will remain constant in *all* states of the system, whether they are stationary or not.

## 1.5.2 Proving the generalized uncertainty principle

Finally, we prove the generalized uncertainty principle. Please note that this proof will not be assessed or examined. However, you are advised to follow it through. You will see that the uncertainty principle is not an independent assumption, but follows directly from very basic principles of quantum mechanics; this is a major success for the methods introduced in this chapter. The proof will also give you useful practice at manipulating Hermitian operators.

The Cauchy–Schwarz inequality was proved in Exercise 1.7.

Our starting point for proving Equation 1.57 is the Cauchy–Schwarz inequality

$$\langle a|a\rangle\langle b|b\rangle \geq |\langle a|b\rangle|^2. \qquad \text{(Eqn 1.19)}$$

For our purposes, it is helpful to express this in a slightly different form. We note that for any complex number $z = \mathrm{Re}(z) + \mathrm{i}\,\mathrm{Im}(z)$,

$$|z|^2 \geq \left|\mathrm{Im}(z)\right|^2 = \left|\frac{z - z^*}{2\mathrm{i}}\right|^2 = \tfrac{1}{4}\left|z - z^*\right|^2.$$

Now, we can set $z = \langle a|b\rangle$ and $z^* = \langle a|b\rangle^* = \langle b|a\rangle$ in this inequality to obtain

$$\left|\langle a|b\rangle\right|^2 \geq \tfrac{1}{4}\left|\langle a|b\rangle - \langle b|a\rangle\right|^2.$$

Combining this with the Cauchy–Schwarz inequality, we obtain

$$\langle a|a\rangle\langle b|b\rangle \geq \tfrac{1}{4}\left|\langle a|b\rangle - \langle b|a\rangle\right|^2. \qquad (1.59)$$

This inequality is valid for any vectors $|a\rangle$ and $|b\rangle$. We have not yet made any connection with the uncertainty principle — but we are about to do so.

We consider a system in a state described by the vector $|\Psi\rangle$, and two observables, $A$ and $B$, that can be measured in this system. The observables are represented by linear Hermitian operators $\widehat{\mathrm{A}}$ and $\widehat{\mathrm{B}}$, and we can introduce the vectors

$$|a\rangle = \widehat{\mathrm{A}}\,|\Psi\rangle \equiv |\widehat{\mathrm{A}}\Psi\rangle,$$
$$|b\rangle = \widehat{\mathrm{B}}\,|\Psi\rangle \equiv |\widehat{\mathrm{B}}\Psi\rangle.$$

Inserting these vectors into Equation 1.59, we obtain

$$\langle\widehat{\mathrm{A}}\Psi|\widehat{\mathrm{A}}\Psi\rangle\langle\widehat{\mathrm{B}}\Psi|\widehat{\mathrm{B}}\Psi\rangle \geq \tfrac{1}{4}\left|\langle\widehat{\mathrm{A}}\Psi|\widehat{\mathrm{B}}\Psi\rangle - \langle\widehat{\mathrm{B}}\Psi|\widehat{\mathrm{A}}\Psi\rangle\right|^2. \qquad (1.60)$$

Now, the crucial point is that the operators $\widehat{\mathrm{A}}$ and $\widehat{\mathrm{B}}$ are *Hermitian*, and this allows us to move them from the left-hand slot of a Dirac bracket to the right-hand slot. Doing this throughout Equation 1.60 gives

$$\langle\Psi|\widehat{\mathrm{A}}\widehat{\mathrm{A}}\Psi\rangle\langle\Psi|\widehat{\mathrm{B}}\widehat{\mathrm{B}}\Psi\rangle \geq \tfrac{1}{4}\left|\langle\Psi|\widehat{\mathrm{A}}\widehat{\mathrm{B}}\Psi\rangle - \langle\Psi|\widehat{\mathrm{B}}\widehat{\mathrm{A}}\Psi\rangle\right|^2,$$

which can be written as

$$\langle\Psi|\,\widehat{\mathrm{A}}^2\,|\Psi\rangle\langle\Psi|\,\widehat{\mathrm{B}}^2\,|\Psi\rangle \geq \tfrac{1}{4}\left|\langle\Psi|\,(\widehat{\mathrm{A}}\widehat{\mathrm{B}} - \widehat{\mathrm{B}}\widehat{\mathrm{A}})\,|\Psi\rangle\right|^2.$$

The quantities $\langle\Psi|\cdots|\Psi\rangle$ appearing in this inequality are all expectation values in the state $\Psi$, so we have

$$\left\langle A^2\right\rangle\left\langle B^2\right\rangle \geq \tfrac{1}{4}\left|\left\langle[\widehat{\mathrm{A}},\widehat{\mathrm{B}}]\right\rangle\right|^2. \qquad (1.61)$$

This is very close to the generalized uncertainty principle. You may recall from Book 1 that the squares of the uncertainties of $A$ and $B$ are given by

$$(\Delta A)^2 = \langle A^2\rangle - \langle A\rangle^2 = \left\langle(A - \langle A\rangle)^2\right\rangle, \qquad (1.62)$$
$$(\Delta B)^2 = \langle B^2\rangle - \langle B\rangle^2 = \left\langle(B - \langle B\rangle)^2\right\rangle. \qquad (1.63)$$

So, in the special case where $\langle A\rangle = \langle B\rangle = 0$, Equation 1.61 becomes

$$(\Delta A)^2\,(\Delta B)^2 \geq \tfrac{1}{4}\left|\left\langle[\widehat{\mathrm{A}},\widehat{\mathrm{B}}]\right\rangle\right|^2,$$

and the generalized uncertainty principle follows on taking the square root of both sides.

The only remaining step is to show that the same conclusion applies when $\langle A\rangle$ and $\langle B\rangle$ are non-zero. The key point is that Equation 1.61 is valid for *any* pair of Hermitian operators. We can therefore replace $\widehat{\mathrm{A}}$ and $\widehat{\mathrm{B}}$ by other Hermitian operators, chosen to make the left-hand side as small as possible.

Now, it is easy to see that $\widehat{\mathrm{A}} - \langle A\rangle$ is a Hermitian operator, since it is the difference of two Hermitian operators ($\widehat{\mathrm{A}}$ and the operator telling us to multiply by the real number $\langle A\rangle$). For similar reasons, $\widehat{\mathrm{B}} - \langle B\rangle$ is Hermitian. We can therefore obtain a valid inequality by making the replacements

$$A \Longrightarrow A - \langle A\rangle \quad \text{and} \quad B \Longrightarrow B - \langle B\rangle$$

consistently throughout Equation 1.61. This gives

$$\left\langle (A - \langle A\rangle)^2\right\rangle \left\langle (B - \langle B\rangle)^2\right\rangle \geq \tfrac{1}{4}\left|\left\langle [\widehat{\mathrm{A}} - \langle A\rangle, \widehat{\mathrm{B}} - \langle B\rangle]\right\rangle\right|^2.$$

Taking the square root of both sides and using the definition of uncertainty (Equations 1.62 and 1.63), we obtain

$$\Delta A\, \Delta B \geq \tfrac{1}{2}\left|\left\langle [\widehat{\mathrm{A}} - \langle A\rangle, \widehat{\mathrm{B}} - \langle B\rangle]\right\rangle\right|. \tag{1.64}$$

The final step is to simplify the commutator on the right-hand side. You can do this in the following exercise.

**Exercise 1.18** Given two linear operators $\widehat{\mathrm{A}}$ and $\widehat{\mathrm{B}}$, show that

$$\left[\widehat{\mathrm{A}} - \langle A\rangle, \widehat{\mathrm{B}} - \langle B\rangle\right] = \left[\widehat{\mathrm{A}}, \widehat{\mathrm{B}}\right],$$

and hence complete the proof of the generalized uncertainty principle. ■

## Summary of Chapter 1

**Section 1.1** The state of a quantum system can be represented by a ket vector in an abstract vector space called function space. For wave mechanics in one dimension, the inner product is given by

$$\langle f|g\rangle = \int_{-\infty}^{\infty} f^*(x)\, g(x)\, \mathrm{d}x.$$

This inner product is a complex number with the properties

$$\langle f|g\rangle^* = \langle g|f\rangle, \quad \langle f|cg\rangle = c\,\langle f|g\rangle \quad \text{and} \quad \langle cf|g\rangle = c^*\,\langle f|g\rangle,$$

and it obeys the inequalities

$$\langle f|f\rangle \geq 0 \quad \text{and} \quad \langle f|f\rangle\langle g|g\rangle \geq |\langle f|g\rangle|^2.$$

**Section 1.2** The Dirac bracket $\langle f|g\rangle$ can be regarded as a joining together of a bra vector $\langle f|$ and a ket vector $|g\rangle$. It is important to remember that the ket vector $|g\rangle = \sum_i c_i\,|g_i\rangle$ corresponds to the bra vector $\langle g| = \sum_i c_i^*\,\langle g_i|$, and vice versa.

**Section 1.3** Observable quantities are represented by linear Hermitian operators. By definition, an operator $\widehat{A}$ is Hermitian if

$$\langle \widehat{A}f|g\rangle = \langle f|\widehat{A}g\rangle$$

for all normalizable functions $f$ and $g$. Hermitian operators have real expectation values and real eigenvalues. If two eigenfunctions (or eigenvectors) of a Hermitian operator correspond to different eigenvalues, they are orthogonal.

If $\widehat{A}$ and $\widehat{B}$ are Hermitian, the product $\widehat{A}\widehat{B}$ is Hermitian if and only if $\widehat{A}$ commutes with $\widehat{B}$. Any power of $\widehat{A}$ is Hermitian, $\widehat{A}\widehat{B} + \widehat{B}\widehat{A}$ is Hermitian, and any linear combination $\alpha\widehat{A} + \beta\widehat{B}$ is Hermitian *provided that* the constants $\alpha$ and $\beta$ are real.

**Section 1.4** The generalized Ehrenfest theorem states that the rate of change of the expectation value of an observable is

$[\widehat{A}, \widehat{H}] = \widehat{A}\widehat{H} - \widehat{H}\widehat{A}$

$$\frac{\mathrm{d}\langle A\rangle}{\mathrm{d}t} = \frac{1}{i\hbar}\left\langle [\widehat{A}, \widehat{H}]\right\rangle,$$

where $\widehat{H}$ is the Hamiltonian operator of the system, and the expectation values on both sides of the equation are calculated for the same state. If $\widehat{A}$ commutes with $\widehat{H}$, the expectation value of $A$ remains constant in time, no matter what state the system is in. This leads to the quantum-mechanical versions of the laws of conservation of energy and momentum. Such conservation laws can be related to symmetries of the system.

**Section 1.5** The generalized uncertainty principle states that

$$\Delta A\,\Delta B \geq \tfrac{1}{2}\left|\left\langle [\widehat{A}, \widehat{B}]\right\rangle\right|,$$

where $\Delta A$ and $\Delta B$ are the uncertainties of any two observables $A$ and $B$ in a given state, and the right-hand side involves the expectation value of the commutator of $\widehat{A}$ and $\widehat{B}$ in the given state.

## Achievements from Chapter 1

*After studying this chapter, you should be able to:*

**1.1** Explain the meanings of the newly defined (emboldened) terms and symbols, and use them appropriately.

**1.2** Explain why it is appropriate to represent a quantum state by a vector in a vector space.

**1.3** Use Dirac brackets and bra and ket vectors in simple calculations.

**1.4** State the properties of Hermitian operators and use them in calculations.

**1.5** Evaluate the commutator of a given pair of operators.

**1.6** State and apply the generalized Ehrenfest theorem.

**1.7** Discuss the relationship between symmetries and conservation laws.

**1.8** State and apply the generalized uncertainty principle.

# Chapter 2 Introduction to angular momentum

## Introduction

This chapter is an introduction to angular momentum in quantum mechanics. You may know something about this concept from your studies of classical mechanics. A rotating wheel, a spinning ball and an orbiting planet all have angular momentum. In many circumstances, the angular momentum of a system is conserved, remaining constant in time. For example, a planet in orbit around the Sun has a constant angular momentum; this explains why the planet has a planar orbit, and why it sweeps out equal areas in equal times (one of Kepler's laws of planetary motion).

Angular momentum also plays a vital role in microscopic systems such as atoms and molecules. Some states of a hydrogen atom or a hydrogen chloride molecule have angular momentum, and so do protons and electrons. Of course, we cannot observe the motion of an electron by viewing it through a microscope, so you might wonder how we can know anything at all about its angular momentum. Fortunately, there is a close link between the angular momentum of a particle and its *magnetic dipole moment* (the quantity that determines how the particle interacts with a magnetic field). We can therefore learn a lot about angular momentum by observing how particles respond to applied magnetic fields. This formed the basis of an experiment carried out by Stern and Gerlach in 1922, which led to the conclusion that the angular momentum of an atom is *quantized*.

A dozen years before quantum mechanics was established, Bohr proposed a semi-quantum model of a hydrogen atom in which he treated the orbiting electron rather like a planet in orbit around the Sun, except that he assumed that the angular momentum of the electron would be quantized. Bohr's model was not satisfactory, but he was right about the quantization of angular momentum. The challenge for quantum mechanics is to explain this fact. Here, you will see how this is done using linear operators and eigenvalue equations. This is the first step towards developing the quantum-mechanical theory of angular momentum.

The chapter is organized as follows. Section 2.1 reviews the classical physics of angular momentum, both for moving particles and for rotating rigid bodies. Section 2.2 uses classical notions to establish a link between angular momentum and the magnetic dipole moment. This leads to a description of an experiment that provided convincing evidence for the quantization of angular momentum. Section 2.3 uses quantum-mechanical principles to show that the Cartesian components of angular momentum are quantized in units of $\hbar$. This section also describes how the magnitude of the angular momentum is quantized, and uses this to interpret the spectra of rotating molecules. Section 2.4 presents the quantum-mechanical version of the law of conservation of angular momentum and relates it to the generalized Ehrenfest theorem. Section 2.5 then shows that different components of angular momentum obey an uncertainty relation. In general, this makes it impossible to find states in which two different components of angular momentum both have definite values. However, in situations where angular momentum is conserved, it is possible to find states where the energy, one component of the angular momentum and the magnitude of the angular momentum all have definite values. This has important consequences for the way quantum states are labelled in atoms.

The present chapter is only an introduction to angular momentum in quantum mechanics. It deals with **orbital angular momentum** — angular momentum that is associated with moving particles or with rotating bodies. This is the type of angular momentum we are familiar with in classical physics. However, at the end of the chapter we shall point the way to another type of angular momentum, called **spin angular momentum**, or *spin* for short. This type of angular momentum is an intrinsic property of certain particles irrespective of any motion they may have. For example, an electron would have spin angular momentum, even if it were stationary. Spin is a purely quantum-mechanical concept which, in spite of its name, cannot be visualized in terms of particles spinning on their axes. The chapter that follows this one is all about spin. Indeed, one of the reasons for discussing orbital angular momentum now is that it will help us understand spin, which is a crucial ingredient for later chapters in the book, dealing with entanglement and the interpretation of quantum mechanics. Later, in Book 3, there will be yet another chapter devoted to angular momentum, in which we discuss aspects that are especially relevant for the description of atoms and molecules.

# 2.1 Review of classical angular momentum

## 2.1.1 The angular momentum of moving particles

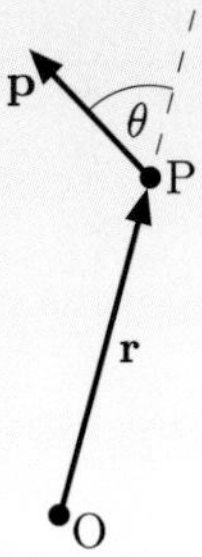


**Figure 2.1** A particle P is in is motion about a fixed origin O; its displacement from O is $\mathbf{r}$, and its momentum is $\mathbf{p} = m\,\mathrm{d}\mathbf{r}/\mathrm{d}t$.

Figure 2.1 shows a particle P, of mass $m$, moving relative to a fixed origin, O. At a given time, the particle's displacement from O is $\mathbf{r}$, and its momentum is $\mathbf{p} = m\,\mathrm{d}\mathbf{r}/\mathrm{d}t$. In general, both these quantities depend on time, although we shall not indicate this in our notation. In classical physics, at any given instant, the **orbital angular momentum** of the particle about O is defined to be

$$\mathbf{L} = \mathbf{r} \times \mathbf{p}. \tag{2.1}$$

For brevity, we shall often refer to this as the **angular momentum** of the particle.

Vector products and the right-hand rule are discussed in Section 8.1.4 of the *Mathematical toolkit*.

The appearance of a vector product in Equation 2.1 is significant. It means that the *magnitude* of the angular momentum is given by $L = rp\sin\theta$, where $\theta$ is the angle between the directions of the vectors $\mathbf{r}$ and $\mathbf{p}$ marked in Figure 2.1. It also means that $\mathbf{L}$ is a vector perpendicular to both $\mathbf{r}$ and $\mathbf{p}$. The precise direction of $\mathbf{L}$ is fixed by the **right-hand rule**; in the situation shown in Figure 2.1, this implies that the angular momentum is directed out of the page, towards you.

**Exercise 2.1** A particle of mass $m$ and constant speed $v$ performs uniform circular motion of radius $r$ in a horizontal plane. Viewed from above, the motion is clockwise. Describe the magnitude and direction of the angular momentum of this particle about an origin at the centre of its circular path. ■

Many physical concepts (such as energy and momentum) are important, in part, because they are subject to conservation laws, and this is true of angular momentum. For example, in the situation shown in Figure 2.1, we can consider what happens when the force acting on the particle is a **central force** — which implies that it always acts along the line joining the particle to the fixed point O.

This would be true for a planet experiencing the gravitational tug of a star, or an electron experiencing the electrostatic attraction of a proton. In general, the rate of change of the angular momentum about O is given by

$$\frac{d\mathbf{L}}{dt} = \frac{d(\mathbf{r} \times \mathbf{p})}{dt} = \dot{\mathbf{r}} \times \mathbf{p} + \mathbf{r} \times \dot{\mathbf{p}}. \tag{2.2}$$

We use dot notation for differentiation with respect to time: $\dot{\mathbf{r}} = d\mathbf{r}/dt$.

However, $\mathbf{p}$ is just $m\dot{\mathbf{r}}$, so the first term is the vector product of two parallel vectors, and must be zero. Using Newton's second law in the form $\mathbf{F} = \dot{\mathbf{p}}$, we can write the second term as $\mathbf{r} \times \mathbf{F}$. Provided that the force is central, this is also a vector product of two parallel (or antiparallel) vectors, and so is equal to zero. We conclude that the angular momentum of a particle subject to a central force remains constant: angular momentum is conserved.

The conservation of angular momentum has many applications in astronomy. For example, the gravitational force of the Sun on a planet is central, so the angular momentum of the planet is conserved. It can be shown that this implies that the radius vector joining the Sun to the planet sweeps out equal areas in equal times, a fact known as Kepler's second law (Figure 2.2).

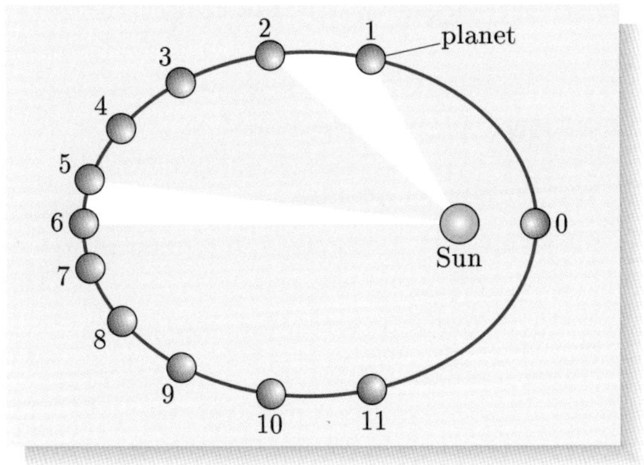


**Figure 2.2** Kepler's second law. The white areas, corresponding to equal intervals of time, are equal.

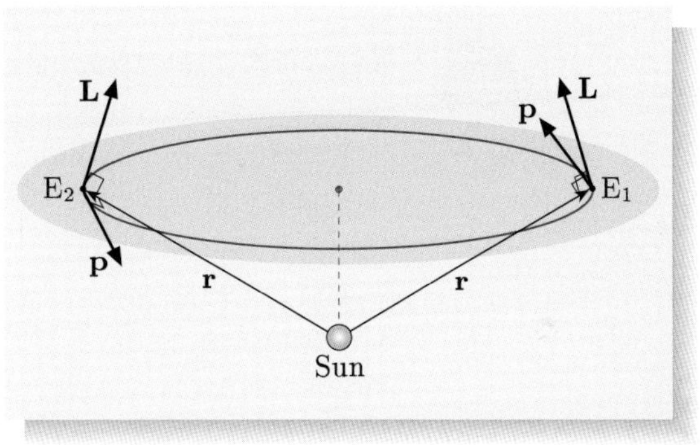


**Figure 2.3** If the plane of the Earth's orbit did not include the Sun, the angular momentum $\mathbf{L}$ of the Earth would point in different directions at different times, e.g. at two points $E_1$ and $E_2$.

- Use the conservation of angular momentum to show that the Sun must lie in the orbital plane of a planet.

- If the Sun were *not* in the orbital plane of the planet, the radius vector $\mathbf{r}$ from the Sun to the planet would lie on something like a cone; the angular momentum $\mathbf{L}$ is always normal to $\mathbf{r}$, and would therefore vary in direction as the planet travelled around its orbit (Figure 2.3). This is impossible because the angular momentum of a planet is conserved, so the vector $\mathbf{L}$ must be constant in both magnitude *and* direction.

We often need the Cartesian components of the angular momentum vector. An easy-to-remember way of writing these down is to express the vector product in terms of a **determinant**, as follows:

Section 8.3.5 of the *Mathematical toolkit* gives a review of determinants.

$$\mathbf{L} = \mathbf{r} \times \mathbf{p} = \begin{vmatrix} \mathbf{e}_x & \mathbf{e}_y & \mathbf{e}_z \\ x & y & z \\ p_x & p_y & p_z \end{vmatrix}, \tag{2.3}$$

where $\mathbf{e}_x$, $\mathbf{e}_y$ and $\mathbf{e}_z$ are **Cartesian unit vectors**. Expanding this determinant, we see that

$$\mathbf{L} = L_x\mathbf{e}_x + L_y\mathbf{e}_y + L_z\mathbf{e}_z, \tag{2.4}$$

where

$$L_x = yp_z - zp_y, \tag{2.5}$$
$$L_y = zp_x - xp_z, \tag{2.6}$$
$$L_z = xp_y - yp_x. \tag{2.7}$$

This procedure of cycling the subscripts is sometimes referred to as a *cyclic permutation*.

All of the expressions for $L_x$, etc. can be obtained from any other one by cycling the indices wherever they appear: $x \Longrightarrow y \Longrightarrow z \Longrightarrow x$. In this way, for example, we get $L_x$ by replacing $z$ by $x$, $x$ by $y$ and $y$ by $z$ in the expression for $L_z$.

**Exercise 2.2** Use Equation 2.3 to confirm that $L_y$ is given by Equation 2.6. ■

## 2.1.2 Angular momentum of rotating rigid bodies

So far we have discussed the angular momentum of particles, but classical physics is also concerned with the angular momentum of extended bodies, such as wheels and boomerangs, and quantum physics deals with the angular momentum of rotating molecules or atomic nuclei. We can restrict the discussion to the rotation of a rigid body about a fixed axis — the rotation of a wheel about a fixed axle, for example (Figure 2.4).

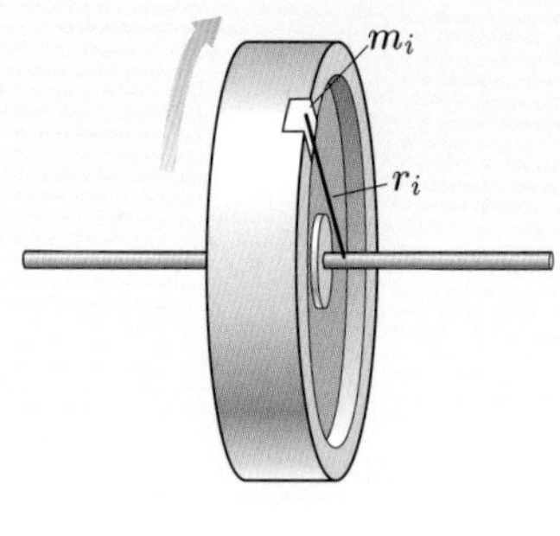


**Figure 2.4** A wheel rotating about a fixed axle can be considered to be made up of many small elements each in orbit about the axle.

Equation 2.1 applies to each particle in an extended body, and the total angular momentum of the body is found by adding together the angular momenta of its particles. This is a vector sum, but if the body rotates about a fixed axis, all contributions to the angular momentum are in the same direction, along the axis of rotation. For a rigid body, each particle has the same angular speed of rotation, $\omega$. It can then be shown that the whole body has an angular momentum of magnitude

$$L = I\omega, \tag{2.8}$$

where the constant $I$ is the body's **moment of inertia** about the given axis of rotation, and $\omega$ is the angular speed of rotation. The moment of inertia of the body is given by $I = \sum m_i d_i^2$, where $m_i$ and $d_i$ are the mass and distance from the axis of rotation of particle $i$, and the sum is taken over all the particles in the body.

We can also add up the kinetic energies of all the particles in the body to obtain the rotational kinetic energy, $E_{\text{rot}}$, of the body. This turns out to be

$$E_{\text{rot}} = \tfrac{1}{2}I\omega^2. \tag{2.9}$$

This expression is correct, but is not in a form suitable for quantizing. When we come to quantize the rotational kinetic energy of a diatomic molecule, we will find it more convenient to combine Equations 2.8 and 2.9 and write

$$E_{\text{rot}} = \frac{L^2}{2I}. \tag{2.10}$$

This is reminiscent of the fact that the kinetic energy of a free particle is best expressed as $p^2/2m$ in quantum mechanics, rather than as $\frac{1}{2}mv^2$.

## 2.2 The Stern–Gerlach experiment

We cannot directly observe the rotations of atoms, so it is not clear how we can measure their angular momenta. However, it turns out that many atoms behave like tiny magnets. The magnetic properties of an atom can be characterized by a quantity called the *magnetic dipole moment* which turns out to be proportional to the angular momentum of the atom. Hence we can find out about the angular momentum of an atom by measuring its magnetic dipole moment.

This is the principle behind a ground-breaking experiment carried out by Otto Stern and Walther Gerlach in 1922. Stern and Gerlach demonstrated that the magnetic dipole moments of atoms are quantized, which is tantamount to showing that their angular momentum is quantized. Before we describe this famous experiment, we shall introduce the concept of magnetic dipole moment, and show how it is related to angular momentum.

### 2.2.1 Magnetic dipoles in magnetic fields

Anyone who has undergone an MRI scan has benefited from the fact that some atomic nuclei behave like tiny magnets, called magnetic dipoles. Magnetism is a pervasive property in the microscopic world, but it is convenient to introduce the concepts we need in the familiar context of classical physics. A simple example of a **magnetic dipole** is provided by a small circular loop of wire carrying a steady electric current. Such a magnetic dipole has some magnetic properties — for example, it produces a magnetic field and it responds to an externally-applied magnetic field. Provided that the area of the loop is small, the magnetic properties of the loop all depend on a single vector quantity, $\boldsymbol{\mu}$, called the **magnetic dipole moment** of the loop. The magnitude of the magnetic dipole moment is

$$\mu = IA, \tag{2.11}$$

where $I$ is the current through the loop and $A$ is the area of the loop (see Figure 2.5). The direction of the magnetic dipole moment is perpendicular to the plane of the loop in the sense defined by the **right-hand grip rule**. This rule involves curling the fingers of the right hand in the direction of current flow around the loop; the extended right thumb then indicates the direction of the magnetic dipole moment. It is convenient to introduce the **oriented area A**, which is a vector quantity of magnitude $A$, pointing in a direction perpendicular to the area of the loop in the sense defined by the right-hand grip rule. The magnetic dipole moment of the current loop can then be expressed as

$$\boldsymbol{\mu} = I\mathbf{A}. \tag{2.12}$$

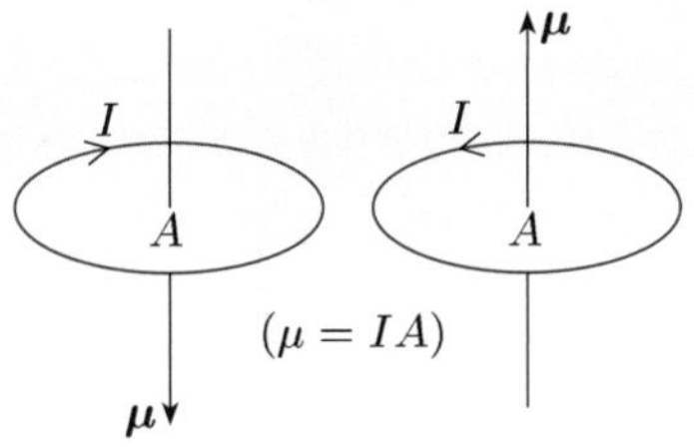


**Figure 2.5** A circular loop of wire of area $A$, carrying a current $I$, has a magnetic dipole moment of magnitude $\mu = IA$ (or $NIA$ if the loop has $N$ turns). The vector $\boldsymbol{\mu}$ is in the directions shown, in agreement with the right-hand grip rule.

Not all magnetic dipoles can be visualized as current loops; a compass needle is a good example to keep in mind. Like a compass needle, any magnetic dipole responds to an external magnetic field as follows: when placed in a magnetic field, a magnetic dipole will experience a torque whose direction is that which would align a stationary magnetic dipole with the magnetic field. This torque is given by the expression

$$\boldsymbol{\Gamma} = \boldsymbol{\mu} \times \mathbf{B}, \tag{2.13}$$

which is zero when $\boldsymbol{\mu}$ and $\mathbf{B}$ are parallel.

Alternatively, we can think in terms of energy. The magnetic dipole has a potential energy in the magnetic field given by

$$E_{\text{mag}} = -\boldsymbol{\mu} \cdot \mathbf{B}. \tag{2.14}$$

This has its smallest value $-\mu B$ when $\boldsymbol{\mu}$ is parallel to $\mathbf{B}$, so it is energetically favourable for the magnetic dipole moment to align with the field.

A magnetic dipole in a *uniform* magnetic field, such as the Earth's field in a local region, feels a torque tending to align it in the direction of the field, but it feels no force pulling it as a whole in any direction. However, the magnetic dipole does feel a force in a *non-uniform* magnetic field. The force experienced by a magnetic dipole in a non-uniform magnetic field is minus the gradient of the potential energy of the magnetic dipole. If the magnetic field points in the $z$-direction, the $z$-component of the force is

$$F_z = -\frac{\partial E_{\text{mag}}}{\partial z} = +\mu_z \frac{\partial B_z}{\partial z}. \tag{2.15}$$

In a uniform magnetic field, this force is equal to zero, though the torque on the magnetic dipole need not be equal to zero, as we have seen. However, if the magnetic field is *non-uniform*, the magnetic dipole will feel a net force pulling it in a direction that depends on the relative orientation of $\boldsymbol{\mu}$ and $\mathbf{B}$. If the magnetic dipole moment is roughly parallel to the magnetic field gradient, it is drawn towards regions of greater field strength; if the magnetic dipole moment is roughly antiparallel to the magnetic field gradient, it is drawn towards regions of lesser field strength.

On a microscopic scale, many atoms and nuclei behave as magnetic dipoles. You will see that the force acting on an atom in a non-uniform magnetic field (Equation 2.15) is a crucial element in the Stern–Gerlach experiment discussed later in this section.

**The SI unit of magnetic dipole moment:** Alternative SI units for magnetic dipole moment can be seen by analyzing Equations 2.12 and 2.14. The first gives units of amperes times square metres ($\text{A m}^2$), while the second gives units of joules per tesla ($\text{J T}^{-1}$); these units are equivalent and can be used interchangeably.

### 2.2.2 Magnetic dipole moments and angular momentum

The link between magnetic dipole moments and angular momenta can be illustrated by a simple classical model. We consider a particle of charge $q$ and mass $m$, moving at constant speed $v$ around a circle of radius $r$. This particle has an angular momentum about the centre of the circle of magnitude $L = mvr$. Because the particle is charged, it also carries a current around the circle, and so produces a magnetic dipole moment whose magnitude we shall now calculate.

The current is equal to the charge per unit time that passes a fixed point. This is equal to the charge $q$ of the particle divided by the time it takes to complete one lap, $T = 2\pi r/v$. So the current has magnitude $|q|/T = |q|\,v/2\pi r$, and the magnetic dipole moment has magnitude

$$\mu = \frac{|q|v}{2\pi r} \times \pi r^2 = \tfrac{1}{2}|q|vr.$$

A particle in circular motion has an angular momentum of magnitude $L = mvr$, so we have

$$\mu = \frac{|q|}{2m}L.$$

For $q > 0$, the magnetic dipole moment vector points in the same direction as the angular momentum vector. For $q < 0$, the magnetic dipole moment vector points in the opposite direction to the angular momentum vector. We therefore have the vector equation

$$\boldsymbol{\mu} = \frac{q}{2m}\mathbf{L}.$$

The important point here is that the magnetic dipole moment and angular momentum vectors are proportional to one another, and the proportionality constant depends only on $q$ and $m$, intrinsic properties of the orbiting particle.

In general,

$$\boldsymbol{\mu} = \gamma\mathbf{L}, \tag{2.16}$$

where the proportionality constant $\gamma$ is called the **gyromagnetic ratio**. This is equal to $q/2m$ for the classical orbiting particle considered above. Other rotating bodies may have different values of $\gamma$ — for example, a rotating compact disc with an extra electron on its rim has a very small ratio of magnetic moment to angular momentum, so its gyromagnetic ratio is much smaller than the magnitude of $q/2m$ for an electron.

The above arguments are based on classical physics. In quantum mechanics, we cannot retain the picture of an electron circulating around a fixed orbit. Nevertheless, it remains true that many atoms have magnetic moments and angular momenta, and these two quantities can be related by Equation 2.16 for some choice of gyromagnetic ratio. So if an experiment shows that the magnetic dipole moment of an atom is quantized, we can infer that the angular momentum of the atom is quantized too. We now describe such an experiment.

### 2.2.3 The Stern–Gerlach experiment: $\mu$ is quantized

The famous experiment carried out by Stern and Gerlach in 1922 was based on the fact that a magnetic dipole experiences a force in a *non-uniform* magnetic field. Stern and Gerlach constructed a magnet with specially-shaped pole pieces, designed to produce a strongly non-uniform magnetic field along the path of a beam of atoms (Figure 2.6).

In the experiment carried out by Stern and Gerlach, the beam was one of silver atoms, created by heating silver to a high temperature in an enclosure (an 'oven') with a small hole. Silver atoms emerging from the hole were collimated into a fine beam which was directed through the magnetic field, the whole experiment being carried out in a very high vacuum. After the silver atoms had passed through the magnetic field, they were detected by letting them fall onto a glass plate, building up a visible deposit of silver in the places where many atoms fell.

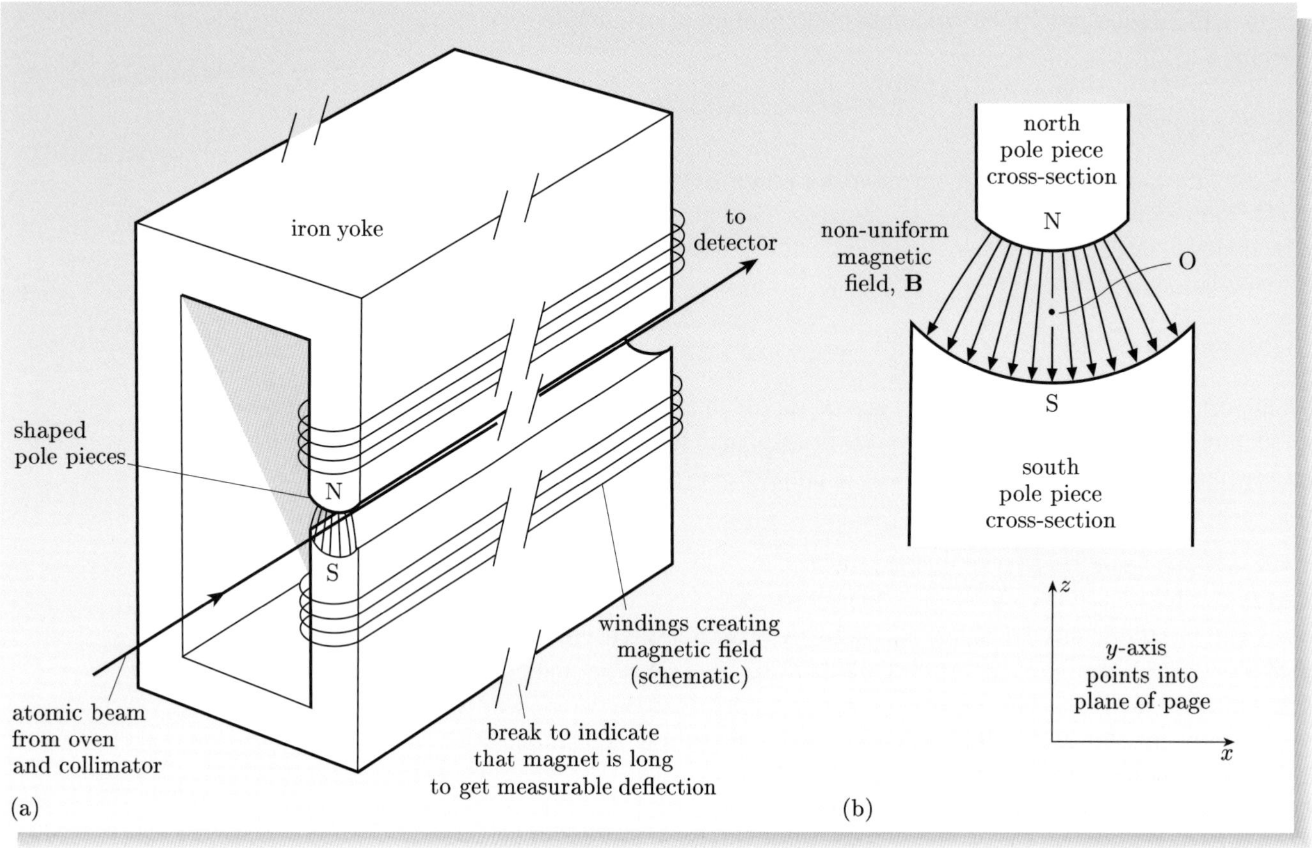


**Figure 2.6** (a) A perspective view of a Stern–Gerlach magnet. (b) Cross-section for a fixed value of $y$ through a non-uniform magnetic field between the specially-shaped pole pieces. The direction of the magnetic field $\mathbf{B}$ at any point is the direction of the field line at that point, and the magnitude of the magnetic field is greater where the field lines are closer together.

Suppose that an atom in the beam with magnetic dipole moment $\boldsymbol{\mu}$ passes through the point O in Figure 2.6b, travelling in the $y$-direction, normal to the plane of the page. Along this path, the atom experiences a steady force in the $z$-direction given by

$$F_z = \mu_z \frac{\partial B_z}{\partial z}. \qquad \text{(Eqn 2.15)}$$

Since $\partial B_z/\partial z < 0$ in Figure 2.6, an atom with a positive value of $\mu_z$ will be deflected downwards, and an atom with a negative value of $\mu_z$ will be deflected upwards.

In classical terms, we would expect the silver atoms to have all orientations of magnetic dipole moment, so the forces on the atoms would be expected to be in the $z$-direction, with values spread throughout the range

$$-\left|\mu \frac{\partial B_z}{\partial z}\right| < F_z < \left|\mu \frac{\partial B_z}{\partial z}\right|. \qquad (2.17)$$

Atoms with $\boldsymbol{\mu}$ directed fully downwards would be deflected most strongly upwards, while atoms with $\boldsymbol{\mu}$ directed fully upwards would be deflected most strongly downwards. Most atoms would end up somewhere in between, randomly distributed, with many being deflected very little. The glass plate would therefore be expected to exhibit a continuous smudge, showing a continuous range of deflections suffered by the silver atoms. Parts (a) and (b) of Figure 2.7 show what might have been expected in classical physics, without, and then with, the non-uniform magnetic field.

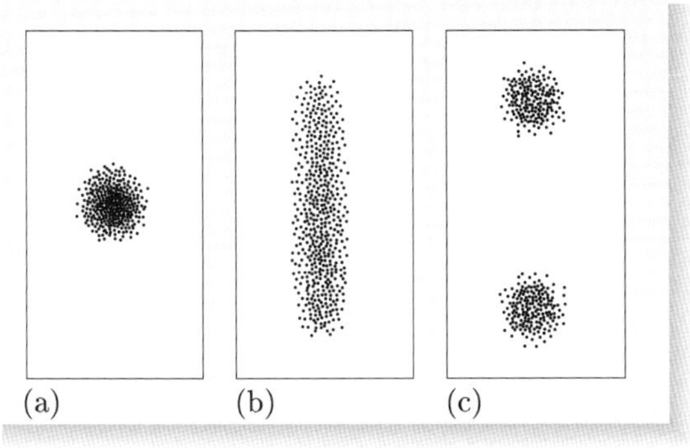


**Figure 2.7** (a) In the absence of a magnetic field, the atoms pass straight through the apparatus, leaving a spot the size of the collimated beam. (b) In a non-uniform magnetic field, atoms are deflected up or down depending on the value of $\mu_z$. According to classical physics, all orientations of $\boldsymbol{\mu}$ are possible, so the atoms would leave a continuous smudge. (c) In quantum physics, only a discrete set of values of $\mu_z$ is allowed, and the atoms leave $n$ spots. The case $n = 2$, appropriate for silver atoms, is shown.

Something very different is observed in practice. Stern and Gerlach found that half of the silver atoms are deflected upwards by some amount, while the other half are deflected downwards by the same amount. In an ideal case, this gives two clear spots on the glass plate, as shown in Figure 2.7c.

In practice, the beam may be so wide in the $x$-direction that different atoms experience different magnetic fields. Atoms passing through the edge of the field will be deflected less than those passing through the middle. The trace formed on the glass plate is therefore like the shape of two lips, as indicated in the upper portion of the plaque reproduced in Figure 2.8. The small graph to the side of this image shows the number of atoms deflected to various values of $z$ above and below the straight-through direction $(x = 0, z = 0)$. It shows just two peaks. The width of these peaks reflects the fact that the atoms emerging from the oven have the usual thermal distribution of speeds, since the deflection depends on the speed as well as the deflecting force. More elaborate experiments, arranged so that all of the atoms have almost the same speed, give two very narrow peaks.

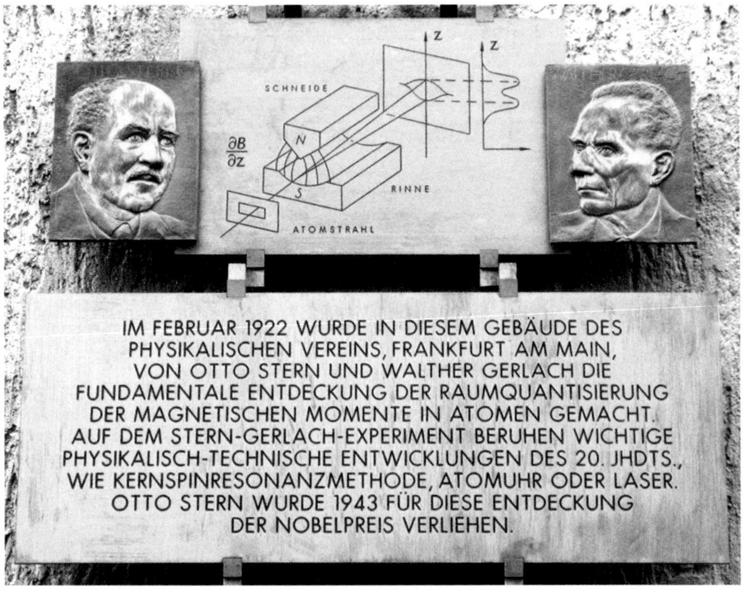


**Figure 2.8** Plaque celebrating the experiment of Otto Stern (1888–1969) and Walther Gerlach (1889–1979). Stern (on the left) was awarded the 1943 Nobel prize for physics for this and other pioneering work involving atomic beams.

What do we conclude? The experiment can only mean that instead of there being a range of possible values of $\mu_z$, ranging from $-|\boldsymbol{\mu}|$ to $|\boldsymbol{\mu}|$, there are just two. Because of the intimate connection between magnetic dipole moment and angular momentum, the experiment implies that there are just two possible values of the $z$-component of the atom's angular momentum. The $z$-component of angular momentum is quantized!

This result is radical, even though Bohr had earlier suggested the quantization of angular momentum in his semi-quantum model of the hydrogen atom. Consider an analogy: if we know that a particle has speed $v$ and there is nothing to favour one direction for the velocity $\mathbf{v}$ over another, then surely $v_z$ can take any value between $-|\mathbf{v}|$ and $|\mathbf{v}|$; more specifically, $v_z = |\mathbf{v}|\cos\theta$, where $\theta$ is the angle between $\mathbf{v}$ and the $z$-axis, ranging continuously from 0 to $\pi$. The Stern–Gerlach experiment showed that $\mu_z$ and $L_z$ do not have continuous values like this.

Why should the $z$-components be special? There is absolutely nothing in the oven, where the silver atoms came from, to favour one orientation of axes over another. With the oven in a fixed orientation, and the whole magnet turned 90° about the axis defined by the beam, we would still find two spots. We therefore conclude that the $x$-component and the $y$-component of angular momentum are quantized as well.

The number of allowed values of angular momentum depends on the type of atom considered. In the case of silver atoms, there are just *two* allowed values of each angular momentum component. That is why Stern and Gerlach observed silver atoms appearing in *two* regions of their glass-plate detector. We shall return to this point later, but the important conclusion for present purposes is that *angular momentum is quantized*. We shall now develop the quantum-mechanical theory of angular momentum, with the aim of explaining this fact.

## 2.3 Angular momentum in quantum mechanics

Experiment has told us that angular momentum is quantized, so we now take up the challenge of seeing how this comes about. The first step follows much the same route as that taken earlier in the course, leading to the quantization of energy.

### 2.3.1 Angular momentum operators $\widehat{\mathrm{L}}_x$, $\widehat{\mathrm{L}}_y$ and $\widehat{\mathrm{L}}_z$

In quantum mechanics, an observable such as $L_z$ is represented by a linear operator which we know, from Chapter 1, must be Hermitian. Our first task in developing a quantum theory of angular momentum is to find suitable operators for the components of angular momentum.

The method of obtaining these operators is very similar to that used to write down the Hamiltonian operator. First we write down an appropriate classical expression, then we replace variables by their corresponding operators. For momentum components, we use the standard replacements

$$\begin{aligned} p_x &\Longrightarrow \widehat{\mathrm{p}}_x = -\mathrm{i}\hbar\,\frac{\partial}{\partial x}, \\ p_y &\Longrightarrow \widehat{\mathrm{p}}_y = -\mathrm{i}\hbar\,\frac{\partial}{\partial y}, \\ p_z &\Longrightarrow \widehat{\mathrm{p}}_z = -\mathrm{i}\hbar\,\frac{\partial}{\partial z}. \end{aligned} \tag{2.18}$$

For position components, we use the rule that the operator $\widehat{\mathrm{x}}$ is simply the act of multiplying by the variable $x$, with similar rules for $\widehat{\mathrm{y}}$ and $\widehat{\mathrm{z}}$. Applying these rules to the $z$-component of angular momentum, we obtain

$$L_z = xp_y - yp_x \quad\Longrightarrow\quad \widehat{\mathrm{L}}_z = -\mathrm{i}\hbar\left[x\,\frac{\partial}{\partial y} - y\,\frac{\partial}{\partial x}\right], \tag{2.19}$$

with similar expressions for $\widehat{\mathrm{L}}_x$ and $\widehat{\mathrm{L}}_y$.

- Write down expressions for the operators $\widehat{\mathrm{L}}_x$ and $\widehat{\mathrm{L}}_y$.

- From Equations 2.5 and 2.6, we have

  $$L_x = yp_z - zp_y \quad\text{and}\quad L_y = zp_x - xp_z.$$

  Substituting $\widehat{\mathrm{p}}_z = -\mathrm{i}\hbar\,\partial/\partial z$ and the corresponding expressions for $\widehat{\mathrm{p}}_x$ and $\widehat{\mathrm{p}}_y$, we obtain

  $$\widehat{\mathrm{L}}_x = -\mathrm{i}\hbar\left[y\,\frac{\partial}{\partial z} - z\,\frac{\partial}{\partial y}\right] \tag{2.20}$$

  and

  $$\widehat{\mathrm{L}}_y = -\mathrm{i}\hbar\left[z\,\frac{\partial}{\partial x} - x\,\frac{\partial}{\partial z}\right]. \tag{2.21}$$

You can verify that all of the expressions for $\widehat{\mathrm{L}}_x$, $\widehat{\mathrm{L}}_y$ and $\widehat{\mathrm{L}}_z$ can be obtained from any one of them, say Equation 2.19, by cycling the indices wherever they appear: $x \Longrightarrow y \Longrightarrow z \Longrightarrow x$. These equations are the starting point for the quantum theory of angular momentum.

### 2.3.2 Spherical coordinates

For many purposes, it is better to use the **spherical coordinates** $r$, $\theta$ and $\phi$ shown in Figure 2.9, rather than the more familiar Cartesian coordinates $x$, $y$ and $z$. The relationship between these two sets of coordinates is given by

$$x = r\sin\theta\cos\phi, \tag{2.22}$$

$$y = r\sin\theta\sin\phi, \tag{2.23}$$

$$z = r\cos\theta, \tag{2.24}$$

which are consistent with $r = \sqrt{x^2 + y^2 + z^2}$.

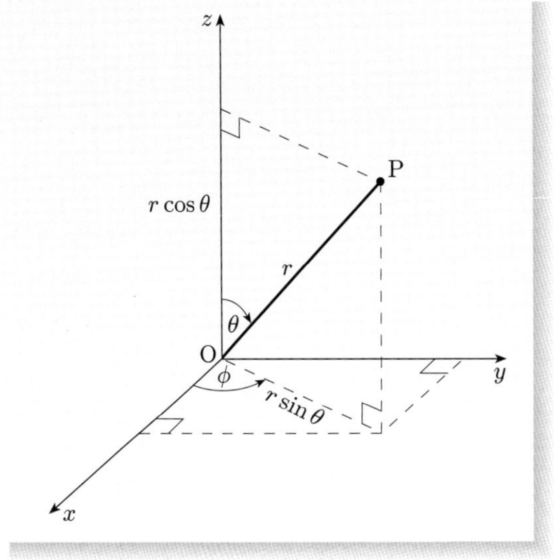


**Figure 2.9** Spherical coordinates: $r$ is called the **radial coordinate**, $\theta$ the **polar angle**, and $\phi$ the **azimuthal angle**. The angle $\theta$ ranges from 0 to $\pi$ and the angle $\phi$ ranges from 0 to $2\pi$.

There are many occasions where the use of spherical coordinates simplifies the description. For example, the following expressions both describe the potential energy of a point charge $q$ due to another point charge $Q$ at the origin:

$$V(r) = \frac{1}{4\pi\varepsilon_0}\frac{qQ}{r},$$

$$V(x,y,z) = \frac{1}{4\pi\varepsilon_0}\frac{qQ}{\sqrt{(x^2+y^2+z^2)}}.$$

The first of these expressions is in spherical coordinates, while the second is in Cartesian coordinates; there is no doubt which looks simpler! Spherical coordinates are useful for systems such as atoms that have spherical symmetry. Angular momentum is also important in situations with spherical symmetry, so it will be useful to express the angular momentum operators in terms of spherical coordinates.

The task of deriving expressions for $\widehat{\mathrm{L}}_x$, $\widehat{\mathrm{L}}_y$ and $\widehat{\mathrm{L}}_z$ in spherical coordinates is a lengthy and non-trivial mathematical exercise, so we shall move directly to the most important conclusion. Starting from Equation 2.19, and using Equations 2.22–2.24, it is possible to show that

$$\widehat{\mathrm{L}}_z = -\mathrm{i}\hbar\frac{\partial}{\partial\phi}. \tag{2.25}$$

This is an expression you should memorize. The expressions for $\widehat{\mathrm{L}}_x$ and $\widehat{\mathrm{L}}_y$ in spherical coordinates are much more complicated, but they are not needed in this course, so we will not write them down.

**Optional check:** If you are familiar with the **chain rule** of partial differentiation, it is not difficult to check that Equation 2.25 is correct. The chain rule tells us that, for any function $f(r,\theta,\phi)$,

$$\frac{\partial f}{\partial\phi} = \frac{\partial x}{\partial\phi}\frac{\partial f}{\partial x} + \frac{\partial y}{\partial\phi}\frac{\partial f}{\partial y} + \frac{\partial z}{\partial\phi}\frac{\partial f}{\partial z}.$$

Using Equations 2.22–2.24 to calculate the three partial derivatives $\partial x/\partial\phi$, $\partial y/\partial\phi$ and $\partial z/\partial\phi$, we therefore see that

$$\frac{\partial f}{\partial\phi} = (-r\sin\theta\sin\phi)\frac{\partial f}{\partial x} + (r\sin\theta\cos\phi)\frac{\partial f}{\partial y} = -y\frac{\partial f}{\partial x} + x\frac{\partial f}{\partial y},$$

so Equation 2.25 is consistent with Equation 2.19.

### 2.3.3 Quantization of $L_z$

In general, the allowed values of an observable $O$ are the eigenvalues of the corresponding quantum-mechanical operator $\widehat{\mathrm{O}}$. We wish to find the allowed values of the angular momentum component $L_z$, and we can do this by finding the eigenvalues of the operator $\widehat{\mathrm{L}}_z$.

Expressed in spherical coordinates, the eigenvalue equation for $\widehat{\mathrm{L}}_z$ takes the form

$$-\mathrm{i}\hbar\frac{\partial}{\partial\phi}\psi(r,\theta,\phi) = \alpha\,\psi(r,\theta,\phi), \tag{2.26}$$

where $\alpha$ is a constant. The operator $-\mathrm{i}\hbar\,\partial/\partial\phi$ does not affect the $r$ and $\theta$ coordinates, so we can assume that the eigenfunctions are of the form

$$\psi(r,\theta,\phi) = g(r,\theta)f(\phi). \tag{2.27}$$

Substituting into Equation 2.26 and cancelling through by $g(r,\theta)$, we then obtain the differential equation

$$-\mathrm{i}\hbar\,\frac{\mathrm{d}f(\phi)}{\mathrm{d}\phi} = \alpha f(\phi), \tag{2.28}$$

An ordinary derivative is used because $f(\phi)$ is a function of a single variable.

which has the general solution

$$f(\phi) = A\,\mathrm{e}^{\mathrm{i}\alpha\phi/\hbar} = A\,\mathrm{e}^{\mathrm{i}m\phi}, \tag{2.29}$$

where $A$ is a constant and $m = \alpha/\hbar$.

- Verify that the function $A\,\mathrm{e}^{\mathrm{i}m\phi}$ is an eigenfunction of $\widehat{\mathrm{L}}_z$, and determine its eigenvalue.

- Substituting $f(\phi) = A\,\mathrm{e}^{\mathrm{i}m\phi}$ into Equation 2.28, we find

$$-\mathrm{i}\hbar\,\frac{\partial}{\partial\phi}\big(A\,\mathrm{e}^{\mathrm{i}m\phi}\big) = -\mathrm{i}\hbar\big(\mathrm{i}mA\,\mathrm{e}^{\mathrm{i}m\phi}\big) = m\hbar\big(A\,\mathrm{e}^{\mathrm{i}m\phi}\big), \tag{2.30}$$

so $f(\phi)$ is an eigenfunction of $\widehat{\mathrm{L}}_z$, with eigenvalue $m\hbar$.

Eigenfunctions are often required to satisfy subsidiary conditions; for example, the energy eigenfunctions that solve the time-independent Schrödinger equation are required to be continuous and finite. In the present case, we impose the condition that the eigenfunctions that satisfy Equation 2.28 must 'join up with themselves' as $\phi$ goes through 360 degrees ($2\pi$ radians), so that $f(\phi + 2\pi) = f(\phi)$. We refer to this as the **single-valuedness condition**. Using Equation 2.29, we require that

$$A\,\mathrm{e}^{\mathrm{i}m(\phi+2\pi)} = A\,\mathrm{e}^{\mathrm{i}m\phi},$$

which gives

$$\mathrm{e}^{\mathrm{i}2\pi m} = 1.$$

This last equation can be satisfied only if $m$ is an integer (positive, negative or zero):

$$m = 0,\ \pm1,\ \pm2,\ \pm3,\ \ldots. \tag{2.31}$$

The integer $m$ is a *quantum number* for $L_z$. The eigenvalues of $\widehat{\mathrm{L}}_z$, and hence the allowed values of $L_z$, are given by $m\hbar$. We therefore conclude that the $z$-component of angular momentum is quantized, coming in $\hbar$-sized lumps. Because of the link between the angular momentum and the magnetic dipole moment, $m$ is called the **magnetic quantum number**.

Some authors call $m$ the *azimuthal quantum number*.

### Normalization and orthogonality of the eigenfunctions

It is conventional to choose the constant $A$ in Equation 2.29 to be equal to $1/\sqrt{2\pi}$. An eigenfunction of $\widehat{\mathrm{L}}_z$, with quantum number $m$, can then be written as

$$f_m(\phi) = \frac{1}{\sqrt{2\pi}}\,\mathrm{e}^{\mathrm{i}m\phi}. \tag{2.32}$$

This choice of $A$ ensures that

$$\int_0^{2\pi} |f_m(\phi)|^2 \, \mathrm{d}\phi = \frac{1}{2\pi} \int_0^{2\pi} |\mathrm{e}^{\mathrm{i}m\phi}|^2 \, \mathrm{d}\phi = \frac{1}{2\pi} \int_0^{2\pi} \mathrm{d}\phi = 1, \tag{2.33}$$

and we say that the eigenfunction is *normalized* .

In a similar vein, we can show that two different eigenfunctions, $f_m(\phi)$ and $f_n(\phi)$, obey

$$\int_0^{2\pi} f_m^*(\phi) \, f_n(\phi) \, \mathrm{d}\phi = 0 \quad \text{for } m \neq n, \tag{2.34}$$

and we describe this by saying that different eigenfunctions of $\widehat{\mathrm{L}}_z$ are *orthogonal* .

**Exercise 2.3** Verify Equation 2.34. ■

### 2.3.4 Quantization of $L_x$, $L_y$ and $L^2$

So far, we have considered the $z$-component of angular momentum, but what about the other two components? Our reason for concentrating on the $z$-component is that the operator $\widehat{\mathrm{L}}_z$ has a simple form in spherical coordinates. The same cannot be said for $\widehat{\mathrm{L}}_x$ and $\widehat{\mathrm{L}}_y$, but their more complicated expressions are not needed here so we shall not write them down.

However, we are free to choose any direction for the $z$-axis and, no matter what direction is chosen, we will always find that the $z$-component of angular momentum is equal to $m\hbar$, where $m$ is an integer. This means that the angular momentum component, taken along any direction in space, can only have the values $0, \pm\hbar, \pm 2\hbar, \ldots$. It follows *without further calculation* that the possible values of $L_x$ and $L_y$ are $0, \pm\hbar, \pm 2\hbar, \ldots$. All three operators, $\widehat{\mathrm{L}}_x$, $\widehat{\mathrm{L}}_y$ and $\widehat{\mathrm{L}}_z$ have the same set of eigenvalues.

There is one very important point about these eigenvalues that must be understood. It is not possible to find a state in which, for example, $L_x = 2\hbar$, $L_y = -\hbar$ and $L_z = 3\hbar$. This is because any state that has a definite non-zero value of $L_z$ does *not* have definite values of $L_x$ and $L_y$. You will see the reasons for this later, but you can think of it as being analogous to the fact that a particle cannot simultaneously have definite values of both position and momentum.

We must also consider the *magnitude* of the angular momentum, $L$, or its square, $L^2$. For example, the classical expression for the rotational energy of a rigid body, rotating about a fixed axis, is $L^2/2I$, where $I$ is the moment of inertia of the body. We therefore need to discuss the quantization of $L^2$.

The quantum-mechanical operator corresponding to $L^2$ is

$$\widehat{\mathrm{L}}^2 = \widehat{\mathrm{L}}_x^2 + \widehat{\mathrm{L}}_y^2 + \widehat{\mathrm{L}}_z^2.$$

With some effort, we could use standard results for $\widehat{\mathrm{L}}_x$, $\widehat{\mathrm{L}}_y$ and $\widehat{\mathrm{L}}_z$ to express this as an explicit differential operator. The result would be quite messy, but we could then, in principle, write down an eigenvalue equation for $\widehat{\mathrm{L}}^2$ and solve it to find the eigenfunctions and eigenvalues; the eigenvalues are the possible values of $L^2$. Here, we simply state the result that emerges for these eigenvalues.

**The eigenvalues of $\widehat{\mathrm{L}}^2$**

The eigenvalues of $\widehat{\mathrm{L}}^2$ are given by the formula $l(l+1)\hbar^2$, where $l$ is any non-negative integer, including zero: $l = 0, 1, 2, 3, \ldots$. So the first few allowed values of $L^2$ are 0, $2\hbar^2$, $6\hbar^2$, $12\hbar^2$, .... The integer $l$ is often called the **orbital angular momentum quantum number**.

## 2.3.5 The spectra of rotating molecules

When infrared radiation with a wide and continuous range of frequencies passes through pure hydrogen chloride (HCl) gas, the radiation is absorbed at a series of specific frequencies. The top part of Figure 2.10 shows a number of dips in the intensity of radiation transmitted through HCl gas; these dips occur at frequencies at which the radiation is strongly absorbed.

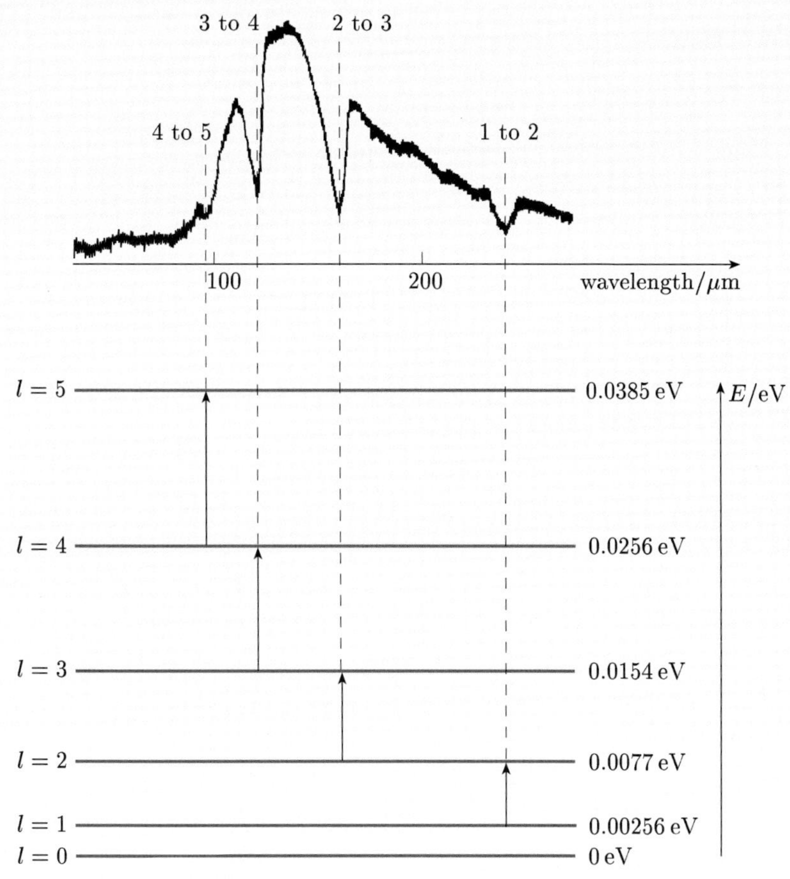


**Figure 2.10** An absorption spectrum for the transmission of infrared radiation through HCl gas (top). The dips correspond to the frequencies at which the radiation is absorbed. The bottom part of the figure shows energy levels and transitions that account for the measured spectrum.

The lower part of Figure 2.10 gives an analysis that explains where the pattern of absorbed frequencies comes from. Each absorption frequency $f$ arises from a transition between two energy levels separated by an energy $hf$. The energy levels marked in the figure account for the dips in the measured absorption spectrum. In the following exercise, you can check that these energy levels are proportional to $l(l+1)$, where $l = 0, 1, 2, \ldots$.

**Exercise 2.4** The lower part of Figure 2.10 shows an excited state at an energy of $0.00256\,\mathrm{eV}$ above the ground state. Calculate from this the next two energy levels, assuming that the energies are proportional to $l(l+1)$, where the ground state has $l = 0$, the $0.00256\,\mathrm{eV}$ state has $l = 1$, etc. Compare your answers with the energies given in the figure, and comment on this. ■

It is not difficult to understand where the $l(l+1)$ rule comes from. We begin with a classical model. The HCl molecule, consisting of one hydrogen and one chlorine atom, can be treated as a rigid body, rather like a lop-sided dumbbell. The rotational energy of the molecule can then be expressed as

$$E_{\text{rot}} = \frac{L^2}{2I}, \qquad \text{(Eqn 2.10)}$$

where $I$ is the moment of inertia about any axis that is perpendicular to the line joining the two atoms and passes through the centre of mass of the molecule.

You might wonder whether this formula (which applies to rotations about a fixed axis) is valid for a molecule that tumbles through space. A more general formula for the rotational energy of the molecule is

$$E_{\text{rot}} = \frac{L_x^2}{2I_x} + \frac{L_y^2}{2I_y} + \frac{L_z^2}{2I_z},$$

where the $z$-axis is chosen to be along the line joining the atoms, and the $x$- and $y$-axes are perpendicular to this line. The moments of inertia $I_x$, $I_y$ and $I_z$ refer to rotations about these axes. Because of the linear shape of the HCl molecule, we can safely neglect $L_z$ in comparison to $L_y$ and $L_x$. Also, by symmetry, we have $I_x = I_y = I$, so we see that

$$E_{\text{rot}} = \frac{L_x^2 + L_y^2}{2I} = \frac{L^2}{2I},$$

as assumed.

Equation 2.10 is an expression for the rotational energy of the molecule expressed in terms of a momentum (albeit an angular momentum). It is the *Hamiltonian function* for the rotational energy of the molecule (there is no potential energy term in this case). The corresponding *Hamiltonian operator* $\widehat{\mathrm{H}}$ is found by replacing $L^2$ with $\widehat{\mathrm{L}}^2$, so that the time-independent Schrödinger equation for the rotating molecule is

$$\widehat{\mathrm{H}}\Psi = \frac{\widehat{\mathrm{L}}^2}{2I}\Psi = E\Psi. \qquad (2.35)$$

The energy eigenvalues of this equation are the allowed rotational energies of the molecule. But $\widehat{\mathrm{H}}$ is just a constant $(1/2I)$ times $\widehat{\mathrm{L}}^2$, and we know that the eigenvalues of $\widehat{\mathrm{L}}^2$ are $l(l+1)\hbar^2$ for $l = 0, 1, 2, \ldots$. Hence we conclude that the rotational energy levels of the molecule are

$$E = \frac{l(l+1)\hbar^2}{2I} \quad \text{for } l = 0, 1, 2, \ldots,$$

which agrees with our analysis of the spectrum in Figure 2.10.

Perhaps you think that such a simple model for an HCl molecule is too good to be true. This molecule is, after all, a complicated system containing 18 electrons and two nuclei. Well, you would be right — there are many other states corresponding to the vibration of the molecule, and different arrangements of the electrons, but these other states are at much higher energies. The low-energy states of HCl are quite well described by our rotational model. Moreover, we can learn a basic fact about the HCl molecule from the spacing between the levels, which depends upon the moment of inertia, $I$. Since the distance between the hydrogen and chlorine atoms determines $I$, this distance can be deduced from the measured spacing of the energy levels. It turns out to be $0.13$ nm.

## 2.4 The conservation of angular momentum

Now that we have operators that describe angular momentum, we can consider the quantum-mechanical version of the law of conservation of angular momentum. Our starting point is the generalized Ehrenfest theorem derived in the preceding chapter. This tells us the time-development of expectation values; if we have an observable $A$ in a given system, the rate of change of its expectation value is

$$\frac{\mathrm{d}\langle A\rangle}{\mathrm{d}t} = \frac{1}{\mathrm{i}\hbar}\left\langle [\widehat{\mathrm{A}},\widehat{\mathrm{H}}]\right\rangle, \qquad \text{(Eqn 1.46)}$$

where $\widehat{\mathrm{H}}$ is the Hamiltonian operator for the system under consideration. We will now apply this general result to the components of angular momentum.

Because our choice of axes is arbitrary, it does not matter, physically, which component of angular momentum we choose to consider. As usual, we shall concentrate on the $z$-component, for which

$$\frac{\mathrm{d}\langle L_z\rangle}{\mathrm{d}t} = \frac{1}{\mathrm{i}\hbar}\left\langle [\widehat{\mathrm{L}}_z,\widehat{\mathrm{H}}]\right\rangle. \qquad (2.36)$$

We immediately see that the expectation value of $L_z$ will remain constant in time provided that $[\widehat{\mathrm{L}}_z,\widehat{\mathrm{H}}] = 0$. We must therefore investigate whether $\widehat{\mathrm{L}}_z$ commutes with the Hamiltonian operator $\widehat{\mathrm{H}}$.

The simplest case to consider is that of a free particle of mass $m$, for which the Hamiltonian operator has the form

$$\widehat{\mathrm{H}} = \frac{1}{2m}\left(\widehat{\mathrm{p}}_x^2 + \widehat{\mathrm{p}}_y^2 + \widehat{\mathrm{p}}_z^2\right).$$

Noting that $\widehat{\mathrm{L}}_z = \widehat{\mathrm{x}}\,\widehat{\mathrm{p}}_y - \widehat{\mathrm{y}}\,\widehat{\mathrm{p}}_x$, we have

$$[\widehat{\mathrm{L}}_z,\widehat{\mathrm{H}}] = \frac{1}{2m}\left[\widehat{\mathrm{x}}\,\widehat{\mathrm{p}}_y - \widehat{\mathrm{y}}\,\widehat{\mathrm{p}}_x,\ \widehat{\mathrm{p}}_x^2 + \widehat{\mathrm{p}}_y^2 + \widehat{\mathrm{p}}_z^2\right].$$

This looks a lot worse than it is! Most of the operators commute with one another — the momentum operators all commute with one another, and $\widehat{\mathrm{p}}_x$ commutes with $\widehat{\mathrm{y}}$, for example. The only pairs of operators that do not commute with one another are $\widehat{\mathrm{x}}$ and $\widehat{\mathrm{p}}_x^2$, and $\widehat{\mathrm{y}}$ and $\widehat{\mathrm{p}}_y^2$, and these are the only pairs of operators for which order matters. Bearing these points in mind, the above expression simplifies to

$$[\widehat{\mathrm{L}}_z,\widehat{\mathrm{H}}] = \frac{1}{2m}\left([\widehat{\mathrm{x}},\widehat{\mathrm{p}}_x^2]\,\widehat{\mathrm{p}}_y - [\widehat{\mathrm{y}},\widehat{\mathrm{p}}_y^2]\,\widehat{\mathrm{p}}_x\right).$$

The commutator $[\widehat{\mathrm{x}}, \widehat{\mathrm{p}}_x^2]$ may look familiar: it was evaluated in Worked Example 1.2 of Chapter 1, where we found that

$$[\widehat{\mathrm{x}}, \widehat{\mathrm{p}}_x^2] = 2\mathrm{i}\hbar\,\widehat{\mathrm{p}}_x.$$

Obviously, a similar result applies to $[\widehat{\mathrm{y}}, \widehat{\mathrm{p}}_y^2]$, which is equal to $2\mathrm{i}\hbar\,\widehat{\mathrm{p}}_y$, so we conclude that

$$[\widehat{\mathrm{L}}_z, \widehat{\mathrm{H}}] = \frac{1}{2m}\left(2\mathrm{i}\hbar\,\widehat{\mathrm{p}}_x\widehat{\mathrm{p}}_y - 2\mathrm{i}\hbar\,\widehat{\mathrm{p}}_y\widehat{\mathrm{p}}_x\right) = 0.$$

The $z$-component of angular momentum commutes with the Hamiltonian operator, so the expectation value of $L_z$ is conserved for a free particle. This is perhaps not a surprise, but we have given a solid proof of this fact using the principles of quantum mechanics.

Now let us consider a system analogous to a planet orbiting the Sun. In classical physics, the planet experiences a force from the Sun, but this force is *central*, acting along the line joining the planet to the Sun. Under these circumstances, classical physics predicts that the angular momentum of the planet is conserved, and Kepler's second law is an observed consequence of this conservation law.

In quantum mechanics, we generally deal with potential energy functions rather than forces. The statement that a force is *central* about a given point O is equivalent to saying that the potential energy function is *spherically symmetric* about O. So if we choose O as our origin and use spherical coordinates, the potential energy function takes the form $V(r)$, which depends only on the radial coordinate, and does not depend on the angular coordinates $\theta$ and $\phi$.

If we consider a system with the Hamiltonian operator

$$\widehat{\mathrm{H}} = \frac{1}{2m}\left(\widehat{\mathrm{p}}_x^2 + \widehat{\mathrm{p}}_y^2 + \widehat{\mathrm{p}}_z^2\right) + \widehat{\mathrm{V}}(r), \tag{2.37}$$

we can ask whether $\widehat{\mathrm{L}}_z$ and $\widehat{\mathrm{H}}$ are commuting operators. We already know that $\widehat{\mathrm{L}}_z$ commutes with the kinetic energy term. To see whether $\widehat{\mathrm{L}}_z$ also commutes with the potential energy term, it is best to use the spherical coordinate form $\widehat{\mathrm{L}}_z = -\mathrm{i}\hbar\,\partial/\partial\phi$. Then, for any function $f(r, \theta, \phi)$, we have

$$\begin{aligned}
\widehat{\mathrm{L}}_z\,\widehat{\mathrm{V}}(r)\,f(r,\theta,\phi) &= -\mathrm{i}\hbar\,\frac{\partial}{\partial\phi}\big(V(r)\,f(r,\theta,\phi)\big) \\
&= -\mathrm{i}\hbar\,V(r)\,\frac{\partial}{\partial\phi}f(r,\theta,\phi) \\
&= \widehat{\mathrm{V}}(r)\,\widehat{\mathrm{L}}_z\,f(r,\theta,\phi).
\end{aligned}$$

Since this is true for any function $f(r, \theta, \phi)$, we conclude that $\widehat{\mathrm{L}}_z$ commutes with the potential energy term, as well as the kinetic energy term, so it commutes with the whole Hamiltonian operator. It follows that the expectation value of $L_z$ is conserved.

We have concentrated on $L_z$ for mathematical reasons, taking advantage of the fact that it is described by a nice simple operator in spherical coordinates. However, the Hamiltonian operator in Equation 2.37 is spherically symmetric, in the sense that it does not depend on how we orient our axes. Since we can choose the $z$-axis to point in any direction in space, this means that the expectation value of the angular momentum component *in any chosen direction* is conserved. This then implies that the expectation values of $L_x$ and $L_y$ are conserved as well as the expectation value of $L_z$.

We see here a particular example of the link between symmetry and conservation laws described in general terms in Chapter 1. *Symmetries give rise to conservation laws.* In the present context, the system is spherically symmetric and this symmetry gives rise to the conservation of angular momentum, which is expressed in quantum mechanics by the fact that the expectation value of any component of angular momentum remains constant in time.

We can also meet situations in which the potential energy function depends on angle.

**Exercise 2.5** Does the operator $\widehat{\mathrm{L}}_z$ commute with the potential energy function in the following cases: (a) a potential energy function $V(r, \theta)$ that depends on the spherical coordinates $r$ and $\theta$, but is independent of $\phi$; (b) a potential energy function $V(r, \phi)$ that depends on the spherical coordinates $r$ and $\phi$, but is independent of $\theta$?

In each case discuss whether a particle subject to the given potential energy function will have a constant expectation value of $L_z$. ■

## 2.5 Compatible and incompatible observables

Section 2.3.4 raised an important issue, which we shall now discuss in detail. We said that it is impossible to find a state in which $L_z$ has a definite non-zero value, and $L_x$ and $L_y$ also have definite values. More generally, if any of these observables has a definite non-zero value, the other two will have uncertain values. This means that we cannot label an arbitrary state by giving simultaneous values for $L_x$, $L_y$ and $L_z$: these three observables are said to be **incompatible**.

### 2.5.1 Commutation relations and compatibility

One way to understand the incompatibility of $L_x$, $L_y$ and $L_z$ is to use the generalized uncertainty principle discussed in the previous chapter. This tells us that the product of the uncertainties of two observables $A$ and $B$ obeys

$$\Delta A \, \Delta B \geq \tfrac{1}{2} \left| \left\langle [\widehat{\mathrm{A}}, \widehat{\mathrm{B}}] \right\rangle \right|, \tag{2.38}$$

where the uncertainties on the left and the expectation value on the right are evaluated in the same state. It turns out to be very difficult (often impossible) to satisfy this inequality if $\Delta A = 0$, $\Delta B = 0$, and $[\widehat{\mathrm{A}}, \widehat{\mathrm{B}}] \neq 0$. The physical interpretation is that observables $A$ and $B$ cannot both have definite values in the same state (ignoring rare exceptions) if the operators $\widehat{\mathrm{A}}$ and $\widehat{\mathrm{B}}$ do not to commute with one another.

In fact, the state involved would have to be an eigenvector of the operator $[\widehat{\mathrm{A}}, \widehat{\mathrm{B}}]$, with zero eigenvalue; such states are truly exceptional.

To apply these ideas to angular momentum, we must evaluate commutators of different angular momentum operators. The following worked example illustrates how this is done.

**Essential skill**

Evaluating a commutator

### Worked Example 2.1

Evaluate the commutator $[\widehat{\mathrm{L}}_x, \widehat{\mathrm{L}}_y]$.

#### Solution

It is convenient here to work in Cartesian coordinates. First let $\widehat{\mathrm{L}}_x\widehat{\mathrm{L}}_y$ act on an arbitrary function $f(x, y, z)$, to obtain

$$\begin{aligned}
\widehat{\mathrm{L}}_x\widehat{\mathrm{L}}_y f &= -\hbar^2\left(y\frac{\partial}{\partial z} - z\frac{\partial}{\partial y}\right)\left(z\frac{\partial}{\partial x} - x\frac{\partial}{\partial z}\right)f \\
&= -\hbar^2\left[y\frac{\partial}{\partial z}\left(z\frac{\partial f}{\partial x}\right) - y\frac{\partial}{\partial z}\left(x\frac{\partial f}{\partial z}\right) - z\frac{\partial}{\partial y}\left(z\frac{\partial f}{\partial x}\right) + z\frac{\partial}{\partial y}\left(x\frac{\partial f}{\partial z}\right)\right] \\
&= -\hbar^2\left[y\frac{\partial f}{\partial x} + \text{four terms involving second-order partial derivatives}\right].
\end{aligned}$$

Now, if we operate on $f(x, y, z)$ with $\widehat{\mathrm{L}}_y\widehat{\mathrm{L}}_x$,

$$\begin{aligned}
\widehat{\mathrm{L}}_y\widehat{\mathrm{L}}_x f &= -\hbar^2\left(z\frac{\partial}{\partial x} - x\frac{\partial}{\partial z}\right)\left(y\frac{\partial}{\partial z} - z\frac{\partial}{\partial y}\right)f \\
&= -\hbar^2\left[z\frac{\partial}{\partial x}\left(y\frac{\partial f}{\partial z}\right) - z\frac{\partial}{\partial x}\left(z\frac{\partial f}{\partial y}\right) - x\frac{\partial}{\partial z}\left(y\frac{\partial f}{\partial z}\right) + x\frac{\partial}{\partial z}\left(z\frac{\partial f}{\partial y}\right)\right] \\
&= -\hbar^2\left[x\frac{\partial f}{\partial y} + \text{four terms involving second-order partial derivatives}\right].
\end{aligned}$$

It turns out that the terms involving second-order partial derivatives are the same in both $\widehat{\mathrm{L}}_x\widehat{\mathrm{L}}_y f$ and $\widehat{\mathrm{L}}_y\widehat{\mathrm{L}}_x f$, so we are left with

$$\begin{aligned}
\left(\widehat{\mathrm{L}}_x\widehat{\mathrm{L}}_y - \widehat{\mathrm{L}}_y\widehat{\mathrm{L}}_x\right)f &= -\hbar^2\left(y\frac{\partial f}{\partial x} - x\frac{\partial f}{\partial y}\right) \\
&= \mathrm{i}\hbar \times (-\mathrm{i}\hbar)\left(x\frac{\partial}{\partial y} - y\frac{\partial}{\partial x}\right)f = \mathrm{i}\hbar\,\widehat{\mathrm{L}}_z f.
\end{aligned}$$

Since this equation applies for any function $f(x, y, z)$, we can write it as an identity between operators:

$$[\widehat{\mathrm{L}}_x, \widehat{\mathrm{L}}_y] = \mathrm{i}\hbar\,\widehat{\mathrm{L}}_z.$$

You saw earlier that a cyclic permutation $x \Longrightarrow y \Longrightarrow z \Longrightarrow x$ converts an equation for one angular momentum component into an equally valid equation for another angular momentum component. The same transformation will convert the commutation relation for $[\widehat{\mathrm{L}}_x, \widehat{\mathrm{L}}_y]$ into valid commutation relations for other angular momentum components. The complete set of commutation relations is

$$[\widehat{\mathrm{L}}_x, \widehat{\mathrm{L}}_y] = \mathrm{i}\hbar\,\widehat{\mathrm{L}}_z, \tag{2.39}$$

$$[\widehat{\mathrm{L}}_y, \widehat{\mathrm{L}}_z] = \mathrm{i}\hbar\,\widehat{\mathrm{L}}_x, \tag{2.40}$$

$$[\widehat{\mathrm{L}}_z, \widehat{\mathrm{L}}_x] = \mathrm{i}\hbar\,\widehat{\mathrm{L}}_y. \tag{2.41}$$

You need remember only *one* of these commutation relations, obtaining the others by cyclically permutating the subscripts.

It is very significant that *different components of angular momentum do not commute with one another.*

Using these commutation relations in the generalized uncertainty principle (Equation 2.38), we see that

$$\Delta L_x \, \Delta L_y \geq \frac{\hbar}{2} \left|\langle L_z \rangle\right|,$$
$$\Delta L_y \, \Delta L_z \geq \frac{\hbar}{2} \left|\langle L_x \rangle\right|,$$
$$\Delta L_z \, \Delta L_x \geq \frac{\hbar}{2} \left|\langle L_y \rangle\right|.$$

These inequalities prevent any pair of angular momentum components from having definite non-zero values in the same state. For, let us suppose that $L_z$ has the definite value $m_z\hbar$ and, *in the same state*, $L_x$ has the definite value $m_x\hbar$. Since $L_z$ and $L_x$ have definite values, we have $\Delta L_z = \Delta L_x = 0$. The above inequalities then tell us that all three expectation values, $\langle L_x \rangle$, $\langle L_y \rangle$ and $\langle L_z \rangle$, must be zero, so $m_z = m_x = 0$. Hence, it is impossible for $L_z$ and $L_x$ to have definite values in the same state, *unless* both of these values are equal to zero. For example, the ground state of a hydrogen atom happens to be a state in which all three components of the angular momentum vanish. Apart from this notable exception, no other state of the atom can be labelled by the values of more than one component of angular momentum.

We can also consider the compatibility of a component of angular momentum (say $L_z$) and $L^2$. The key issue is whether the operators $\widehat{\mathrm{L}}_z$ and $\widehat{\mathrm{L}}^2$ commute with one another. It is possible to show (we do not give the proof here) that

$$\left[\widehat{\mathrm{L}}^2, \widehat{\mathrm{L}}_x\right] = \left[\widehat{\mathrm{L}}^2, \widehat{\mathrm{L}}_y\right] = \left[\widehat{\mathrm{L}}^2, \widehat{\mathrm{L}}_z\right] = 0. \tag{2.42}$$

In other words, $\widehat{\mathrm{L}}^2$ commutes with all three components of angular momentum. This means that the generalized uncertainty principle places no bar on $L^2$ and, say, $L_z$ having definite values in the same state.

Strictly speaking, the fact that the generalized uncertainty principle raises no objections does not show that it is possible to find states in which $L^2$ and $L_z$ both have definite values. However, there is a separate theorem (again not proved here) that if a set of Hermitian operators $\widehat{\mathrm{A}}, \widehat{\mathrm{B}}, \ldots$ all commute with one another, then their eigenfunctions can always be chosen to be *simultaneous eigenfunctions* of all the mutually commuting operators. Given this fact, we can be confident that states can be found in which both $L^2$ and $L_z$ have definite values.

$L^2$ and $L_z$ are said to be **compatible observables**.

### 2.5.2 Simultaneous eigenfunctions of $\widehat{\mathrm{L}}^2$ and $\widehat{\mathrm{L}}_z$

We have just seen that the operators $\widehat{\mathrm{L}}^2$ and $\widehat{\mathrm{L}}_z$ commute with one another, and that this means that these operators have a set of simultaneous eigenfunctions, representing states in which both $L^2$ and $L_z$ have definite values. We shall now describe these states in more detail.

In spherical coordinates, the operator $\widehat{\mathrm{L}}^2$ is a complex expression involving $\theta$ and $\phi$. Earlier on, we did not bother to write this down, but asked you to imagine the process of forming the appropriate eigenvalue equation and finding its eigenvalues and eigenfunctions. The eigenvalues are of the form $l(l+1)\hbar^2$, where

$l = 0, 1, 2, \ldots$. The eigenfunctions are functions of $\theta$ and $\phi$, such as $\cos\theta\, e^{i\phi}$, but again we shall avoid the details in this book.

The term **eigenstate** is sometimes used for a quantum state that is represented by an eigenfunction or eigenvector of a given operator.

Fortunately, Dirac notation allows us to specify particular eigenstates of $\widehat{L}^2$ and $\widehat{L}_z$ without writing down the lengthy expressions for the operators or eigenfunctions. We shall use the notation $|l, m\rangle$ to represent an eigenfunction of $\widehat{L}^2$ with eigenvalue $l(l+1)\hbar^2$, that is simultaneously an eigenfunction of $\widehat{L}_z$ with eigenvalue $m\hbar$, so we have

$$\widehat{L}^2|l, m\rangle = l(l+1)\hbar^2|l, m\rangle, \tag{2.43}$$

$$\widehat{L}_z|l, m\rangle = m\hbar|l, m\rangle. \tag{2.44}$$

Note that the ket vector is labelled not by the eigenvalues but by the *quantum numbers* $l$ and $m$, which are sufficient to specify the eigenvalues $l(l+1)\hbar^2$ and $m\hbar$, respectively.

Now, the quantum numbers $l$ and $m$ are not completely independent of one another. This is not surprising: it would certainly be very strange if the $z$-component of the angular momentum were greater in magnitude than the angular momentum itself. We therefore have the condition $|m\hbar| \leq \sqrt{l(l+1)}\hbar$. Given that $m$ and $l$ are integers, this implies that $|m| \leq l$. It turns out that $m$ can have all integer values consistent with this condition; in other words, for a given value of $l$, the possible values of $m$ are

$$m = 0,\ \pm 1,\ \pm 2,\ \ldots,\ \pm l,$$

that is, $2l + 1$ values in all.

**Exercise 2.6**

(a) Write out all the possible kets associated with quantum number $l = 3$.

(b) Use ket notation to write out two explicit eigenvalue equations, for $\widehat{L}_z$ and $\widehat{L}^2$, for the state in which $l = 4$ and $m$ has its minimum possible value. ■

### 2.5.3 Describing angular momentum and energy

We often have to deal with a spherically-symmetric system — that is, a system whose Hamiltonian does not depend on the orientation of our coordinate axes. An isolated atom is a good example. Where there is spherical symmetry, the expectation values of $L_x$, $L_y$ and $L_z$ are all conserved. We shall now consider another aspect of spherical symmetry, which is important for the way we describe atoms.

In a spherically-symmetric system, we have seen that the operators $\widehat{L}_x$, $\widehat{L}_y$ and $\widehat{L}_z$ all commute with the Hamiltonian operator $\widehat{H}$. It immediately follows that $\widehat{L}_x^2$, $\widehat{L}_y^2$ and $\widehat{L}_z^2$ also commute with $\widehat{H}$. For example, we have

$$\widehat{L}_z^2\,\widehat{H} = \widehat{L}_z\widehat{L}_z\widehat{H} = \widehat{L}_z\widehat{H}\,\widehat{L}_z = \widehat{H}\,\widehat{L}_z\widehat{L}_z = \widehat{H}\,\widehat{L}_z^2.$$

Consequently, $\widehat{L}^2 = \widehat{L}_x^2 + \widehat{L}_y^2 + \widehat{L}_z^2$ also commutes with $\widehat{H}$. We therefore have the following situation:

- $\widehat{L}_z$ commutes with $\widehat{L}^2$ (it always does);
- $\widehat{L}_z$ commutes with $\widehat{H}$ (in a spherically-symmetric system);
- $\widehat{L}^2$ commutes with $\widehat{H}$ (in a spherically-symmetric system).

So, in a spherically-symmetric system, $\widehat{L}_z$, $\widehat{L}^2$ and $\widehat{H}$ form a set of *mutually* commuting operators, in which each operator commutes with the other two. It is therefore possible to find a set of functions that are simultaneous eigenfunctions of all three operators, and these eigenfunctions correspond to states in which the system simultaneously has definite values of the $z$-component of angular momentum, the square of the magnitude of the angular momentum, and the energy. This allows us to put labels on the energy eigenfunctions of a hydrogen atom, as you will see later in the course. This result is very important because the spectral lines that are emitted by atoms in the laboratory correspond to transitions between quantum states that can be labelled by angular momentum quantum numbers.

### 2.5.4 A two-dimensional model 'atom'

The above ideas can be illustrated with a simple model. In this chapter, we cannot discuss real, three-dimensional atoms. Instead, we do what physicists often do to get insight into a tricky problem. We consider an analogous system in a smaller number of dimensions. Even though unrealistic, such models often lead to insights into the workings of real systems.

If you are really pressed for study time, Section 2.5.4 could be omitted at this stage. We shall return to this topic in Chapter 1 of Book 3.

In this spirit, we consider a two-dimensional 'atom' consisting of a particle of mass $M$, confined to the $z = 0$ plane and subject to an attractive potential energy function $V(x, y)$ that depends only on $x$ and $y$. The only angular momentum component we need to consider is $L_z$, represented by the operator $\widehat{L}_z$. There is no need to consider a separate operator $\widehat{L}^2$.

● Write down the Hamiltonian operator and Schrödinger's time-independent equation for a particle of mass $M$ subject to such a potential energy function.

❍ The Hamiltonian operator is the sum of kinetic and potential energy terms

$$\widehat{H} = -\frac{\hbar^2}{2M}\left[\frac{\partial^2}{\partial x^2} + \frac{\partial^2}{\partial y^2}\right] + V(x,y), \tag{2.45}$$

so the time-independent Schrödinger equation is

$$-\frac{\hbar^2}{2M}\left[\frac{\partial^2\psi(x,y)}{\partial x^2} + \frac{\partial^2\psi(x,y)}{\partial y^2}\right] + V(x,y)\,\psi(x,y) = E\,\psi(x,y). \tag{2.46}$$

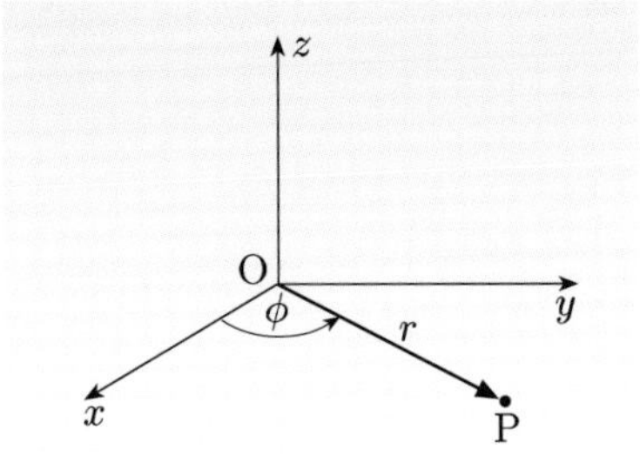


**Figure 2.11** Polar coordinates $r$ and $\phi$ can be used instead of $x$ and $y$ to specify the position of a point in a plane.

We shall suppose that $V(x, y)$ is symmetric under rotations, i.e. it depends only on the distance $\sqrt{x^2 + y^2}$ from the origin. This prompts us to use the **polar coordinates** $r$ and $\phi$ shown in Figure 2.11. The potential energy function is then written as $V(r)$ and the energy eigenfunction as $\psi(r, \phi)$.

It is also necessary to transform the kinetic energy term in the Hamiltonian operator into polar coordinates. This is a tedious task, so we shall simply state the result: the Hamiltonian operator becomes

You are not expected to recall or derive the form of $\widehat{\mathrm{H}}$ in polar coordinates.

$$\widehat{\mathrm{H}} = -\frac{\hbar^2}{2M}\left[\frac{\partial^2}{\partial r^2} + \frac{2}{r}\frac{\partial}{\partial r} + \frac{1}{r^2}\frac{\partial^2}{\partial \phi^2}\right] + V(r). \qquad (2.47)$$

Look at the third term in the square brackets, involving the second derivative of $\phi$. It is just $1/2Mr^2$ times $\widehat{\mathrm{L}}_z^2$, because we can write

$$\widehat{\mathrm{L}}_z^2 = \left(-\mathrm{i}\hbar\frac{\partial}{\partial\phi}\right)\left(-\mathrm{i}\hbar\frac{\partial}{\partial\phi}\right) = -\hbar^2\frac{\partial^2}{\partial\phi^2}. \qquad (2.48)$$

As a result, Schrödinger's time-independent equation for a particle of mass $M$, moving in two dimensions under the influence of a rotationally-symmetric potential energy function, can be written as

$$-\frac{\hbar^2}{2M}\left[\frac{\partial^2\psi}{\partial r^2} + \frac{2}{r}\frac{\partial\psi}{\partial r}\right] + \frac{1}{2Mr^2}\widehat{\mathrm{L}}_z^2\,\psi(r,\phi) + V(r)\,\psi(r,\phi) = E\,\psi(r,\phi). \qquad (2.49)$$

Rather than solve this equation for any specific $V(r)$, we look at properties that apply for any $V(r)$. We shall look for solutions that are in the product form $\psi(r,\phi) = R(r)f(\phi)$. Substituting this into Equation 2.49 and using the usual technique of separation of variables, we obtain two ordinary differential equations linked by a separation constant, $K$:

$$\frac{1}{2M}\widehat{\mathrm{L}}_z^2 f(\phi) = -\frac{\hbar^2}{2M}\frac{\mathrm{d}^2 f}{\mathrm{d}\phi^2} = K f(\phi), \qquad (2.50)$$

$$-\frac{\hbar^2}{2M}\left[\frac{\mathrm{d}^2 R}{\mathrm{d}r^2} + \frac{2}{r}\frac{\mathrm{d}R}{\mathrm{d}r}\right] + V(r)\,R(r) = \left[E - \frac{K}{r^2}\right]R(r). \qquad (2.51)$$

The first of these equations is easily solved with the aid of Equation 2.30.

- Show that $f(\phi) = \mathrm{e}^{\mathrm{i}m\phi}$ is an eigenfunction of Equation 2.50, with eigenvalue $K = \hbar^2 m^2/2M$.

- Substituting the given expression for $f(\phi)$ into Equation 2.50, we obtain

$$-\frac{\hbar^2}{2M}\frac{\mathrm{d}^2}{\mathrm{d}\phi^2}\left(\mathrm{e}^{\mathrm{i}m\phi}\right) = \frac{\hbar^2 m^2}{2M}\mathrm{e}^{\mathrm{i}m\phi},$$

from which we conclude that $\mathrm{e}^{\mathrm{i}m\phi}$ is an eigenfunction, with eigenvalue $K = \hbar^2 m^2/2M$.

The function $f(\phi)$ must be single-valued as before, so $m$ is restricted to positive, negative or zero integer values. Using $K = \hbar^2 m^2/2M$, the differential equation for $R(r)$ can be written as

$$-\frac{\hbar^2}{2M}\left[\frac{\mathrm{d}^2 R}{\mathrm{d}r^2} + \frac{2}{r}\frac{\mathrm{d}R}{\mathrm{d}r}\right] + \frac{\hbar^2 m^2}{2Mr^2}R(r) + V(r)\,R(r) = E\,R(r). \qquad (2.52)$$

We can imagine solving this equation for each allowed value of $m$. The solutions have to satisfy various boundary conditions (they must not diverge at infinity, for example) and this generally means that, for each value of $m$, there is a discrete set of solutions, which we label by another quantum number, $n$. The allowed radial solutions are therefore written as $R_{nm}(r)$, and the corresponding energy eigenvalues as $E_{nm}$.

Assembling the product solutions from their separate parts, we conclude that the time-independent Schrödinger equation has a discrete set of solutions

$$\psi_{mn}(r, \phi) = R_{mn}(r)\, e^{im\phi}. \tag{2.53}$$

The function in Equation 2.53 is an eigenfunction of the Hamiltonian operator $\widehat{H}$, with eigenvalue $E_{nm}$, and it is *simultaneously* an eigenfunction of $\widehat{L}_z$, with eigenvalue $m\hbar$. Our simple model therefore provides a concrete example of the way in which energy eigenfunctions and eigenvalues can be labelled by sets of quantum numbers that include those for angular momentum, a consequence of the fact that the potential energy function has rotational symmetry.

## 2.6 A remaining puzzle

The quantum theory of angular momentum presented in this chapter has had a number of successes:

**1. Quantization** We showed why the components of angular momentum come in $\hbar$-sized lumps.

**2. Rotating molecules** We explained the overall pattern of the infrared absorption spectrum produced by rotating hydrogen chloride molecules.

**3. The labelling of atomic states** We showed how atomic states can be labelled, using the quantum numbers $m$ and $l$ that determine the $z$-component and the magnitude of the angular momentum. The correct labelling of atomic states is a first step towards understanding atomic spectra.

The Stern–Gerlach experiment supports the idea that angular momentum is quantized, and so can be regarded as providing further evidence in favour of our theory. However, there is a snag. When Stern and Gerlach carried out their experiment on silver atoms, they observed just *two* regions where silver was deposited on their detecting screen. However, you have seen that the allowed values of $l$ are $0, 1, 2, \ldots$ (integers) and that, for each value of $l$, there are $2l + 1$ different values of $m$ ($0, \pm 1, \pm 2, \pm l$). Each value of $m$ gives a different value of $L_z$, and hence a different value of $\mu_z$. We would therefore expect to find silver atoms appearing at $2l + 1$ places; this is always an odd number because $l$ is an integer. The fact that silver atoms are detected at *two* places is therefore beyond the powers of explanation of this chapter.

The solution to this difficulty will be given in the next chapter. You will see that there is a different type of angular momentum, not describable in classical terms, whose components have two different values, $+\hbar/2$ and $-\hbar/2$. This new form of angular momentum is called *spin*.

## Summary of Chapter 2

**Section 2.1** In classical physics, the $z$-component of the angular momentum of a particle is $L_z = xp_y - yp_z$. The $x$- and $y$-components can be obtained from this by a cyclic permutation of the subscripts: $x \Longrightarrow y \Longrightarrow z \Longrightarrow x$. The magnitude of the angular momentum of a rigid body rotating about a fixed axis is $L = I\omega$, where $I$ is the moment of inertia about the axis and $\omega$ is the angular speed of the body. The corresponding rotational energy is $E_{\text{rot}} = L^2/2I$.

**Section 2.2** Many atoms, nuclei and particles behave as magnetic dipoles, characterized by a magnetic dipole moment $\boldsymbol{\mu}$. In a magnetic field $\mathbf{B}$, a magnetic dipole has potential energy $E_{\text{mag}} = -\boldsymbol{\mu} \cdot \mathbf{B}$. In a non-uniform magnetic field pointing in the $z$-direction, a magnetic dipole experiences a force $F_z = \mu_z \, \partial B_z/\partial z$. The magnetic dipole moment due to an orbiting charge is related to the orbital angular momentum by $\boldsymbol{\mu} = \gamma\mathbf{L}$, where $\gamma$ is the gyromagnetic ratio.

The Stern–Gerlach experiment shows that the magnetic dipole moments of atoms are quantized. Because of the intimate link between magnetic dipole moments and angular momentum, the experiment also provides evidence for the quantization of angular momentum.

**Section 2.3** The quantum-mechanical operator for the $z$-component of angular momentum is $\widehat{\mathrm{L}}_z = (-\mathrm{i}\hbar)(x\,\partial/\partial y - y\,\partial/\partial x)$. Similar results for $\widehat{\mathrm{L}}_x$ and $\widehat{\mathrm{L}}_y$ are obtained by cyclic permutation of the subscripts. In spherical coordinates,

$$\widehat{\mathrm{L}}_z = -\mathrm{i}\hbar \frac{\partial}{\partial \phi}.$$

The eigenfunctions of $\widehat{\mathrm{L}}_z$ are of the form $A\,\mathrm{e}^{\mathrm{i}m\phi}$, and single-valuedness imposes the requirement that $m$ is an integer (positive, negative or zero). The corresponding eigenvalues are $m\hbar$.

The square of the magnitude of angular momentum is represented by the operator $\widehat{\mathrm{L}}^2 = \widehat{\mathrm{L}}_x^2 + \widehat{\mathrm{L}}_y^2 + \widehat{\mathrm{L}}_z^2$. This has eigenvalues $l(l+1)\hbar^2$, where $l$ is any non-negative integer. Using these eigenvalues we can explain the infrared absorption spectrum of HCl, caused by transitions between rotational energy levels.

**Section 2.4** The expectation value $L_z$ remains constant in time if $\widehat{\mathrm{L}}_z$ commutes with the Hamiltonian operator of the system. The expectation values of all the components of angular momentum are conserved if the Hamiltonian operator is spherically symmetric. This is an example of the profound link between symmetries and conservation laws.

**Section 2.5** Mutually commuting Hermitian operators have simultaneous eigenfunctions. Angular momentum operators obey the commutation relations

$$\left[\widehat{\mathrm{L}}_x, \widehat{\mathrm{L}}_y\right] = \mathrm{i}\hbar\,\widehat{\mathrm{L}}_z \quad \text{and} \quad \left[\widehat{\mathrm{L}}_z, \widehat{\mathrm{L}}^2\right] = 0,$$

with similar results obtained by cyclic permutation. Apart from an exceptional case, where all three angular momentum components are equal to zero, it is impossible for any two components of angular momentum to have definite values in the same state. However, it is possible to find states $|l, m\rangle$ that are simultaneous eigenfunctions of $\widehat{\mathrm{L}}_z$ and $\widehat{\mathrm{L}}^2$, with

$$\widehat{\mathrm{L}}_z|l, m\rangle = m\hbar|l, m\rangle \quad \text{and} \quad \widehat{\mathrm{L}}^2|l, m\rangle = l(l+1)\hbar^2|l, m\rangle.$$

For a given value of $l$, the values of $m$ are restricted to $m = 0, \pm 1, \pm 2, \ldots, \pm l$.

The energy eigenfunctions of any spherically-symmetric system can be chosen to be simultaneous eigenfunctions of $\widehat{\mathrm{H}}$, $\widehat{\mathrm{L}}_z$ and $\widehat{\mathrm{L}}^2$.

**Section 2.6** The two lines appearing in the Stern–Gerlach experiment for silver atoms cannot be explained by the otherwise successful theory. They point to a distinct (non-orbital) kind of angular momentum called spin.

# Achievements from Chapter 2

*After studying this chapter, you should be able to:*

**2.1** Explain the meanings of the newly defined (emboldened) terms and symbols, and use them appropriately.

**2.2** Give classical expressions for the angular momentum of a particle, and for the angular momentum and rotational kinetic energy of a rigid body rotating about a fixed axis.

**2.3** Give an account of the behaviour of a magnetic dipole in uniform and non-uniform magnetic fields.

**2.4** Describe the relationship between angular momentum and magnetic dipole moment, and define the gyromagnetic ratio.

**2.5** Give an account of the Stern–Gerlach experiment, its interpretation and its significance.

**2.6** Write down expressions for the angular momentum operators $\widehat{\mathrm{L}}_x$, $\widehat{\mathrm{L}}_y$ and $\widehat{\mathrm{L}}_z$ in Cartesian coordinates.

**2.7** Recall the expression for $\widehat{\mathrm{L}}_z$ in spherical coordinates, and obtain its eigenfunctions and eigenvalues.

**2.8** Recall the eigenvalues of $\widehat{\mathrm{L}}^2$, and give the allowed values of $L_z$ for a given value of $L^2$.

**2.9** State and use the basic commutation relations for angular momentum operators.

**2.10** Discuss the conservation of angular momentum in quantum mechanics, and interpret this in terms of rotational symmetry.

**2.11** Explain why different components of angular momentum cannot simultaneously have non-zero values; discuss the labelling of energy eigenfunctions by angular momentum quantum numbers.

# Chapter 3 Spin angular momentum

## Introduction

The previous chapter ended with a puzzle. There was a hint that the solution to this puzzle is a new kind of angular momentum, one without parallel in the everyday world. This chapter introduces this new property: *spin*. To give a quantum-mechanical description of spin, we must go beyond the wave mechanics of Book 1 and call upon the more general ideas introduced in Chapter 1, including the representation of quantum states as vectors in a vector space.

This chapter falls into two unequal parts: the first section uses the Stern–Gerlach experiment to set out some basic phenomena that the formalism must explain. The rest of the chapter is devoted to a step-by-step presentation of the quantum theory of spin. This theory will be used throughout the rest of this course, to explain the behaviour of identical particles in atoms and solids and to explore mysterious phenomena such as quantum entanglement and quantum teleportation, which lie at the frontiers of our current understanding of the quantum world.

The structure of this chapter is as follows. Section 3.1 returns to the Stern–Gerlach experiment, presenting a range of characteristic *phenomena* that a quantum theory of spin must explain. Section 3.2 describes how spin states can be represented by *vectors* in a two-dimensional vector space, and Section 3.3 shows how observable quantities related to spin can be represented by *matrices*. These descriptions are very different to those of wave mechanics, where quantum states were represented by wave functions and observables by differential operators. Nevertheless, both wave mechanics and spin theory have a common structure, and many similarities become evident in the Dirac notation of Chapter 1.

As always in quantum mechanics, we are interested in calculating the probabilities of the outcomes of experiments. Section 3.4 shows how this is done for spin measurements, and goes on to calculate expectation values. Like all states, the state describing the spin of a particle can change in time. Section 3.5 shows how Schrödinger's equation can be applied to spin states, and uses it to predict the time-development of a spin state in the presence of an external magnetic field.

## 3.1 Spin: what the formalism must explain

In this section we examine several variations of the Stern–Gerlach experiment which reveal the basic phenomena that a quantum theory of spin must reproduce.

### 3.1.1 Observations with Stern–Gerlach apparatus

Figure 3.1 shows a schematic diagram of the simplest type of Stern–Gerlach experiment. In this arrangement, a beam of silver atoms from an oven is sent through an *inhomogeneous* magnetic field produced by a magnet with specially-shaped pole pieces — a Stern–Gerlach magnet, as described in Chapter 2. Throughout this discussion, we shall take the pointed pole piece to be a north pole (N), and the notched pole piece to be a south pole (S). The red arrow in

Figure 3.1 indicates the **orientation vector** of the magnet. This is chosen to point along the line of symmetry from the south pole piece to the north pole piece, in the direction of increasing magnetic field strength; it will help us compare the alignments of different Stern–Gerlach magnets.

With this choice, it will turn out that atoms with spin 'up' in the direction of the orientation vector are deflected upwards, while atoms with spin 'down' are deflected downwards.

We use a fixed coordinate system, $x$, $y$, $z$; in Figure 3.1 the beam is incident along the $y$-direction and the magnet is oriented in the $z$-direction. These choices will simplify the analysis in subsequent sections. In this idealization, all details of the oven, the collimation of the beam, the production of a high vacuum for the beam, and the detection process have been omitted.

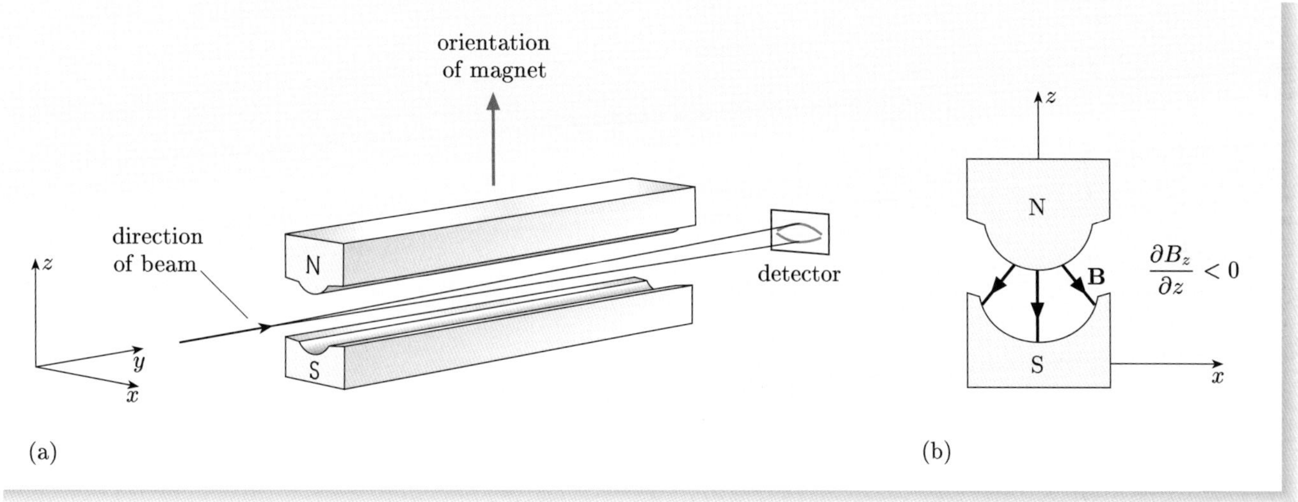


**Figure 3.1** A schematic diagram of a Stern–Gerlach experiment: (a) perspective view and (b) cross-sectional view. The magnet is oriented in the $z$-direction and the beam travels in the $y$-direction.

Figure 3.1 shows that an incident beam of silver atoms is split into two emerging beams (or components), which are detected when they strike a measurement screen. One component consists of atoms that have been deflected in the direction of the orientation vector of the magnet, which in this case is the positive $z$-direction. The other component consists of atoms that have been deflected in the opposite direction. The key result is that only *two* components are detected, corresponding to *two* allowed values of $\mu_z$, the $z$-component of the magnetic dipole moment of the atoms. Classically, one would expect a continuous distribution of deflections, corresponding to a continuous range of allowed values of $\mu_z$.

In the previous chapter, the quantization of $\mu_z$ was attributed to the quantization of the $z$-component of orbital angular momentum. However, the quantum-mechanical theory of orbital angular momentum predicts that there is always an *odd* number of emerging beams (1, 3, 5, etc.), and this cannot be reconciled with the observed *pair* of emerging beams. We shall continue to assume that the magnetic dipole moments of silver atoms are due to a type of angular momentum, but this cannot be orbital angular momentum; it is an entirely new type of angular momentum called **spin angular momentum** or **spin** for short. Our interpretation is that a silver atom has two possible values of $S_z$, the $z$-component of its spin. We cannot obtain the numerical values of these two possible values directly from the Stern–Gerlach experiment, but for the moment, we will simply assert that the two possible values are $S_z = +\hbar/2$ and $S_z = -\hbar/2$. These two values correspond to two different values of $\mu_z$, and hence produce the two emerging beams that we see in Figure 3.1.

Of course, the atom does not know how the $z$-axis has been chosen, and the same two-valuedness of a component of spin is observed in the set-up of Figure 3.2.

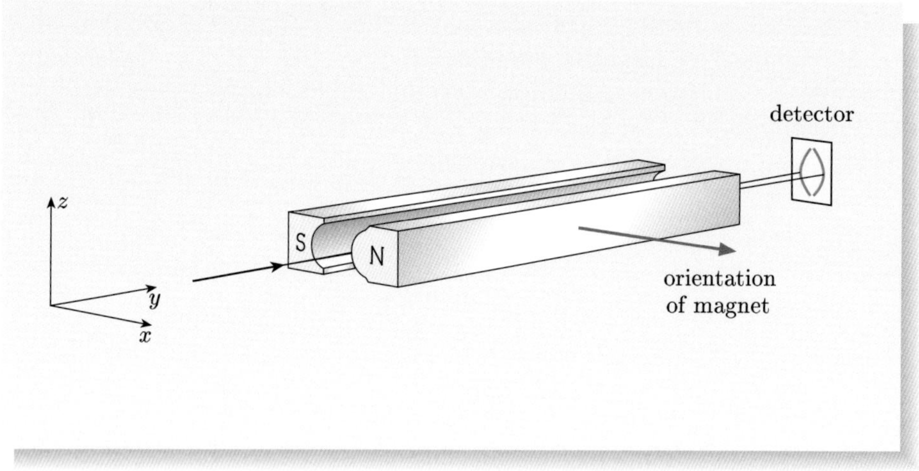


**Figure 3.2** The Stern–Gerlach magnet of Figure 3.1 is rotated so that it is oriented in the $x$-direction.

**Exercise 3.1** When the magnet of Figure 3.1 is rotated through 90° to give the orientation of Figure 3.2, two components are detected, deflected in the positive and negative $x$-directions. The magnitudes of the deflections are unchanged. Interpret this result in terms of the possible outcomes of measurements of $S_x$, the component of spin in the $x$-direction. ■

The next type of Stern–Gerlach experiment we consider involves two magnets in series. Figure 3.3 shows what is observed when we take *one* component of the beam and pass it through a second magnet with the *same* orientation as the first.

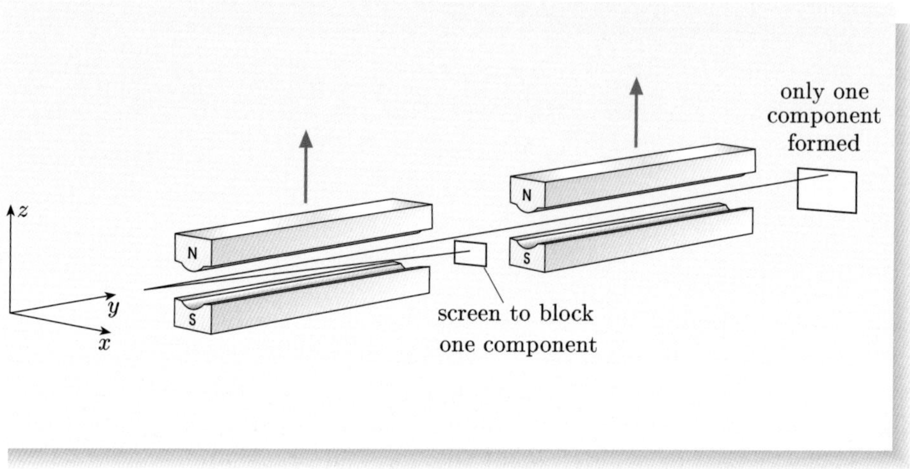


**Figure 3.3** Two identically oriented Stern–Gerlach magnets in series. A screen placed after the first magnet allows only the upper component of the beam to reach the second magnet.

The result is not very surprising. Taking the component that is deflected in the positive $z$-direction by the first magnet, we find only one component emerging from the second magnet, and it has been further deflected in the positive $z$-direction. But what happens if the orientation of the second magnet differs from that of the first? Figure 3.4 illustrates the result of such an experiment.

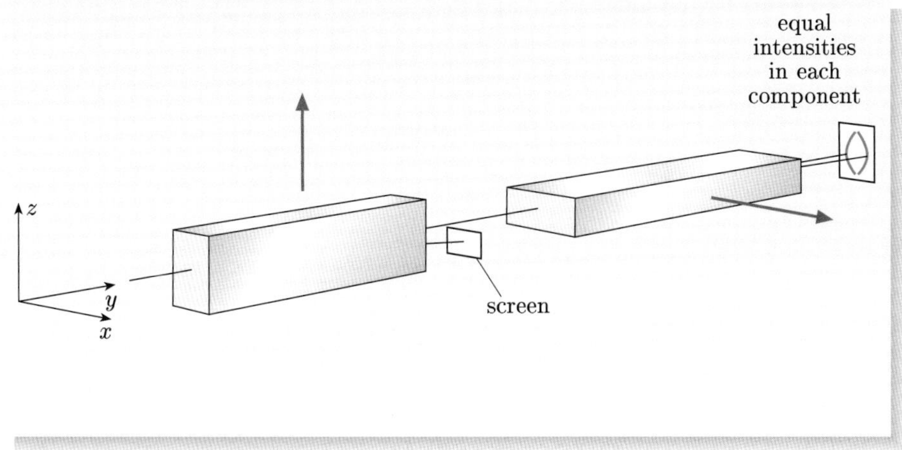


**Figure 3.4** Taking one component from a Stern–Gerlach magnet oriented in the $z$-direction, we obtain two components, of equal intensity, from a magnet oriented in the $x$-direction. (From now on, the magnets will be drawn in simplified box form.)

When the second magnet is rotated through $90°$ about the incident beam, two components are detected, with deflections in the $\pm x$-directions, corresponding to atoms with $S_x = \pm\hbar/2$. Moreover, *equal* numbers of atoms from the beam prepared by the first magnet are found to have $S_x = +\hbar/2$ and $S_x = -\hbar/2$, when analyzed by the second magnet.

A Stern–Gerlach apparatus that stops and detects both emerging beams will be called a **spin analyzer**. By contrast, a Stern–Gerlach apparatus that allows one of the emerging beams to pass undetected, while blocking off the other, will be called a **spin preparer**, because it *prepares* particles with a definite component of spin along the orientation direction of the apparatus. We adopt the convention of retaining the beam with a *positive* spin component in the orientation direction. Thus Figure 3.3 depicts a spin preparer oriented in the $z$-direction, and this prepares a beam of atoms with $S_z = +\hbar/2$. A spin analyzer oriented in the $z$-direction reveals this fact by detecting only the value $S_z = +\hbar/2$. The result shown in Figure 3.4, on the other hand, is that a spin analyzer oriented in the $x$-direction detects equal numbers of atoms with $S_x = +\hbar/2$ and $S_x = -\hbar/2$.

The general rule for what is found when the analyzer's orientation makes an angle $\theta$ with the preparer's orientation can be stated as follows.

### The $\cos^2(\theta/2)$ rule

Suppose that a spin preparer and a spin analyzer are collinear, with an angle $\theta$ between their orientation vectors (Figure 3.5). Then an atom emerging with a positive spin component along the orientation of the spin preparer has a probability $\cos^2(\theta/2)$ of being detected with a positive spin component along the orientation of the spin analyzer. (By our conventions, such an atom is deflected in the direction of the orientation vector of the analyzer.)

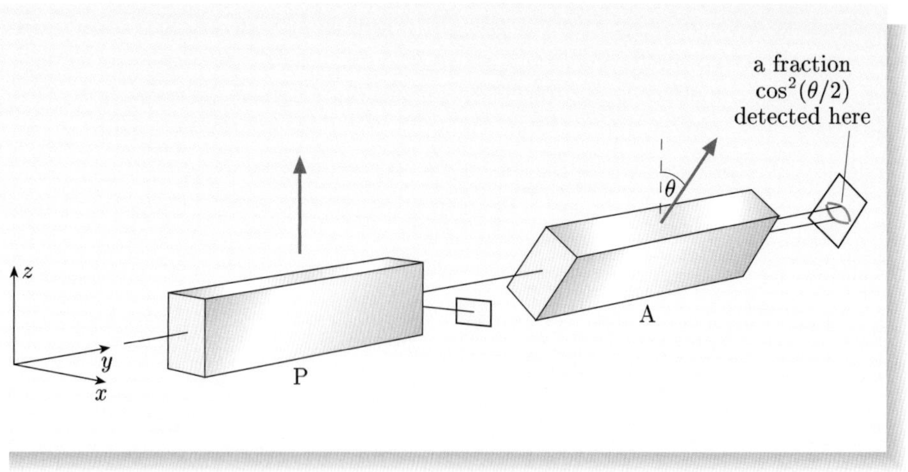


**Figure 3.5** An experiment in which the spin analyzer A is rotated at an angle $\theta$ with respect to the orientation of the spin preparer P, illustrating the $\cos^2(\theta/2)$ rule.

The appearance of $\theta/2$ rather than $\theta$ in this rule may be surprising, but spin is an entirely quantum-mechanical concept whose properties do not necessarily agree with classical intuition. It is also important to note that the $\cos^2(\theta/2)$ rule gives the *probability* of a particular outcome; the fate of any given atom cannot be predicted with certainty unless $\theta$ is $0°$, or is some multiple of $180°$. As with all quantum-mechanical phenomena governed by probabilities, the probability $\cos^2(\theta/2)$ estimates the fractional frequency that will be observed in the limit of a very large number of measurements. If only one atom passes through the apparatus, and $\theta = 90°$, we will not find that half an atom has gone each way!

- What is the probability that an atom's spin component along the direction of the analyzer's orientation vector will be detected to have the value $-\hbar/2$?

- There are two possible values of the atom's spin component along the direction of the analyzer's orientation vector: $+\hbar/2$ and $-\hbar/2$. The probability of getting a value $+\hbar/2$ is $\cos^2(\theta/2)$, so the probability of getting a value $-\hbar/2$ is $1 - \cos^2(\theta/2) = \sin^2(\theta/2)$.

### Exercise 3.2

(a) Verify that the $\cos^2(\theta/2)$ rule correctly describes the results of the experiments in Figures 3.3 and 3.4.

(b) Use the rule to predict what will happen when the second magnet of Figure 3.3 is rotated by $180°$ about the beam.

(c) Use the rule to predict what will happen when the second magnet of Figure 3.4 is rotated by $180°$ about the beam. ■

Now consider the three-magnet situation shown in Figure 3.6, where the second magnet now acts as a spin preparer, P′, and the third acts as a spin analyzer, A, oriented in the same direction as the first spin preparer, P.

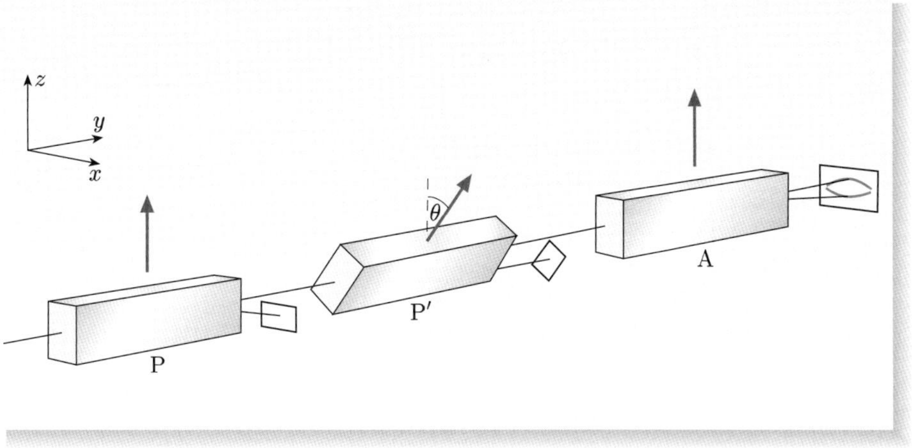


**Figure 3.6** The experimental arrangement for Worked Example 3.1.

**Worked Example 3.1**

What fraction of the beam prepared by P in Figure 3.6 is detected in the *lower* component by A?

**Essential skill**

Applying the $\cos^2(\theta/2)$ rule

**Solution**

The angle between the orientations of P and P′ is $\theta$, so the fraction of atoms prepared by P that emerges in the positive direction of the orientation vector of P′ is $\cos^2(\theta/2)$. Of these atoms, a fraction $1 - \cos^2(\theta/2) = \sin^2(\theta/2)$ is deflected in the opposite direction to the orientation vector of A and is therefore detected in the lower component by A. So a fraction

$$\cos^2(\theta/2)\sin^2(\theta/2) = \tfrac{1}{4}\sin^2(\theta)$$

of the beam prepared by P is eventually detected in the lower component by A.

Standard trigonometrical identities are listed inside the back cover of the book.

Worked Example 3.1 reveals a remarkable fact: if P′ is oriented at right angles to P ($\theta = 90°$), about a quarter of the atoms prepared by P will be detected in the lower component of A. But if P′ were removed, *none* of the atoms prepared by P would be detected in the lower component of A. The spin preparer P′ does not simply act as a sort of filter, selecting atoms that are somehow already predetermined to be deflected along its orientation vector. Instead, its presence radically changes the state of atoms. Some go into the blocked beam and do not emerge; the remainder are prepared in a state with a spin component parallel to the orientation of P′; this is not the same as the state of the atoms entering P′. Having passed through P′, these atoms have some chance of being detected in the lower component by A; without passing through P′, they would have no such chance.

**Exercise 3.3** Consider a series of spin preparers, $P_1$ to $P_n$, followed by a spin analyzer, A, which is oriented at right angles to the first spin preparer $P_1$. The angles between successive spin preparers, and the angle between the last spin preparer and A, are all equal to one another. Calculate the fraction of the beam prepared by $P_1$ that is deflected along the orientation vector of A for $n = 1$, $n = 2$ and $n = 3$. Evaluate your answers to two significant figures. ■

These applications of the $\cos^2(\theta/2)$ rule show that the presence of one or more spin preparers between an initial spin preparer and a final analyzer can radically affect the probabilities of the outcomes measured by the analyzer.

**What have we studied the properties of?**

The original Stern–Gerlach experiment was carried out with silver atoms. Why silver? Wouldn't it be more interesting to study the spin of fundamental particles such as electrons? Maybe — but there are formidable practical difficulties in doing so. The reason is that electrons are charged particles, and moving charges experience magnetic forces in a magnetic field. Electrons would be strongly deflected by the magnetic fields in a Stern–Gerlach apparatus, simply because they are moving charged particles. Such a deflection would overwhelm the much more delicate deflection due to the magnetic dipole moment of an electron in an inhomogeneous magnetic field, and prevent us from observing effects directly associated with spin.

Neutral silver atoms, however, have no charge. What is more, the electrons in a silver atom are arranged in such a way that the magnetic dipole moments of all but one of the electrons cancel out. The remaining electron has no orbital angular momentum ($l = 0$) so there is no orbital contribution to its magnetic dipole moment. This means that the magnetic dipole moment of a silver atom can be regarded as being due to the spin of a single electron. By carrying out the Stern–Gerlach experiment with silver atoms we are, in effect, studying the spin of a single free electron, without the unwanted side effects associated with its charge. Other atoms, such as sodium or potassium, can also be used for this purpose.

Finally, we remark that the experiments just described are really 'thought experiments': for technical reasons it is quite hard to do experiments of exactly the kind described here, particularly with three Stern–Gerlach magnets in series. However, the basic phenomena described here have been abundantly verified with experiments of one kind or another.

### 3.1.2 The quantum mysteries of spin

The series of thought experiments outlined above bring out the key points that a quantum theory of spin must explain. Developing such a theory is the challenge taken up by the rest of this chapter, but first it is worth looking back at the experiments to note their characteristic quantum features.

We first correct an impression that might have been left by the way we have drawn the figures. From Figure 3.1 onwards, we have shown diverging paths along which the atoms travel. This must not be taken too literally! Quantum mechanics has done away with the notion of a 'trajectory'. An atom is not an 'up' atom or a 'down' atom until it has *actually been measured* to be so. Just as a particle that has passed through a slit does not 'decide' where to materialize in a diffraction pattern until it reaches a detecting screen, so an atom does not 'decide' whether it has been deflected up or down until it has been detected. Once the atom has been detected at a particular point, it is *as if* it had followed a path to that point.

The first key point is that the Stern–Gerlach experiment, carried out with silver atoms, produces just two regions on the detecting screen where atoms appear.

This means that the magnetic dipole moment of a silver atom (which is also the magnetic dipole moment due to the spin of a single electron) cannot be due to orbital angular momentum; if it were, there would be an *odd* number of components. Instead, we assume that the magnetic dipole moment is due to a new, non-classical type of angular momentum, called spin. Even if an electron were at rest at a single point in space, it would possess spin, together with an associated magnetic dipole moment. Spin is therefore regarded as an intrinsic property of an electron and, for this reason, it is sometimes called **intrinsic angular momentum**.

The other key point is that a spin preparer creates a beam of atoms, all in a state with a definite value of a given spin component — say, with $S_z = +\hbar/2$. We say that $S_z$ has a definite value because every measurement of $S_z$ gives the value $+\hbar/2$. If we measure the spin component in some other direction, we always get either $+\hbar/2$ or $-\hbar/2$, but we cannot say which of these two outcomes will occur for any single atom. Instead, when large numbers of atoms pass through the apparatus, we can use the $\cos^2(\theta/2)$ rule to predict the proportion of measurements that give $+\hbar/2$ and the proportion that give $-\hbar/2$.

Spin was proposed by Goudsmit and Uhlenbeck in 1925. Their evidence was based on a detailed analysis of the spectral lines of hydrogen atoms in a magnetic field, but they were also inspired by Pauli's famous exclusion principle. Pauli had found that the regularities of the Periodic Table could be explained if a maximum of two electrons were allowed to occupy each atomic orbital. He referred to this as a '*classically non-describable two-valuedness*', but was reluctant to interpret it in terms of spin.

A measure of how surprising spin seemed at the time is provided by the story that the great Lorentz tried to dissuade Goudsmit and Uhlenbeck from publishing on the grounds that he had calculated that a spinning electron, with the correct magnetic dipole moment, would have a surface speed greater than that of light. Uhlenbeck was about to withdraw the paper, but it had been sent to the journal already! Lorentz's model of an electron proved to be incorrect; the quantum concept of spin *cannot be modelled by anything so classical as a spinning ball.* Perhaps by now we should be used to the fact that quantum mechanics springs surprises on us. Spin *is* a form of angular momentum, but is not one that can be pictured in classical terms.

Finally, we note that the theory we shall develop applies to any type of particle whose spin components have two possible values, $+\hbar/2$ and $-\hbar/2$. For reasons that will emerge later, particles with this property are called **spin-$\frac{1}{2}$ particles**. The family of spin-$\frac{1}{2}$ particles is large and important, and includes electrons, muons, protons, neutrons and quarks. However, some particles (such as photons) have a different type of spin, and they are not described by the formalism of this chapter.

## 3.2 Representing spin states

We shall assume that it makes sense to talk about the **spin state** of a particle, independently of its other properties. When we do this, it is obvious that spin states cannot be represented by ordinary wave functions, which are functions of position. Amongst other things, a wave function tells us the probability density for finding a particle at different points in space. But this has nothing to do with the spin state of an electron. So far as we know, electrons are point-like entities; their spin at each instant has a direction, but no spatial extent.

Fortunately, Chapter 1 gave us an alternative way of representing quantum states, using vectors in an abstract vector space. This notation gave us a compact way of writing the equations of wave mechanics, and it also suggests a different way of thinking about quantum mechanics. You may recall that a wave function $\Psi(x,t)$ corresponds to a state vector $|\Psi\rangle$ in *function space* — an infinite-dimensional vector space with an inner product defined by

$$\langle f|g\rangle = \int_{-\infty}^{\infty} f^*(x)\, g(x)\, \mathrm{d}x. \tag{3.1}$$

In a system such as a harmonic oscillator, the energy eigenfunctions $\psi_i(x)$ provide an orthonormal basis for function space. The energy eigenfunctions are orthonormal because

$$\langle \psi_i|\psi_j\rangle = \int_{-\infty}^{\infty} \psi_i^*(x)\, \psi_j(x)\, \mathrm{d}x = \delta_{ij}, \tag{3.2}$$

and they provide a basis for function space because *any* state vector $|\Psi\rangle$ can be expressed as a linear combination of the eigenvectors $|\psi_i\rangle$:

$$|\Psi\rangle = \sum_{i=0}^{\infty} a_i |\psi_i\rangle.$$

This sum generally contains an infinite number of mutually orthogonal eigenvectors $|\psi_i\rangle$, which is why function space is said to be infinite-dimensional. The coefficients $a_i$ are interpreted as probability amplitudes: $|a_i|^2$ is the probability that an energy measurement in the state $|\Psi\rangle$ will give the $i$th energy eigenvalue, $E_i$. Because one or other of the energy eigenvalues must be obtained, we have

$$\sum_{i=0}^{\infty} |a_i|^2 = 1.$$

You will see that spin states can be described in a similar way. We shall suppose that the spin state of a spin-$\frac{1}{2}$ particle can be represented by a vector in an abstract vector space, which we shall call **spin space**.

### 3.2.1 Representing spin states by vectors

You have seen that a spin analyzer oriented in the $z$-direction measures the $z$-component of spin, with two possible values: $S_z = +\hbar/2$ and $S_z = -\hbar/2$. There is a special spin state that is certain to give the value $S_z = +\hbar/2$. We call this the **spin-up state** relative to the $z$-axis, and represent it by the vector $|\uparrow_z\rangle$. Another special spin state is certain to give the value $S_z = -\hbar/2$. We call this the **spin-down state** relative to the $z$-axis, and represent it by the vector $|\downarrow_z\rangle$.

The possibilities of an atom being 'spin-up' or 'spin-down' are mutually exclusive, so to is natural to assume that $|\uparrow_z\rangle$ and $|\downarrow_z\rangle$ are orthogonal to one another in spin space. We shall also assume that these vectors are normalized, although the interpretation of 'orthogonal' and 'normalized' will be left rather vague for the moment.

There are many possible spin states, which can be produced by spin preparers oriented in arbitrary directions. However, we shall assume that:

Any spin state $|A\rangle$ can be written as a linear combination of $|\uparrow_z\rangle$ and $|\downarrow_z\rangle$, so

$$|A\rangle = a_1|\uparrow_z\rangle + a_2|\downarrow_z\rangle, \tag{3.3}$$

where $a_1$ and $a_2$ are complex numbers.

In other words, $|\uparrow_z\rangle$ and $|\downarrow_z\rangle$ provide an *orthonormal basis* for spin space. Because any spin state $|A\rangle$ can be written as a linear combination of just *two* basis vectors, we say that the spin space of a spin-$\frac{1}{2}$ particle is *two-dimensional.*

We shall assume that the coefficients $a_1$ and $a_2$ have the usual quantum-mechanical interpretation of being probability amplitudes. When a silver atom in the state $|A\rangle$ of Equation 3.3 enters a spin analyzer and has the $z$-component of its spin measured, the probability of getting $+\hbar/2$ is $|a_1|^2$, and the probability of getting $-\hbar/2$ is $|a_2|^2$. Since these probabilities must sum to one, we require that

$$|a_1|^2 + |a_2|^2 = 1. \tag{3.4}$$

**Exercise 3.4** A spin preparer produces atoms in the spin state

$$|A\rangle = \frac{\sqrt{3}}{2}|\uparrow_z\rangle + \frac{1}{2}|\downarrow_z\rangle.$$

(a) If a single atom is prepared in the state $|A\rangle$, what prediction can be made about the result of measuring $S_z$ for this atom?

(b) If a million atoms are prepared in the state $|A\rangle$, what prediction can be made about the results of measuring $S_z$ for this collection of atoms? ■

We said earlier that the basis vectors $|\uparrow_z\rangle$ and $|\downarrow_z\rangle$ are 'orthogonal to one another' and 'normalized'. Terms such as these are part of a wider issue: how do we define an **inner product** between vectors in spin space? We cannot use Equation 3.1 because spin states are not described by wave functions. However, we can proceed as follows.

First, we shall use the familiar bra-ket notation of Dirac. Given two vectors $|A\rangle$ and $|B\rangle$ in spin space, we denote their inner product by $\langle A|B\rangle$. Then we express the fact that the basis vectors are normalized and orthogonal to one another by writing

$$\langle\uparrow_z|\uparrow_z\rangle = \langle\downarrow_z|\downarrow_z\rangle = 1, \tag{3.5}$$

$$\langle\uparrow_z|\downarrow_z\rangle = \langle\downarrow_z|\uparrow_z\rangle = 0. \tag{3.6}$$

We shall assume that the inner product in spin space obeys similar rules to the inner product in function space. This is a reasonable assumption, based on the belief that there is an underlying unity to quantum mechanics.

In particular, we shall assume that the inner product of $|A\rangle = a_1|\uparrow_z\rangle + a_2|\downarrow_z\rangle$ with $|B\rangle = b_1|\uparrow_z\rangle + b_2|\downarrow_z\rangle$ can be evaluated as follows. We write

$$\langle A|B\rangle = \Big(a_1^*\langle\uparrow_z| + a_2^*\langle\downarrow_z|\Big)\Big(b_1|\uparrow_z\rangle + b_2|\downarrow_z\rangle\Big),$$

where the complex conjugates in the first set of round brackets are a typical feature of taking inner products in complex vector spaces. Then, multiplying out the brackets gives

$$\langle A|B\rangle = a_1^*b_1\langle\uparrow_z|\uparrow_z\rangle + a_1^*b_2\langle\uparrow_z|\downarrow_z\rangle + a_2^*b_1\langle\downarrow_z|\uparrow_z\rangle + a_2^*b_2\langle\downarrow_z|\downarrow_z\rangle.$$

Finally, there is a great simplification because the basis vectors $|\uparrow_z\rangle$ and $|\downarrow_z\rangle$ are normalized and orthogonal, obeying Equations 3.5 and 3.6. We conclude that

$$\langle A|B\rangle = a_1^*b_1 + a_2^*b_2. \tag{3.7}$$

This equation tells us how to evaluate the inner product of vectors in spin space. In fact, its derivation follows the same lines as Worked Example 1.1 in Chapter 1. The only difference is that vectors in spin space have only two components, while vectors in function space have an infinite number of them; in many ways, the quantum mechanics of spin is much simpler than wave mechanics.

In the special case where $|B\rangle = |A\rangle$, Equations 3.7 and 3.4 combine to give

$$\langle A|A\rangle = a_1^*a_1 + a_2^*a_2 = |a_1|^2 + |a_2|^2 = 1.$$

Any spin state vector must be normalized in this way. If a spin state vector is not correctly normalized, we must multiply it by a suitable normalization constant.

The result of Exercise 3.5 is important and will be used later.

**Exercise 3.5** Use Equation 3.7 to verify that $\langle A|B\rangle^* = \langle B|A\rangle$ for vectors in spin space.

**Exercise 3.6** Find normalization constants so that the following three spin vectors are normalized, and write out the corresponding normalized forms:

(a) $|\uparrow_z\rangle + |\downarrow_z\rangle$, (b) $|\uparrow_z\rangle + \mathrm{i}|\downarrow_z\rangle$, (c) $5|\uparrow_z\rangle - 12|\downarrow_z\rangle$. ■

We generally choose the normalization constant to be real and positive, but this is done only for convenience. You may recall that a wave function $\Psi(x,t)$ can be multiplied by an overall phase factor $e^{\mathrm{i}\alpha}$, where $\alpha$ is real, without making any difference to the state being described. The same is true for spin states. This means that two spin vectors which look quite different may actually describe the same state. For example, the vectors

$$|A\rangle = \frac{1}{\sqrt{2}}\big(|\uparrow_z\rangle + \mathrm{i}|\downarrow_z\rangle\big) \quad \text{and} \quad |B\rangle = \frac{1}{\sqrt{2}}\big(-\mathrm{i}|\uparrow_z\rangle + |\downarrow_z\rangle\big) \tag{3.8}$$

describe the *same* spin state because $|B\rangle = -\mathrm{i}|A\rangle$. Note carefully that while overall phase factors (multiplying all terms in a spin vector) make no difference, the phases of individual terms generally do matter. For example, the vectors

$$|A\rangle = \frac{1}{\sqrt{2}}\big(|\uparrow_z\rangle + \mathrm{i}|\downarrow_z\rangle\big) \quad \text{and} \quad |C\rangle = \frac{1}{\sqrt{2}}\big(\mathrm{i}|\uparrow_z\rangle + |\downarrow_z\rangle\big) \tag{3.9}$$

correspond to *different* states because $|C\rangle$ is not a multiple of $|A\rangle$.

**Exercise 3.7** Show that $|C\rangle$ in Equation 3.9 cannot be expressed as a multiple of $|A\rangle$. ■

### 3.2.2 Representing spin states by matrices

We now introduce an alternative representation of spin states which simplifies many calculations. We represent $|\uparrow_z\rangle$ and $|\downarrow_z\rangle$ by the following column matrices:

Section 8.3 of the *Mathematical toolkit* reviews matrices.

$$|\uparrow_z\rangle = \begin{bmatrix}1\\0\end{bmatrix} \quad \text{and} \quad |\downarrow_z\rangle = \begin{bmatrix}0\\1\end{bmatrix}. \tag{3.10}$$

These matrices have two elements because spin space is two-dimensional. Note that we have chosen very simple matrices to represent states that are spin-up or spin-down *relative to the $z$-direction*. There is nothing special about the $z$-axis, and it can be chosen to point in any direction in space, but spin states with definite values of $S_z$ are *always* represented by the matrices of Equation 3.10. This convention is universally accepted and should not be broken.

Any vector $|A\rangle$ in spin space can be expressed as a linear combination of $|\uparrow_z\rangle$ and $|\downarrow_z\rangle$. This means that we can express $|A\rangle$ in Equation 3.3 as

$$|A\rangle = a_1\begin{bmatrix}1\\0\end{bmatrix} + a_2\begin{bmatrix}0\\1\end{bmatrix} = \begin{bmatrix}a_1\\a_2\end{bmatrix}. \tag{3.11}$$

So any spin state of a spin-$\frac{1}{2}$ particle can be represented as a two-element matrix, which is called a **spinor**.

The mathematics of matrices fits exactly the manipulations we need to carry out on vectors in spin space. For example, given two spinors

$$|A\rangle = \begin{bmatrix}a_1\\a_2\end{bmatrix} \quad \text{and} \quad |B\rangle = \begin{bmatrix}b_1\\b_2\end{bmatrix},$$

and a constant $k$, we can use the rules of matrix algebra to write

$$|A\rangle + |B\rangle = \begin{bmatrix}a_1\\a_2\end{bmatrix} + \begin{bmatrix}b_1\\b_2\end{bmatrix} = \begin{bmatrix}a_1+b_1\\a_2+b_2\end{bmatrix}$$

and

$$k|A\rangle = k\begin{bmatrix}a_1\\a_2\end{bmatrix} = \begin{bmatrix}ka_1\\ka_2\end{bmatrix}.$$

These equations make good sense because the vectors on the left-hand sides are correctly represented by matrices on the right-hand sides.

We can also write the inner product of two vectors in matrix form. To do this, we first recall that

$$\langle A|B\rangle = a_1^*b_1 + a_2^*b_2, \tag{Eqn 3.7}$$

and then note that

$$a_1^*b_1 + a_2^*b_2 = \begin{bmatrix}a_1^* & a_2^*\end{bmatrix}\begin{bmatrix}b_1\\b_2\end{bmatrix},$$

where the product on the right-hand side involves matrix multiplication (going along the row of the first matrix, and down the column of the second matrix, multiplying corresponding elements and adding the results). We therefore see that the inner product of two spin vectors can be written in the matrix form

$$\langle A|B\rangle = \begin{bmatrix}a_1^* & a_2^*\end{bmatrix}\begin{bmatrix}b_1\\b_2\end{bmatrix}. \tag{3.12}$$

The inner product $\langle A|B\rangle$ can be regarded as a simple joining together of a bra vector $\langle A|$ and a ket vector $|B\rangle$. We can therefore identify the separate bra and ket vectors as follows:

$$\langle A| = \begin{bmatrix} a_1^* & a_2^* \end{bmatrix} \quad \text{and} \quad |B\rangle = \begin{bmatrix} b_1 \\ b_2 \end{bmatrix}.$$

A ket spin vector is represented by a **column spinor**, and a bra spin vector is represented by a **row spinor**. To convert a column spinor into the corresponding row spinor, the rule is to turn the column into a row and take the complex conjugate of all elements,

$$\text{so if} \quad |A\rangle = \begin{bmatrix} a_1 \\ a_2 \end{bmatrix}, \quad \text{then} \quad \langle A| = \begin{bmatrix} a_1^* & a_2^* \end{bmatrix}. \tag{3.13}$$

**Essential skill**

Manipulation of spinors

### Worked Example 3.2

Consider the pair of spinors

$$|c\rangle = \begin{bmatrix} 1 \\ \mathrm{i} \end{bmatrix} \quad \text{and} \quad |d\rangle = \begin{bmatrix} \mathrm{i} \\ 1 \end{bmatrix}.$$

Use spinor notation to normalize these spinors, and find the corresponding normalized spinors, $|C\rangle$ and $|D\rangle$. Show that $|C\rangle$ and $|D\rangle$ are orthogonal to one another (i.e. $\langle C|D\rangle = 0$).

**Solution**

Using matrix multiplication, we have

$$\langle c|c\rangle = \begin{bmatrix} 1 & -\mathrm{i} \end{bmatrix} \begin{bmatrix} 1 \\ \mathrm{i} \end{bmatrix} = 1 + 1 = 2,$$

$$\langle d|d\rangle = \begin{bmatrix} -\mathrm{i} & 1 \end{bmatrix} \begin{bmatrix} \mathrm{i} \\ 1 \end{bmatrix} = 1 + 1 = 2.$$

The normalization factor can be taken to be $1/\sqrt{2}$ in both cases, and the corresponding normalized spinors are

$$|C\rangle = \frac{1}{\sqrt{2}} \begin{bmatrix} 1 \\ \mathrm{i} \end{bmatrix} \quad \text{and} \quad |D\rangle = \frac{1}{\sqrt{2}} \begin{bmatrix} \mathrm{i} \\ 1 \end{bmatrix}.$$

To check that $|C\rangle$ and $|D\rangle$ are orthogonal, we must show that their inner product is equal to zero:

$$\langle C|D\rangle = \frac{1}{\sqrt{2}} \begin{bmatrix} 1 & -\mathrm{i} \end{bmatrix} \frac{1}{\sqrt{2}} \begin{bmatrix} \mathrm{i} \\ 1 \end{bmatrix} = \frac{1}{2}(\mathrm{i} - \mathrm{i}) = 0.$$

There is no need to show explicitly that $\langle D|C\rangle = 0$, since we know that $\langle D|C\rangle = \langle C|D\rangle^*$ (see Exercise 3.5).

**Exercise 3.8** Show that the spin vectors

$$|U\rangle = \frac{1}{\sqrt{2}} \begin{bmatrix} 1 \\ 1 \end{bmatrix} \quad \text{and} \quad |V\rangle = \frac{1}{\sqrt{2}} \begin{bmatrix} -1 \\ 1 \end{bmatrix}$$

are orthonormal (i.e. $\langle U|U\rangle = \langle V|V\rangle = 1$ and $\langle U|V\rangle = 0$). ■

### Alternative pairs of orthonormal basis vectors

The vectors $|\uparrow_z\rangle$ and $|\downarrow_z\rangle$ provide an *orthonormal basis* for spin space. They are orthonormal because

$$\langle\uparrow_z|\uparrow_z\rangle = \langle\downarrow_z|\downarrow_z\rangle = 1 \quad \text{and} \quad \langle\uparrow_z|\downarrow_z\rangle = \langle\downarrow_z|\uparrow_z\rangle = 0,$$

and they provide a basis because any spin state can be written as

$$|A\rangle = a_1|\uparrow_z\rangle + a_2|\downarrow_z\rangle,$$

where $a_1$ and $a_2$ are complex numbers.

Orthonormality, in this context, refers to inner products in spin space; it does *not* mean that $|\uparrow_z\rangle$ and $|\downarrow_z\rangle$ relate to perpendicular directions in real space. In real space, of course, $|\uparrow_z\rangle$ and $|\downarrow_z\rangle$ refer to *opposite* spins along the $z$-axis; in measurements of the $z$-component of spin, $|\uparrow_z\rangle$ always gives the value $+\hbar/2$, and $|\downarrow_z\rangle$ always gives the value $-\hbar/2$.

Now, there is nothing special about the $z$-direction. It is possible to prepare atoms in states that are spin-up or spin-down relative to any direction. For example, there is a spin-up state $|\uparrow_x\rangle$, and a spin-down state $|\downarrow_x\rangle$, relative to the $x$-direction. In measurements of the $x$-component of spin, $|\uparrow_x\rangle$ always gives the value $+\hbar/2$, and $|\downarrow_x\rangle$ always gives the value $-\hbar/2$.

The vectors $|\uparrow_x\rangle$ and $|\downarrow_x\rangle$ provide an alternative orthonormal basis in spin space. This means that any spin state $|A\rangle$ can be written as

$$|A\rangle = b_1|\uparrow_x\rangle + b_2|\downarrow_x\rangle,$$

where the complex numbers $b_1$ and $b_2$ are interpreted as probability amplitudes for spin measurements made in the $x$-direction. When the $x$-component of spin is measured in the state $|A\rangle$, the probability of getting the value $+\hbar/2$ is $|b_1|^2$ and the probability of getting $-\hbar/2$ is $|b_2|^2$.

This idea can be generalized to spin measurements taken in any direction. If $|\uparrow_\mathbf{n}\rangle$ and $|\downarrow_\mathbf{n}\rangle$ are spin-up and spin down states relative to a direction $\mathbf{n}$, we can write any spin state as

$$|A\rangle = c_1|\uparrow_\mathbf{n}\rangle + c_2|\downarrow_\mathbf{n}\rangle, \tag{3.14}$$

and interpret $|c_1|^2$ as the probability of getting the value $+\hbar/2$, and $|c_2|^2$ as the probability of getting the value $-\hbar/2$, when the spin component in the direction $\mathbf{n}$ is measured.

Section 3.1 described thought experiments in which silver atoms were prepared in specific spin states, and spin components along various directions were measured. The above discussion suggests that we might be able to explain the probabilities quoted in Section 3.1 by taking the modulus squared of coefficients such as $c_1$ or $c_2$. But there is a difficulty. We must first write the given spin state in terms of spin-up and spin-down states corresponding to the orientation of the spin analyzer. We do not know how to find such states. The next section will show how this is done, using the quantum-mechanical operator that represents the spin component measured in a given direction (an observable quantity).

**Exercise 3.9** It turns out that the vectors $|U\rangle$ and $|V\rangle$ in Exercise 3.8 are the spin-up and spin-down vectors $|\uparrow_x\rangle$ and $|\downarrow_x\rangle$ relative to the $x$-direction. Use this fact to show that

$$|\uparrow_z\rangle = \frac{1}{\sqrt{2}}|\uparrow_x\rangle - \frac{1}{\sqrt{2}}|\downarrow_x\rangle,$$

and hence show that when the $x$-component of spin is measured in the state $|\uparrow_z\rangle$, there is a 50% chance of getting the value $S_x = +\hbar/2$. ■

## 3.3 Spin observables in quantum mechanics

In the previous section, we introduced spinors to represent the spin states of a spin-$\frac{1}{2}$ particle. This leaves a large gap in the formalism still to be filled. In wave mechanics, we have wave functions that represent the state of a system; we also have operators that represent various observables. For example, the Hamiltonian operator $\widehat{\text{H}}$ represents the energy of the system. In the context of spin, the most important observables are the spin components $S_x$, $S_y$ and $S_z$ of a particle. We therefore ask: what operators should be used to represent these observables in quantum mechanics?

### 3.3.1 Matrices representing $S_x$, $S_y$ and $S_z$

In wave mechanics, states are described by wave functions, and observables are represented by operators such as $\widehat{\text{p}}_x = -i\hbar\,\partial/\partial x$ or $\widehat{\text{L}}_z = -i\hbar\,\partial/\partial\phi$, which act on functions to give new functions.

In this chapter, we place hats on $2 \times 2$ matrices to show that they act as operators.

Spin states, however, are represented by column spinors ($2 \times 1$ matrices), and spin observables are represented by $2 \times 2$ matrices that act on column spinors to give new column spinors. We seek the matrices $\widehat{\text{S}}_x$, $\widehat{\text{S}}_y$ and $\widehat{\text{S}}_z$ that represent the spin components $S_x$, $S_y$ and $S_z$. We start with $\widehat{\text{S}}_z$.

From the Stern–Gerlach experiment, we know that a measurement of $S_z$ has two possible outcomes: $+\hbar/2$ and $-\hbar/2$. According to the general principles of quantum mechanics, this means that the eigenvalues of $\widehat{\text{S}}_z$ are $\pm\hbar/2$. We also know that the spin-up state $|\uparrow_z\rangle$ gives $+\hbar/2$ with certainty, while the spin-down state $|\downarrow_z\rangle$ gives $-\hbar/2$ with certainty. This means that $|\uparrow_z\rangle$ is an eigenvector of $\widehat{\text{S}}_z$ with eigenvalue $+\hbar/2$, while $|\downarrow_z\rangle$ is an eigenvector of $\widehat{\text{S}}_z$ with eigenvalue $-\hbar/2$. We therefore require that

$$\widehat{\text{S}}_z|\uparrow_z\rangle = \widehat{\text{S}}_z \begin{bmatrix}1\\0\end{bmatrix} = +\frac{\hbar}{2}\begin{bmatrix}1\\0\end{bmatrix}, \tag{3.15}$$

$$\widehat{\text{S}}_z|\downarrow_z\rangle = \widehat{\text{S}}_z \begin{bmatrix}0\\1\end{bmatrix} = -\frac{\hbar}{2}\begin{bmatrix}0\\1\end{bmatrix}. \tag{3.16}$$

We are looking for a $2 \times 2$ matrix $\widehat{\text{S}}_z$ that satisfies both these equations. Denoting the elements of this matrix by $a$, $b$, $c$ and $d$, Equation 3.15 gives

$$\begin{bmatrix}a & b\\c & d\end{bmatrix}\begin{bmatrix}1\\0\end{bmatrix} = \frac{\hbar}{2}\begin{bmatrix}1\\0\end{bmatrix}.$$

Multiplying out the matrices on the left-hand side gives

$$\begin{bmatrix}a\\c\end{bmatrix} = \frac{\hbar}{2}\begin{bmatrix}1\\0\end{bmatrix},$$

so $a = \hbar/2$ and $c = 0$. In a similar way, Equation 3.16 gives

$$\begin{bmatrix} a & b \\ c & d \end{bmatrix} \begin{bmatrix} 0 \\ 1 \end{bmatrix} = -\frac{\hbar}{2} \begin{bmatrix} 0 \\ 1 \end{bmatrix} \quad \text{and hence} \quad \begin{bmatrix} b \\ d \end{bmatrix} = -\frac{\hbar}{2} \begin{bmatrix} 0 \\ 1 \end{bmatrix},$$

leading to $b = 0$ and $d = -\hbar/2$. Thus we have found that

$$\widehat{S}_z = \frac{\hbar}{2} \begin{bmatrix} 1 & 0 \\ 0 & -1 \end{bmatrix}. \tag{3.17}$$

The matrices representing $S_y$ and $S_z$ are harder to establish. We shall not go into the details here, but will only briefly outline the clues that allow suitable matrices to be found.

First, recall that spin is assumed to be a type of angular momentum. This assumption is supported by the fact that charged particles with spin have magnetic properties similar to those of orbiting charges. Now, we know that the *orbital* angular momentum operators $\widehat{L}_x$, $\widehat{L}_y$ and $\widehat{L}_z$ satisfy the commutation relations

$$\widehat{L}_x\widehat{L}_y - \widehat{L}_y\widehat{L}_x = i\hbar\,\widehat{L}_z, \qquad \text{(Eqn 2.39)}$$
$$\widehat{L}_y\widehat{L}_z - \widehat{L}_z\widehat{L}_y = i\hbar\,\widehat{L}_x, \qquad \text{(Eqn 2.40)}$$
$$\widehat{L}_z\widehat{L}_x - \widehat{L}_x\widehat{L}_z = i\hbar\,\widehat{L}_y. \qquad \text{(Eqn 2.41)}$$

We therefore assume that the spin matrices $\widehat{S}_x$, $\widehat{S}_y$ and $\widehat{S}_z$ obey similar commutation relations :

$$\widehat{S}_x\widehat{S}_y - \widehat{S}_y\widehat{S}_x = i\hbar\,\widehat{S}_z, \tag{3.18}$$
$$\widehat{S}_y\widehat{S}_z - \widehat{S}_z\widehat{S}_y = i\hbar\,\widehat{S}_x, \tag{3.19}$$
$$\widehat{S}_z\widehat{S}_x - \widehat{S}_x\widehat{S}_z = i\hbar\,\widehat{S}_y. \tag{3.20}$$

Given Equation 3.17 for $\widehat{S}_z$, these equations place strong restrictions on $\widehat{S}_x$ and $\widehat{S}_y$. In addition we know that the eigenvalues of all three matrices are $\pm\hbar/2$. Finally, because $\widehat{S}_x$, $\widehat{S}_y$ and $\widehat{S}_z$ represent observable quantities, they must behave as linear *Hermitian* operators when they act on spinors.

Section 8.3.4 of the *Mathematical toolkit* shows that the square matrix $\widehat{A}$ acts as a Hermitian operator only if $A_{ij} = A^*_{ji}$ for all $i$ and $j$. Any matrix satisfying this condition is said to be a **Hermitian matrix**.

The algebra involved in imposing these requirements is straightforward but tedious; we skip to the final result. The three observables $S_x$, $S_y$ and $S_z$, corresponding to spin components measured along the $x$-, $y$- and $z$-directions, can be represented by the following set of matrices:

$$\widehat{S}_x = \frac{\hbar}{2} \begin{bmatrix} 0 & 1 \\ 1 & 0 \end{bmatrix}, \quad \widehat{S}_y = \frac{\hbar}{2} \begin{bmatrix} 0 & -i \\ i & 0 \end{bmatrix}, \quad \widehat{S}_z = \frac{\hbar}{2} \begin{bmatrix} 1 & 0 \\ 0 & -1 \end{bmatrix}. \tag{3.21}$$

**Exercise 3.10** Show that the spin matrices $\widehat{S}_x$, $\widehat{S}_y$ and $\widehat{S}_z$ do satisfy Equation 3.18.

**Exercise 3.11** Show that $\widehat{S}_y$ has eigenvectors $\dfrac{1}{\sqrt{2}} \begin{bmatrix} 1 \\ i \end{bmatrix}$ and $\dfrac{1}{\sqrt{2}} \begin{bmatrix} i \\ 1 \end{bmatrix}$, with corresponding eigenvalues $+\hbar/2$ and $-\hbar/2$. What is the physical significance of these results? ■

### 3.3.2 Spin in an arbitrary direction

By adjusting the orientation of a spin analyzer, we can measure the component of spin in any direction — not just along the $x$-, $y$- and $z$-axes. Such a general spin component is an observable quantity, and is represented by a $2 \times 2$ matrix. We shall obtain an expression for this general spin matrix. We shall then be able to explain what happens in Figures 3.5 and 3.6, where the directions chosen for preparing and analyzing spins are related by an arbitrary angle.

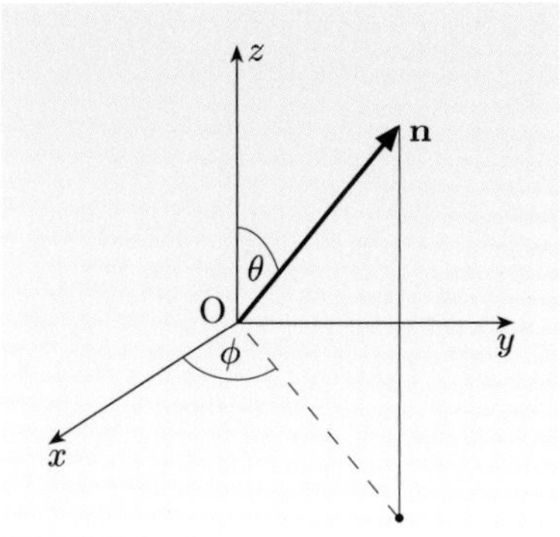


**Figure 3.7** A unit vector $\mathbf{n}$ with polar angle $\theta$ and azimuthal angle $\phi$ in spherical coordinates. The vector $\mathbf{n}$ has Cartesian components $n_x = \sin\theta\cos\phi$, $n_y = \sin\theta\sin\phi$ and $n_z = \cos\theta$, which are the $x$-, $y$- and $z$-coordinates of the tip of the arrow representing $\mathbf{n}$.

In classical physics, given a unit vector $\mathbf{n}$, we define the component of a vector $\mathbf{S}$ along $\mathbf{n}$ to be

$$S_{\mathbf{n}} = \mathbf{n} \cdot \mathbf{S} = S\cos\alpha,$$

where $\alpha$ is the angle between the direction of $\mathbf{S}$ and the direction of $\mathbf{n}$.

The vector $\mathbf{n}$ can be specified in terms of the polar and azimuthal angles of spherical coordinates. The geometry of Figure 3.7 gives

$$\mathbf{n} = \sin\theta\cos\phi\,\mathbf{e}_x + \sin\theta\sin\phi\,\mathbf{e}_y + \cos\theta\,\mathbf{e}_z.$$

So, if spin were a classical vector $\mathbf{S}$, its component $S_{\mathbf{n}}$ in the direction of the unit vector $\mathbf{n}$ would be

$$S_{\mathbf{n}} = \mathbf{n} \cdot \mathbf{S} = \sin\theta\cos\phi\,S_x + \sin\theta\sin\phi\,S_y + \cos\theta\,S_z.$$

To obtain the corresponding quantum-mechanical operator, we replace the classical observables $S_x$, $S_y$ and $S_z$ by the corresponding spin matrices. Using Equation 3.21, this gives

$$\widehat{\mathrm{S}}_{\mathbf{n}} = \frac{\hbar}{2}\left(\sin\theta\cos\phi\begin{bmatrix}0 & 1\\ 1 & 0\end{bmatrix} + \sin\theta\sin\phi\begin{bmatrix}0 & -\mathrm{i}\\ \mathrm{i} & 0\end{bmatrix} + \cos\theta\begin{bmatrix}1 & 0\\ 0 & -1\end{bmatrix}\right),$$

which can be simplified to give

Remember:
$\mathrm{e}^{\pm\mathrm{i}\phi} = \cos\phi \pm \mathrm{i}\sin\phi$.

$$\widehat{\mathrm{S}}_{\mathbf{n}} = \frac{\hbar}{2}\begin{bmatrix}\cos\theta & \mathrm{e}^{-\mathrm{i}\phi}\sin\theta\\ \mathrm{e}^{\mathrm{i}\phi}\sin\theta & -\cos\theta\end{bmatrix}. \tag{3.22}$$

This is the matrix form of the operator that represents the component of spin in the direction of the unit vector $\mathbf{n}$ shown in Figure 3.7. We call it the **general spin matrix**.

In the Stern–Gerlach experiments of Figures 3.1–3.6, the beam points along the $y$-axis. This ensures that all the spin preparers and spin analyzers are oriented in the $xz$-plane, with $\phi = 0$. In the special case where $\phi = 0$, Equation 3.22 reduces to

$$\widehat{\mathrm{S}}_{\mathbf{n}} = \frac{\hbar}{2}\begin{bmatrix}\cos\theta & \sin\theta\\ \sin\theta & -\cos\theta\end{bmatrix} \quad \text{(restricted form for } \phi = 0\text{).} \tag{3.23}$$

This is the spin matrix for a direction $\mathbf{n}$ that lies in the $xz$-plane and makes an angle $\theta$ with the $z$-direction. The simpler form of Equation 3.23 is the main reason we chose to have atoms incident in the $y$-direction in our discussions of Stern–Gerlach experiments.

The general spin matrix has two eigenvalues, $+\hbar/2$ and $-\hbar/2$. These are the possible values of a spin component in any given direction. Corresponding to these two values, there are two eigenvectors, which we denote by $|\uparrow_{\mathbf{n}}\rangle$ and $|\downarrow_{\mathbf{n}}\rangle$. In other words, we have

$$\widehat{S}_{\mathbf{n}}|\uparrow_{\mathbf{n}}\rangle = +\frac{\hbar}{2}|\uparrow_{\mathbf{n}}\rangle,$$
$$\widehat{S}_{\mathbf{n}}|\downarrow_{\mathbf{n}}\rangle = -\frac{\hbar}{2}|\downarrow_{\mathbf{n}}\rangle.$$

If the spin component in the $\mathbf{n}$-direction is measured, the state $|\uparrow_{\mathbf{n}}\rangle$ is certain to give the value $+\hbar/2$, while the state $|\downarrow_{\mathbf{n}}\rangle$ is certain to give the value $-\hbar/2$. We say that $|\uparrow_{\mathbf{n}}\rangle$ is spin-up and $|\downarrow_{\mathbf{n}}\rangle$ is spin-down, *relative to the* $\mathbf{n}$*-direction.*

The eigenvectors $|\uparrow_{\mathbf{n}}\rangle$ and $|\downarrow_{\mathbf{n}}\rangle$ can be represented by specific spinors. At this point, we simply state the results (for more details, see Exercise 3.14 below). For a general direction $\mathbf{n}$, the spin-up and spin-down eigenvectors are

$$|\uparrow_{\mathbf{n}}\rangle = \begin{bmatrix}\cos(\theta/2)\\ e^{i\phi}\sin(\theta/2)\end{bmatrix} \quad\text{and}\quad |\downarrow_{\mathbf{n}}\rangle = \begin{bmatrix}-e^{-i\phi}\sin(\theta/2)\\ \cos(\theta/2)\end{bmatrix}. \qquad (3.24)$$

These two vectors provide an orthonormal basis for spin space. In other words, *any* spin state $|A\rangle$ can be written as

$$|A\rangle = c_1|\uparrow_{\mathbf{n}}\rangle + c_2|\downarrow_{\mathbf{n}}\rangle,$$

where $c_1$ and $c_2$ are complex numbers.

**Exercise 3.12** Verify that $|\uparrow_{\mathbf{n}}\rangle$ and $|\downarrow_{\mathbf{n}}\rangle$ are normalized and orthogonal to each other.

**Exercise 3.13** Find spinors corresponding to:

(a) an eigenvector of $\widehat{S}_x$ with eigenvalue $+\hbar/2$;

(b) an eigenvector of $\widehat{S}_y$ with eigenvalue $-\hbar/2$;

(c) a state that definitely has $+\hbar/2$ along an axis that lies in the $xz$-plane and makes angles of 60° and 30° with the positive $z$- and $x$-axes.

**Exercise 3.14** Verify that $|\uparrow_{\mathbf{n}}\rangle$, as given in Equations 3.24, is an eigenvector of $\widehat{S}_{\mathbf{n}}$ with eigenvalue $+\hbar/2$. ■

### 3.3.3 Compatible and incompatible spin observables

In Section 2.5 we met compatible and incompatible observables of orbital angular momentum. Here we shall see that very similar ideas apply to spin.

If a spin-$\frac{1}{2}$ atom is in a state $|\uparrow_{\mathbf{n}}\rangle$, then a measurement of its spin component in the positive $\mathbf{n}$-direction will certainly give the value $+\hbar/2$, and a measurement of its spin component in the negative $\mathbf{n}$-direction will certainly give the value $-\hbar/2$. However, if we measure spin in some other direction, for example the $z$-direction, we will *not* be able to predict the outcome with certainty; this is because the eigenvectors of $\widehat{S}_{\mathbf{n}}$ are a superposition of $|\uparrow_z\rangle$ and $|\downarrow_z\rangle$. Obviously, this result cannot depend on our choice of axes, so we can make a general statement:

> If a particle is in a state with a definite value of the spin component in a given direction $\mathbf{n}$, it does not have a definite value of the spin component in any other direction (except for the opposite direction, $-\mathbf{n}$, where the sign of the spin component is reversed).

Spin components along different axes in space are *incompatible observables*. Incompatibility is linked to the fact that $\widehat{S}_x$, $\widehat{S}_y$ and $\widehat{S}_z$ do not commute with one another. If, for example, $\widehat{S}_z$ and $\widehat{S}_x$ did commute, it would be possible to find a complete set of vectors that are eigenvectors of both $\widehat{S}_z$ and $\widehat{S}_x$, corresponding to states in which both $S_z$ and $S_x$ have definite values. However, these simultaneous eigenvectors do not exist because Equation 3.20 shows that $\widehat{S}_z\widehat{S}_x \neq \widehat{S}_x\widehat{S}_z$.

This situation follows the general pattern of the last chapter, where you saw that a particle cannot simultaneously have definite values of $L_z$ and $L_x$ (unless both are zero). But in that chapter there was an operator,

$$\widehat{L}^2 = \widehat{L}_x^2 + \widehat{L}_y^2 + \widehat{L}_z^2,$$

representing the square of the magnitude of the orbital angular momentum, which did commute with the three operators $\widehat{L}_x$, $\widehat{L}_y$ and $\widehat{L}_z$ for the components of orbital angular momentum. Thus, $L^2$ could have a definite value at the same time as $L_z$.

The same is true for spin in the sense that the operator defined by

$$\widehat{S}^2 = \widehat{S}_x^2 + \widehat{S}_y^2 + \widehat{S}_z^2,$$

representing the square of the magnitude of spin, commutes with the three matrices $\widehat{S}_x$, $\widehat{S}_y$ and $\widehat{S}_z$ for the components of spin. To see why, we first note that it is easy to verify that

$$\widehat{S}_x^2 = \widehat{S}_y^2 = \widehat{S}_z^2 = \frac{\hbar^2}{4}\begin{bmatrix} 1 & 0 \\ 0 & 1 \end{bmatrix} = \frac{\hbar^2}{4}\widehat{I}, \tag{3.25}$$

where $\widehat{I}$ is the $2 \times 2$ unit matrix.

- Verify Equation 3.25 for the case of $\widehat{S}_x$.

- Using Equation 3.21 and multiplying out the matrices gives

$$\widehat{S}_x^2 = \frac{\hbar^2}{4}\begin{bmatrix} 0 & 1 \\ 1 & 0 \end{bmatrix}\begin{bmatrix} 0 & 1 \\ 1 & 0 \end{bmatrix} = \frac{\hbar^2}{4}\begin{bmatrix} 1 & 0 \\ 0 & 1 \end{bmatrix} = \frac{\hbar^2}{4}\widehat{I}.$$

Using Equation 3.25, we see that

$$\widehat{S}^2 = \widehat{S}_x^2 + \widehat{S}_y^2 + \widehat{S}_z^2 = \frac{3\hbar^2}{4}\widehat{I}. \tag{3.26}$$

If we now apply $\widehat{S}^2$ to an arbitrary spinor, we obtain

$$\widehat{S}^2\begin{bmatrix} a \\ b \end{bmatrix} = \frac{3\hbar^2}{4}\begin{bmatrix} 1 & 0 \\ 0 & 1 \end{bmatrix}\begin{bmatrix} a \\ b \end{bmatrix} = \frac{3\hbar^2}{4}\begin{bmatrix} a \\ b \end{bmatrix},$$

so any spinor is an eigenvector of $\widehat{S}^2$ with eigenvalue $3\hbar^2/4$. This means that any state of a spin-$\frac{1}{2}$ particle has $S^2 = 3\hbar^2/4$, and we can say that $S_z$ and $S^2$ are *compatible observables* — they can both have definite values in the same state.

You may recall from Chapter 2 that the allowed values of $L^2$ are $l(l+1)\hbar^2$, where $l = 0, 1, 2, \ldots$, and the allowed values of $L_z$ are $m\hbar$, where $m$ is an integer ranging from $-l$ to $+l$.

Now for spin we have something very similar. If we write $S^2 = s(s+1)\hbar^2$, we see that the particles described in this chapter have $s = 1/2$, which gives

$$S^2 = \tfrac{1}{2}(\tfrac{1}{2}+1)\hbar^2 = 3\hbar^2/4,$$

and the allowed values of $S_z$ are $m_s\hbar$ where $m_s = \pm\frac{1}{2}$. Here, at last, is the reason we refer to electrons as being 'spin-$\frac{1}{2}$ particles'.

$l$ and $m$ are called the *orbital angular momentum quantum number* and the *magnetic quantum number*; $s$ and $m_s$ are called the **spin quantum number** and the **spin magnetic quantum number**.

## 3.4 Predicting the results of measurements

In this section, we show how the formalism developed so far can be used to predict the outcomes of spin measurements, including Stern–Gerlach experiments of the type discussed in Section 3.1. As always in the quantum world, there are limitations to what can be predicted with certainty.

### 3.4.1 Some general remarks about spin measurements

Before carrying out calculations, we first make some general remarks about spin measurements and their interpretation, referring back to experiments using Stern–Gerlach apparatus (Figure 3.8).

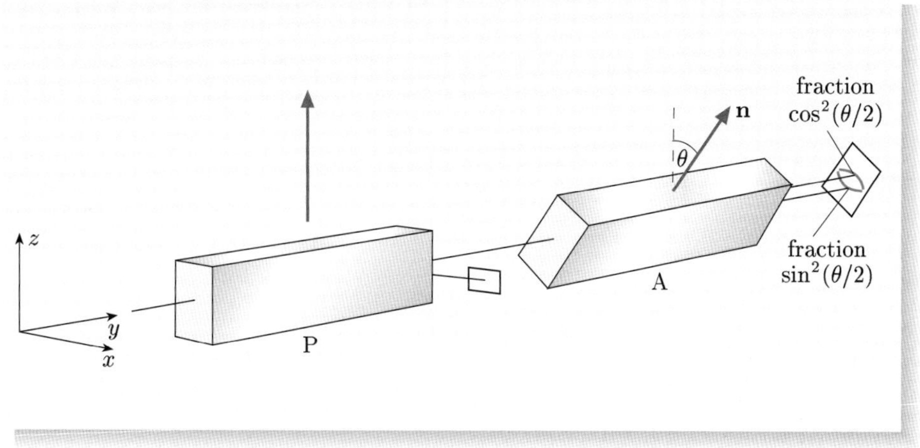


**Figure 3.8** An example of an experiment involving Stern–Gerlach magnets.

We have already stressed that it is incorrect to think of an atom as following a definite trajectory through a Stern–Gerlach apparatus. We should not say that an atom is spin-up relative to a given direction until we have actually measured it to be so. Rather than thinking of a beam of atoms as being split by a Stern–Gerlach magnet, with some atoms going one way and other atoms the other way, we should think of each atom as being in a linear superposition of two states. *The spin component of an atom along a given axis is undetermined until it is measured.*

A number of questions come to mind. What constitutes a measurement? When does the measurement take place? What does the measurement do to the state of the particle?

The spin analyzer in Figure 3.8 lets atoms fall on a detecting screen. If a particular atom is detected as arriving in the upper trace on the screen, this means (for our choice of magnets) that the atom is spin-up *immediately after the measurement.* Before the measurement, the atom is in a linear superposition of states that are spin-up and spin-down relative to the orientation vector of the magnet. This linear superposition changes abruptly into a spin-up state the instant the atom is recorded in the upper trace. It is also possible for the atom to arrive in the lower trace, and the linear superposition then changes abruptly into a spin-down state at the instant of detection.

The abrupt change from a linear superposition state to a spin-up or spin-down state is a characteristic feature of quantum mechanics. You met something similar at the beginning of Book 1: an extended wave function, describing a diffracted particle, collapses down to a single pixel when the particle is detected on a screen. In Book 1, this was called the *collapse of the wave function.* Here, we shall use a more general term — the **collapse of the state vector**, reflecting the fact that spin states are described by vectors, not functions.

If this collapse seems mysterious, it is because it is mysterious. There is no satisfactory description in terms of any underlying mechanism. There is a great deal of controversy about this topic. It does seem, however, that the collapse of the state vector occurs when there is an irreversible event such as a particle colliding with a screen and leaving its mark. Without such an event, collapse does not take place. For example, we can imagine guiding the two beams in a Stern–Gerlach analyzer and allowing them to merge together, well before they are detected. If this were done, quantum mechanics predicts that there would be no collapse, and that the final state emerging from the Stern–Gerlach apparatus would be the same as that entering it. In other words, it is not the Stern–Gerlach magnets that cause the collapse, but the detectors.

We assume that the state produced immediately after a measurement is a state that is certain to give the value found in the measurement. This makes good sense because if we carry out the same measurement twice, in very rapid succession, we would expect to get the same results in both cases. In terms of the formalism we have developed, this means that:

When a spin component in the $\mathbf{n}$-direction is measured, the spin state collapses onto an eigenvector of $\widehat{\mathrm{S}}_{\mathbf{n}}$ — the one whose eigenvalue is the value obtained in the measurement. For example, if we measure $S_x$ and obtain the value $-\hbar/2$, the spin state collapses onto $|\downarrow_x\rangle$, which is the eigenvector of $\widehat{\mathrm{S}}_x$ corresponding to the eigenvalue $-\hbar/2$.

You might wonder how we can investigate the state of an atom after a spin measurement. In a spin analyzer, the measurement takes the atom out of the beam, making it unavailable for further measurements. However, it is also possible to think of a spin preparer as a kind of measurer.

Suppose that a spin preparer blocks off particles with $S_z = -\hbar/2$ and allows particles with $S_z = +\hbar/2$ to pass though. We consider an atom that is in a linear superposition of spin-up and spin-down states before it enters the preparer. If this atom enters the preparer, *and we do not detect it in the blocked-off path*, we can infer that it has $S_z = +\hbar/2$, and that the initial superposition of spin-up and spin-down states has collapsed onto a spin-up state. In effect, this simulates a measurement of $S_z$ — by a method reminiscent of the Sherlock Holmes story, where a vital clue was that a dog failed to bark. Having passed through the preparer, the atom is still in a beam and further measurements can be carried out on it. We can confirm that it does have $S_z = \hbar/2$ after the measurement, and this is exactly what the apparatus sketched in Figure 3.3 would do.

### 3.4.2 Calculating probabilities

The result of sending an atom through a Stern–Gerlach apparatus is uncertain; for most initial states, the atom could emerge in either the spin-up beam or the spin-down beam. We now show how the probabilities of these two outcomes can be calculated. You will see, in particular, how the quantum theory of spin explains the $\cos^2(\theta/2)$ rule of Section 3.1.

Suppose that a spin analyzer is oriented in the $\mathbf{n}$-direction, so that it measures $S_\mathbf{n}$, the spin component in the $\mathbf{n}$-direction. The corresponding spin matrix $\widehat{\mathrm{S}}_\mathbf{n}$ has eigenvectors $|\uparrow_\mathbf{n}\rangle$ and $|\downarrow_\mathbf{n}\rangle$, and these provide an orthonormal basis for spin space. This means that any spin state $|A\rangle$ can be written as

The subscript u stands for spin-*up*, while d stands for spin-*down*, relative to the direction $\mathbf{n}$.

$$|A\rangle = a_\mathrm{u}|\uparrow_\mathbf{n}\rangle + a_\mathrm{d}|\downarrow_\mathbf{n}\rangle, \tag{3.27}$$

where the complex numbers $a_\mathrm{u}$ and $a_\mathrm{d}$ are the probability amplitudes for measuring spin-up or spin-down in the $\mathbf{n}$-direction; the corresponding probabilities are $|a_\mathrm{u}|^2$ and $|a_\mathrm{d}|^2$.

If the orientations of the spin preparer and the spin analyzer are known, we can easily find appropriate spinors for $|A\rangle$, $|\uparrow_\mathbf{n}\rangle$ and $|\downarrow_\mathbf{n}\rangle$. The remaining problem is to find the coefficients $a_\mathrm{u}$ and $a_\mathrm{d}$. We shall now present an efficient way of doing this.

To find $a_\mathrm{u}$, we take the inner product of both sides of Equation 3.27 with $|\uparrow_\mathbf{n}\rangle$ to get

$$\langle\uparrow_\mathbf{n}|A\rangle = a_\mathrm{u}\langle\uparrow_\mathbf{n}|\uparrow_\mathbf{n}\rangle + a_\mathrm{d}\langle\uparrow_\mathbf{n}|\downarrow_\mathbf{n}\rangle.$$

The eigenvectors are normalized and orthogonal, so $\langle\uparrow_\mathbf{n}|\uparrow_\mathbf{n}\rangle = 1$ and $\langle\uparrow_\mathbf{n}|\downarrow_\mathbf{n}\rangle = 0$, and we are left with

$$a_\mathrm{u} = \langle\uparrow_\mathbf{n}|A\rangle. \tag{3.28}$$

A similar argument, based on taking the inner product with $|\downarrow_\mathbf{n}\rangle$, gives

$$a_\mathrm{d} = \langle\downarrow_\mathbf{n}|A\rangle. \tag{3.29}$$

The corresponding probabilities are then given by

$$p_\mathrm{u} = |a_\mathrm{u}|^2 = |\langle\uparrow_\mathbf{n}|A\rangle|^2 \tag{3.30}$$

$$p_\mathrm{d} = |a_\mathrm{d}|^2 = |\langle\downarrow_\mathbf{n}|A\rangle|^2 \tag{3.31}$$

The only remaining step is to evaluate the inner products with the appropriate spinors. To illustrate this process, let us suppose that the orientation vector of the spin preparer makes an angle $\theta_1$ with the $z$-direction and has $\phi_1 = 0$. Let us also suppose that the spin analyzer is oriented in the direction of the vector $\mathbf{n}$, which makes an angle $\theta_2$ with the $z$-direction and has $\phi_2 = 0$. Then, inserting these angles into Equation 3.24, we see that the initial state is

$$|A\rangle = \begin{bmatrix}\cos(\theta_1/2)\\ \sin(\theta_1/2)\end{bmatrix},$$

and the eigenvector characterizing the measurement result is

$$|\uparrow_{\mathbf{n}}\rangle = \begin{bmatrix}\cos(\theta_2/2)\\ \sin(\theta_2/2)\end{bmatrix}.$$

We therefore have

$$\begin{aligned}\langle\uparrow_{\mathbf{n}}|A\rangle &= \begin{bmatrix}\cos(\theta_2/2) & \sin(\theta_2/2)\end{bmatrix}\begin{bmatrix}\cos(\theta_1/2)\\ \sin(\theta_1/2)\end{bmatrix}\\ &= \cos(\theta_2/2)\cos(\theta_1/2) + \sin(\theta_2/2)\sin(\theta_1/2)\\ &= \cos\big((\theta_2-\theta_1)/2\big),\end{aligned}$$

Standard trigonometric identities are listed inside the back cover of the book.

and the probability of measuring spin-up in the $\mathbf{n}$-direction is

$$p_{\mathrm{u}} = |\langle\uparrow_{\mathbf{n}}|A\rangle|^2 = \cos^2\big((\theta_2-\theta_1)/2\big),$$

where $\theta_2 - \theta_1$ is the angle between the orientations of the preparer and the analyzer. So our formalism does indeed explain the $\cos^2(\theta/2)$ rule, which was stated without proof in Section 3.1.

**Exercise 3.15** Express $|\uparrow_z\rangle$ as a linear combination of $|\uparrow_y\rangle$ and $|\downarrow_y\rangle$, and hence find the probability of getting the values $+\hbar/2$ and $-\hbar/2$ when $S_y$ is measured in the state $|\uparrow_z\rangle$. ■

### 3.4.3 Calculating expectation values

Now that we know how to calculate the probabilities of getting particular outcomes in a spin measurement, we can find the expectation value of a given spin component in a given state.

Suppose that a spin-$\frac{1}{2}$ particle is in a spin state represented by $|A\rangle$, and that we measure its spin component in the direction $\mathbf{n}$. The possible values are $+\hbar/2$ and $-\hbar/2$, and the corresponding probabilities are $p_{\mathrm{u}}$ and $p_{\mathrm{d}}$. We then define the **expectation value** of $S_{\mathbf{n}}$ in the state $|A\rangle$ to be

$$\langle S_{\mathbf{n}}\rangle = p_{\mathrm{u}}\left(\frac{\hbar}{2}\right) + p_{\mathrm{d}}\left(-\frac{\hbar}{2}\right), \qquad (3.32)$$

$$= |\langle\uparrow_{\mathbf{n}}|A\rangle|^2\left(\frac{\hbar}{2}\right) - |\langle\downarrow_{\mathbf{n}}|A\rangle|^2\left(\frac{\hbar}{2}\right). \qquad (3.33)$$

This formula can be used directly, with $p_{\mathrm{u}}$ and $p_{\mathrm{d}}$, the spin-up and spin-down probabilities, found by the methods described in the previous subsection.

However, there is another way of calculating the expectation value of a spin component, analogous to the sandwich integral rule of wave mechanics. In wave mechanics, the expectation value of momentum is given by

$$\langle p_x\rangle = \langle\Psi|\widehat{\mathrm{p}}_x|\Psi\rangle \equiv \int_{-\infty}^{\infty} \Psi^*(x,t)\,\widehat{\mathrm{p}}_x\Psi(x,t)\,\mathrm{d}x.$$

A similar **sandwich rule** applies in the case of spin. It can be shown that

$$\langle S_{\mathbf{n}}\rangle = \langle A|\,\widehat{\mathrm{S}}_{\mathbf{n}}\,|A\rangle, \tag{3.34}$$

where $\langle A|$ and $|A\rangle$ are the bra and ket vectors representing the spin state of the particle. To evaluate the expectation value, we express the bras and kets as row and column spinors, use an appropriate spin matrix $\widehat{\mathrm{S}}_{\mathbf{n}}$, and multiply out all the matrices. The next example shows why this works.

### Worked Example 3.3

Show that Equations 3.32 and 3.34 are equivalent.

**Essential skill**

Evaluating expectation values of spin observables using spinors

#### Solution

We will start with the expression of Equation 3.34 and show that Equation 3.32 follows. First, we express $|A\rangle$ as a linear combination of the eigenvectors of $\widehat{\mathrm{S}}_{\mathbf{n}}$:

$$|A\rangle = a_{\mathrm{u}}|\uparrow_{\mathbf{n}}\rangle + a_{\mathrm{d}}|\downarrow_{\mathbf{n}}\rangle. \tag{3.35}$$

The corresponding bra vector is found, as usual, by replacing all the kets by bras and taking the complex conjugates of the coefficients. This gives

$$\langle A| = a_{\mathrm{u}}^*\langle\uparrow_{\mathbf{n}}| + a_{\mathrm{d}}^*\langle\downarrow_{\mathbf{n}}|.$$

Now, $|\uparrow_{\mathbf{n}}\rangle$ and $|\downarrow_{\mathbf{n}}\rangle$ are eigenvectors of $\widehat{\mathrm{S}}_{\mathbf{n}}$ with eigenvalues $+\hbar/2$ and $-\hbar/2$, respectively, so we have

$$\widehat{\mathrm{S}}_{\mathbf{n}}|A\rangle = \frac{\hbar}{2}\Big(a_{\mathrm{u}}|\uparrow_{\mathbf{n}}\rangle - a_{\mathrm{d}}|\downarrow_{\mathbf{n}}\rangle\Big).$$

Combining the last two expressions, we obtain

$$\langle S_{\mathbf{n}}\rangle = \langle A|\,\widehat{\mathrm{S}}_{\mathbf{n}}\,|A\rangle = \frac{\hbar}{2}\Big(a_{\mathrm{u}}^*\langle\uparrow_{\mathbf{n}}| + a_{\mathrm{d}}^*\langle\downarrow_{\mathbf{n}}|\Big)\Big(a_{\mathrm{u}}|\uparrow_{\mathbf{n}}\rangle - a_{\mathrm{d}}|\downarrow_{\mathbf{n}}\rangle\Big),$$

which can be simplified, using the orthonormality of $|\uparrow_{\mathbf{n}}\rangle$ and $|\downarrow_{\mathbf{n}}\rangle$, to

$$\langle S_{\mathbf{n}}\rangle = \frac{\hbar}{2}\left(a_{\mathrm{u}}^*a_{\mathrm{u}} - a_{\mathrm{d}}^*a_{\mathrm{d}}\right) = \frac{\hbar}{2}\left(|a_{\mathrm{u}}|^2 - |a_{\mathrm{d}}|^2\right).$$

Finally, we can write this in the form of Equation 3.32:

$$\langle S_{\mathbf{n}}\rangle = p_{\mathrm{u}}\left(\frac{\hbar}{2}\right) + p_{\mathrm{d}}\left(-\frac{\hbar}{2}\right),$$

since $p_{\mathrm{u}} = |a_{\mathrm{u}}|^2$ is the probability for spin-up in the $\mathbf{n}$-direction and $p_{\mathrm{d}} = |a_{\mathrm{d}}|^2$ is the probability for spin-down in the $\mathbf{n}$-direction.

**Exercise 3.16** Find the expectation value of $S_y$ for the state in which the particle definitely has spin $S_z = +\hbar/2$. Do the calculation two ways, first using Equation 3.34, then using Equation 3.32. ■

## 3.5 Energy levels and time-development

A spin-$\frac{1}{2}$ particle, such as a silver atom, behaves like a tiny magnetic dipole. That is why silver atoms are deflected by the inhomogeneous magnetic field of a Stern–Gerlach magnet. In the simpler case of a uniform magnetic field, a spin-$\frac{1}{2}$ particle will have a magnetic potential energy that depends on the orientation of its spin relative to the magnetic field.

In this section, we will use these ideas to obtain a Hamiltonian operator that describes the energy associated with spin orientation. We will then address two important questions about a spin-$\frac{1}{2}$ particle in a magnetic field:

- What are its energy levels?
- How does a given spin state evolve in time?

These questions will be answered by writing down and solving the time-independent Schrödinger equation and the Schrödinger equation for a spin-$\frac{1}{2}$ particle in a magnetic field.

### 3.5.1 The Hamiltonian operator and energy levels

Chapter 2 explained that there is a relationship between the orbital angular momentum $\mathbf{L}$ of a charged particle, and the resulting magnetic dipole moment $\boldsymbol{\mu}$:

$$\boldsymbol{\mu} = \gamma\mathbf{L},$$

where the proportionality constant $\gamma$ is the gyromagnetic ratio. This constant is proportional to the charge-to-mass ratio of the orbiting particle, and is negative for an electron because of its negative charge.

Something very similar applies to spin. In this case, we have

$$\boldsymbol{\mu} = \gamma_s\mathbf{S}, \tag{3.36}$$

where the proportionality constant $\gamma_s$ is called the **spin gyromagnetic ratio**. The value of this constant depends on the type of particle, and is negative for an electron. In general, $\gamma_s \neq \gamma$.

The classical expression for the potential energy of a magnetic dipole, of magnetic dipole moment $\boldsymbol{\mu}$, in a magnetic field $\mathbf{B}$ is

$$E_{\text{mag}} = -\boldsymbol{\mu}\cdot\mathbf{B}. \tag{3.37}$$

Combining Equations 3.36 and 3.37, we obtain

$$E_{\text{mag}} = -\gamma_s\mathbf{S}\cdot\mathbf{B}. \tag{3.38}$$

Let us suppose that the magnetic field has magnitude $B$ and points in the direction of the unit vector $\mathbf{n}$. Then $\mathbf{B} = B\mathbf{n}$, and Equation 3.38 takes the form

$$E_{\text{mag}} = -\gamma_s B\mathbf{n}\cdot\mathbf{S} = -\gamma_s BS_{\mathbf{n}}, \tag{3.39}$$

where $S_{\mathbf{n}}$ is the spin component in the direction of the magnetic field.

Equation 3.39 is the energy contribution associated with the alignment of the spin relative to the magnetic field. A real particle would have other forms of energy, including kinetic energy, but we shall assume that these do not influence the behaviour of its spin, and so can be omitted from our discussion. Equation 3.39 is a classical Hamiltonian function which contains no kinetic energy terms. We can obtain the corresponding Hamiltonian operator $\widehat{\text{H}}$ by replacing the observable $S_{\mathbf{n}}$ by the corresponding general spin matrix, $\widehat{\text{S}}_{\mathbf{n}}$. This gives

$$\widehat{\text{H}} = -\gamma_{\text{s}} B\,\widehat{\text{S}}_{\mathbf{n}} = -\frac{\gamma_{\text{s}} B\hbar}{2}\begin{bmatrix}\cos\theta & \text{e}^{-\text{i}\phi}\sin\theta \\ \text{e}^{\text{i}\phi}\sin\theta & -\cos\theta\end{bmatrix}. \tag{3.40}$$

In the special case where the magnetic field points along the $z$-axis, for example, we have

$$\widehat{\text{H}} = -\gamma_{\text{s}} B\,\widehat{\text{S}}_z = -\frac{\gamma_{\text{s}} B\hbar}{2}\begin{bmatrix}1 & 0 \\ 0 & -1\end{bmatrix}.$$

In general, the quantity $\widehat{\text{H}}$ defined in Equation 3.40 is called the **Hamiltonian matrix**. The equation shows that the Hamiltonian matrix $\widehat{\text{H}}$ is proportional to the general spin matrix $\widehat{\text{S}}_{\mathbf{n}}$, where $\mathbf{n}$ is a unit vector in the direction of the magnetic field. Hence $\widehat{\text{H}}$ and $\widehat{\text{S}}_{\mathbf{n}}$ share the same eigenvectors, $|\uparrow_{\mathbf{n}}\rangle$ and $|\downarrow_{\mathbf{n}}\rangle$, and we can write

The subscript u stands for spin-*up*, while d stands for spin-*down*, relative to the direction $\mathbf{n}$ of the magnetic field.

$$\widehat{\text{H}}|\uparrow_{\mathbf{n}}\rangle = -\frac{\gamma_{\text{s}} B\hbar}{2}|\uparrow_{\mathbf{n}}\rangle \quad \text{and} \quad \widehat{\text{H}}|\downarrow_{\mathbf{n}}\rangle = +\frac{\gamma_{\text{s}} B\hbar}{2}|\downarrow_{\mathbf{n}}\rangle. \tag{3.41}$$

In other words,

$$\widehat{\text{H}}|\uparrow_{\mathbf{n}}\rangle = E_{\text{u}}|\uparrow_{\mathbf{n}}\rangle \quad \text{and} \quad \widehat{\text{H}}|\downarrow_{\mathbf{n}}\rangle = E_{\text{d}}|\downarrow_{\mathbf{n}}\rangle, \tag{3.42}$$

where

$$E_{\text{u}} = -\frac{\gamma_{\text{s}} B\hbar}{2} \quad \text{and} \quad E_{\text{d}} = +\frac{\gamma_{\text{s}} B\hbar}{2}. \tag{3.43}$$

Equation 3.42 is just the time-independent Schrödinger equation, written out for both of its solutions. The energy eigenvectors are $|\uparrow_{\mathbf{n}}\rangle$ and $|\downarrow_{\mathbf{n}}\rangle$, and the energy eigenvalues are $E_{\text{u}}$ and $E_{\text{d}}$.

We therefore have two energy levels, $E_{\text{u}}$ and $E_{\text{d}}$. Which of these is lower in energy depends on the sign of $\gamma_{\text{s}}$. For particles such as electrons, $\gamma_{\text{s}} < 0$ so $E_{\text{u}} > E_{\text{d}}$. Other particles, such as protons, have $\gamma_{\text{s}} > 0$, and in this case $E_{\text{u}} < E_{\text{d}}$. In both cases there are two energy levels, separated by

$$\Delta E = |\gamma_{\text{s}}|B\hbar = \hbar\omega,$$

where $\omega = |\gamma_{\text{s}}|B$ is a positive quantity called the **Larmor frequency**. The lower level is $-\hbar\omega/2$ and the upper level is $+\hbar\omega/2$, but which of these levels corresponds to spin-up or spin-down relative to the direction of the magnetic field depends on the particle involved, as shown in Figure 3.9.

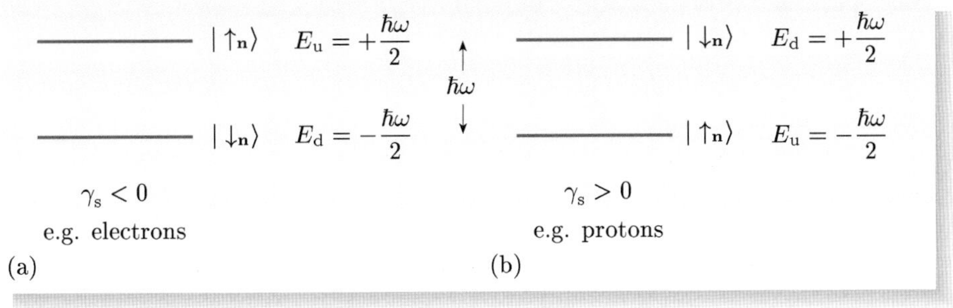


**Figure 3.9** Energy levels for a spin-$\frac{1}{2}$ particle in a magnetic field: (a) particles such as electrons with $\gamma_{\text{s}} < 0$; (b) particles such as protons with $\gamma_{\text{s}} > 0$.

These ideas have important applications. A magnetic resonance imaging (MRI) scanner applies a strong magnetic field to ensure that the spin-up and spin-down states of protons in living tissue have slightly different energies. It then uses a radio frequency pulse to transfer protons from the spin-up state to the spin-down state. By monitoring the subsequent behaviour of the protons, it is possible produce detailed maps of internal body organs (Figure 3.10).

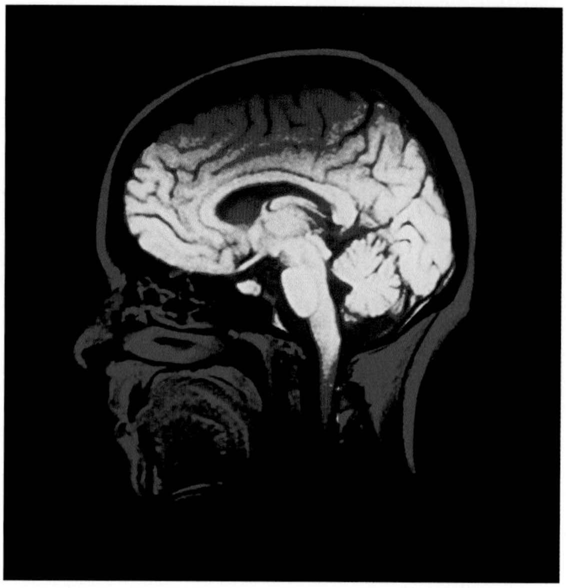

**Figure 3.10** An MRI image showing a vertical 'slice' through a human head.

**Exercise 3.17** A proton has a spin gyromagnetic ratio $\gamma_s = 4.26 \times 10^7\,\mathrm{Hz\,T^{-1}}$. It is placed in a magnetic field of magnitude $3.00\,\mathrm{T}$. What frequency of electromagnetic radiation is required to promote a proton from the spin-up state to the spin-down state? ■

### 3.5.2 Time-development of spin states

Finally, we discuss the time-development of spin states in a magnetic field. This is also an important part of the way an MRI scanner works, as it gives us the ability to monitor the protons after they have been excited by a radio frequency pulse.

To predict how states evolve in time, we use Schrödinger's equation. For a spin-$\frac{1}{2}$ particle, the Hamiltonian operator is a $2 \times 2$ matrix, and it acts on a $2 \times 1$ spinor. Nevertheless, Schrödinger's equation still applies and it takes the form

$$i\hbar \frac{\mathrm{d}|A\rangle}{\mathrm{d}t} = \widehat{\mathrm{H}}|A\rangle, \tag{3.44}$$

where $|A\rangle$ is the spin state of a particle at any time $t$. Now, suppose that we know the initial spin state, $|A\rangle_{\text{initial}}$, at time $t = 0$. How can we predict the spin state $|A\rangle$ at some future time $t$? The secret is to represent spin states in a suitable basis — one that simplifies the calculation. The 'right' choice is provided by the eigenvectors of $\widehat{\mathrm{H}}$, namely $|\uparrow_{\mathbf{n}}\rangle$ and $|\downarrow_{\mathbf{n}}\rangle$.

Given a magnetic field $\mathbf{B} = B\mathbf{n}$, the first step is to find the eigenvectors $|\uparrow_{\mathbf{n}}\rangle$ and $|\downarrow_{\mathbf{n}}\rangle$, and the next step is to expand the initial state $|A\rangle_{\text{initial}}$ in terms of these vectors:

$$|A\rangle_{\text{initial}} = a_{\text{u}}|\uparrow_{\mathbf{n}}\rangle + a_{\text{d}}|\downarrow_{\mathbf{n}}\rangle.$$

Both of these steps were explored in previous sections. The key point, which we now introduce, is that the spin state at any later time is given by

$$|A\rangle = a_{\text{u}}\text{e}^{-\text{i}E_{\text{u}}t/\hbar}|\uparrow_{\mathbf{n}}\rangle + a_{\text{d}}\text{e}^{-\text{i}E_{\text{d}}t/\hbar}|\downarrow_{\mathbf{n}}\rangle. \tag{3.45}$$

This is reminiscent of the formula used to predict the time-development of a wave packet in a harmonic oscillator (Book 1, Chapter 6). To see why it works, we first note that the exponential factors in Equation 3.45 become equal to 1 at $t = 0$, so $|A\rangle$ becomes equal to $|A\rangle_{\text{initial}}$ at $t = 0$, as it must. Secondly, we can show that the above expression for $|A\rangle$ satisfies Schrödinger's equation. To establish this, we substitute Equation 3.45 into Equation 3.44. Substituting into the left-hand side gives

$$\begin{aligned}\text{i}\hbar\,\frac{\text{d}|A\rangle}{\text{d}t} &= \text{i}\hbar\left((-\text{i}E_{\text{u}}/\hbar)\,a_{\text{u}}\text{e}^{-\text{i}E_{\text{u}}t/\hbar}|\uparrow_{\mathbf{n}}\rangle + (-\text{i}E_{\text{d}}/\hbar)\,a_{\text{d}}\text{e}^{-\text{i}E_{\text{d}}t/\hbar}|\downarrow_{\mathbf{n}}\rangle\right)\\ &= E_{\text{u}}a_{\text{u}}\text{e}^{-\text{i}E_{\text{u}}t/\hbar}|\uparrow_{\mathbf{n}}\rangle + E_{\text{d}}a_{\text{d}}\text{e}^{-\text{i}E_{\text{d}}t/\hbar}|\downarrow_{\mathbf{n}}\rangle,\end{aligned} \tag{3.46}$$

while substituting into the right-hand side gives

$$\widehat{\text{H}}|A\rangle = E_{\text{u}}a_{\text{u}}\text{e}^{-\text{i}E_{\text{u}}t/\hbar}|\uparrow_{\mathbf{n}}\rangle + E_{\text{d}}a_{\text{d}}\text{e}^{-\text{i}E_{\text{d}}t/\hbar}|\downarrow_{\mathbf{n}}\rangle, \tag{3.47}$$

because $|\uparrow_{\mathbf{n}}\rangle$ and $|\downarrow_{\mathbf{n}}\rangle$ are eigenvectors of $\widehat{\text{H}}$ with eigenvalues $E_{\text{u}}$ and $E_{\text{d}}$. Since the right-hand sides of Equations 3.46 and 3.47 are equal, the left-hand sides must also be equal. Thus $|A\rangle$ satisfies both the initial condition and Schrödinger's equation; it therefore describes the spin state of the particle at all times (so long as the particle remains undisturbed by measurements).

**Essential skill**

Predicting the time-dependence of a spin state in a magnetic field

### Worked Example 3.4

At time $t = 0$, a silver atom is prepared in the initial spin state $|A\rangle_{\text{initial}} = |\uparrow_z\rangle$. The atom has a spin gyromagnetic ratio $\gamma_{\text{s}} < 0$, and is in a uniform magnetic field $\mathbf{B} = B\mathbf{e}_x$, so its Larmor frequency is $\omega = -\gamma_{\text{s}}B$. Predict the spin state of the atom at any later time $t$, and hence obtain $\langle S_z\rangle$ as a function of time, expressing your answers in terms of the Larmor frequency.

#### Solution

The Hamiltonian matrix is $\widehat{\text{H}} = -\gamma_{\text{s}}B\,\widehat{\text{S}}_x = \omega\widehat{\text{S}}_x$. Using Equations 3.24 with $\theta = \pi/2$ and $\phi = 0$, we see that this matrix has eigenvectors

$$|\uparrow_x\rangle = \frac{1}{\sqrt{2}}\begin{bmatrix}1\\1\end{bmatrix} \quad\text{and}\quad |\downarrow_x\rangle = \frac{1}{\sqrt{2}}\begin{bmatrix}-1\\1\end{bmatrix},$$

with the eigenvalues $E_{\text{u}} = +\hbar\omega/2$ and $E_{\text{d}} = -\hbar\omega/2$ shown in Figure 3.9a.

We must expand the initial spin state in terms of these eigenvectors. To do this, we write

$$|A\rangle_{\text{initial}} = |\uparrow_z\rangle = a_{\text{u}}|\uparrow_x\rangle + a_{\text{d}}|\downarrow_x\rangle,$$

and then find the coefficients from

$$a_{\rm u} = \langle \uparrow_x \mid \uparrow_z \rangle = \frac{1}{\sqrt{2}} \begin{bmatrix} 1 & 1 \end{bmatrix} \begin{bmatrix} 1 \\ 0 \end{bmatrix} = \frac{1}{\sqrt{2}},$$

$$a_{\rm d} = \langle \downarrow_x \mid \uparrow_z \rangle = \frac{1}{\sqrt{2}} \begin{bmatrix} -1 & 1 \end{bmatrix} \begin{bmatrix} 1 \\ 0 \end{bmatrix} = -\frac{1}{\sqrt{2}}.$$

This gives

$$|A\rangle_{\rm initial} = \frac{1}{\sqrt{2}} \Big( | \uparrow_x \rangle - | \downarrow_x \rangle \Big),$$

so, for any time $t$,

$$\begin{aligned} |A\rangle &= \frac{1}{\sqrt{2}} \Big( e^{-iE_{\rm u}t/\hbar} | \uparrow_x \rangle - e^{-iE_{\rm d}t/\hbar} | \downarrow_x \rangle \Big) \\ &= \frac{1}{\sqrt{2}} \Big( e^{-i\omega t/2} | \uparrow_x \rangle - e^{+i\omega t/2} | \downarrow_x \rangle \Big) \\ &= \frac{1}{2} e^{-i\omega t/2} \begin{bmatrix} 1 \\ 1 \end{bmatrix} - \frac{1}{2} e^{+i\omega t/2} \begin{bmatrix} -1 \\ 1 \end{bmatrix} \\ &= \frac{1}{2} \begin{bmatrix} e^{-i\omega t/2} + e^{+i\omega t/2} \\ e^{-i\omega t/2} - e^{+i\omega t/2} \end{bmatrix} = \begin{bmatrix} \cos(\omega t/2) \\ -i\sin(\omega t/2) \end{bmatrix}. \end{aligned}$$

Remember: $e^{ix} = \cos x + i \sin x$.

The expectation value of $S_z$ at time $t$ is then given by

$$\begin{aligned} \langle S_z \rangle &= \langle A | \widehat{S}_z | A \rangle \\ &= \frac{\hbar}{2} \begin{bmatrix} \cos(\omega t/2) & i\sin(\omega t/2) \end{bmatrix} \begin{bmatrix} 1 & 0 \\ 0 & -1 \end{bmatrix} \begin{bmatrix} \cos(\omega t/2) \\ -i\sin(\omega t/2) \end{bmatrix} \\ &= \frac{\hbar}{2} \begin{bmatrix} \cos(\omega t/2) & i\sin(\omega t/2) \end{bmatrix} \begin{bmatrix} \cos(\omega t/2) \\ i\sin(\omega t/2) \end{bmatrix} \\ &= \frac{\hbar}{2} \left( \cos^2(\omega t/2) - \sin^2(\omega t/2) \right) \\ &= \frac{\hbar}{2} \cos(\omega t). \end{aligned}$$

**Exercise 3.18** How does the expectation value of $S_y$ vary with time in the state described in Worked Example 3.4?

**Exercise 3.19** A spin-$\frac{1}{2}$ particle with $\gamma_{\rm s} > 0$ is in a uniform magnetic field that points in the $y$-direction. At time $t = 0$, it is in the spin state $| \uparrow_z \rangle$. Find the spinor that represents the state of the particle at any time $t$, expressing your answer in terms of the Larmor frequency. (The results of Exercise 3.15 may be useful.) ■

# Summary of Chapter 3

**Section 3.1** Any spin component of a spin-$\frac{1}{2}$ particle has two possible values, $+\hbar/2$ and $-\hbar/2$, corresponding to the two beams that emerge from a Stern–Gerlach magnet. The probability that an atom will be measured to be spin-up relative to one Stern–Gerlach magnet, when it has been prepared to be spin-up relative to another Stern–Gerlach magnet, is equal to $\cos^2(\theta/2)$, where $\theta$ is the angle between the orientation vectors of the two magnets.

**Section 3.2** The spin state of a spin-$\frac{1}{2}$ particle is represented by a vector in spin space, which can be conveniently written as a two-element matrix called a spinor. The inner product of $|A\rangle = \begin{bmatrix} a_1 \\ a_2 \end{bmatrix}$ and $|B\rangle = \begin{bmatrix} b_1 \\ b_2 \end{bmatrix}$ is given by

$$\langle A|B\rangle = \begin{bmatrix} a_1^* & a_2^* \end{bmatrix} \begin{bmatrix} b_1 \\ b_2 \end{bmatrix} = a_1^* b_1 + a_2^* b_2.$$

As always, we have $\langle A|B\rangle^* = \langle B|A\rangle$.

**Section 3.3** The spin component in a given direction $\mathbf{n}$ is an observable quantity, represented in quantum mechanics by a $2 \times 2$ matrix

$$\widehat{\mathrm{S}}_{\mathbf{n}} = \frac{\hbar}{2} \begin{bmatrix} \cos\theta & \mathrm{e}^{-\mathrm{i}\phi} \sin\theta \\ \mathrm{e}^{\mathrm{i}\phi} \sin\theta & -\cos\theta \end{bmatrix}.$$

This matrix has eigenvectors

$$|\uparrow_{\mathbf{n}}\rangle = \begin{bmatrix} \cos(\theta/2) \\ \mathrm{e}^{\mathrm{i}\phi} \sin(\theta/2) \end{bmatrix} \quad \text{and} \quad |\downarrow_{\mathbf{n}}\rangle = \begin{bmatrix} -\mathrm{e}^{-\mathrm{i}\phi} \sin(\theta/2) \\ \cos(\theta/2) \end{bmatrix},$$

and eigenvalues $+\hbar/2$ and $-\hbar/2$. The two eigenvectors form an orthonormal basis in spin space. They are the only states that have definite values of the spin component in the $\mathbf{n}$-direction.

Spin matrices along different Cartesian axes obey commutation relations similar to those for the components of orbital angular momentum. As a result, it is impossible for two (different and non-opposite) components of spin to have definite values in the same state. The matrix $\widehat{\mathrm{S}}^2 = \widehat{\mathrm{S}}_x^2 + \widehat{\mathrm{S}}_y^2 + \widehat{\mathrm{S}}_z^2$ commutes with all spin matrices and has the value $s(s+1)\hbar^2$ in any state, where $s = 1/2$. This is the origin of the term 'spin-$\frac{1}{2}$ particle'.

**Section 3.4** Spin components are undetermined until they are measured. On measurement of $S_{\mathbf{n}}$, the spin state vector collapses onto an eigenvector of $\widehat{\mathrm{S}}_{\mathbf{n}}$ — the one whose eigenvalue is equal to the value obtained in the measurement.

If a particle is in the spin state

$$|A\rangle = a_{\mathrm{u}}|\uparrow_{\mathbf{n}}\rangle + a_{\mathrm{d}}|\downarrow_{\mathbf{n}}\rangle,$$

and the spin component in the $\mathbf{n}$-direction is measured, the probability of getting the spin-up value $+\hbar/2$ is $|a_{\mathrm{u}}|^2 = |\langle\uparrow_{\mathbf{n}}|A\rangle|^2$, and the probability of getting the spin-down value $-\hbar/2$ is $|a_{\mathrm{d}}|^2 = |\langle\downarrow_{\mathbf{n}}|A\rangle|^2$. Detailed calculations confirm the $\cos^2(\theta/2)$ rule.

The expectation value of $S_{\mathbf{n}}$ is given by the sandwich rule $\langle S_{\mathbf{n}}\rangle = \langle A|\,\widehat{\mathrm{S}}_{\mathbf{n}}\,|A\rangle$.

**Section 3.5** A spin-$\frac{1}{2}$ particle in a magnetic field $\mathbf{B} = B\mathbf{n}$ has the Hamiltonian matrix $\widehat{\mathrm{H}} = -\gamma_{\mathrm{s}} B\, \widehat{\mathrm{S}}_{\mathbf{n}}$, where $\gamma_{\mathrm{s}}$ is the spin gyromagnetic ratio of the particle.

The time-independent Schrödinger equation has two energy eigenvectors that are the eigenvectors of $\widehat{\mathrm{S}}_{\mathbf{n}}$: $|\uparrow_{\mathbf{n}}\rangle$ and $|\downarrow_{\mathbf{n}}\rangle$, and two energy eigenvalues, $\pm\hbar\omega/2$, where $\omega = |\gamma_{\mathrm{s}}|B$ is the Larmor frequency. The (time-dependent) Schrödinger equation is solved by expanding the initial spin state in terms of $|\uparrow_{\mathbf{n}}\rangle$ and $|\downarrow_{\mathbf{n}}\rangle$. The time-dependent spin-state is then obtained by inserting appropriate factors of $\mathrm{e}^{\pm\mathrm{i}\omega t/2}$.

## Achievements from Chapter 3

*After studying this chapter, you should be able to:*

**3.1** Explain the meanings of the newly defined (emboldened) terms and symbols, and use them appropriately.

**3.2** Describe the behaviour of spin-$\frac{1}{2}$ particles in various combinations of Stern–Gerlach magnets.

**3.3** Explain the roles of spin preparers and spin analyzers. Recall and use the $\cos^2(\theta/2)$ rule.

**3.4** Write spin states in terms of ket vectors and spinors, using appropriate conventions. Explain what is meant by an orthonormal basis.

**3.5** Use spinors to evaluate inner products of vectors in spin space, and to normalize spinors.

**3.6** Given expressions for the general spin matrix and its eigenvectors, find specific forms appropriate in given circumstances.

**3.7** Find the probabilities of the possible outcomes of a given spin measurement in a given spin state.

**3.8** Find the expectation value of a given spin observable in a given spin state.

**3.9** Write down a Hamiltonian matrix that describes the interaction of a spin-$\frac{1}{2}$ particle with a uniform magnetic field; find the corresponding energy eigenvectors and eigenvalues.

**3.10** Use Schrödinger's equation to predict the time-dependence of a spin state describing a spin-$\frac{1}{2}$ particle in a magnetic field.

# Chapter 4 Many-particle systems and indistinguishability

## Introduction: many-particle systems

In this chapter, the systems we study become more realistic in one important respect: they involve more than one particle. It will not have escaped your attention that virtually all the systems we have studied so far consist of a single particle bound in a well, or tunnelling through a barrier, etc. But all the interesting systems we would like to describe, such as atoms, molecules, solids, etc., contain many particles. The main part of this chapter presents the quantum theory of systems of two particles. Although this might not seem like a great leap forward, the basic ideas are those required to describe systems with *any* number of particles. Two-particle systems also prepare the way for the remarkable consequences of *quantum entanglement*, the subject of the final chapters of this book.

The quantum world differs from the classical world in a radical way that becomes apparent when we study systems of more than one particle. In the quantum world, particles of a given type (such as electrons, protons, helium atoms, etc.) are *identical* in a way that has no parallel in the everyday world. Manufacturers try hard to make all their white snooker balls identical, but they cannot succeed. All electrons on the other hand *are absolutely identical*, a fact that has profound consequences for the behaviour of matter; it lies behind the *Pauli exclusion principle* which will feature later in this chapter. The properties of atoms and, in fact, of all the 'stuff' that surrounds us, are crucially dependent upon this principle. That is why much of this chapter deals with the mathematical formalism for dealing with identical particles. Before that, however, we must start with the quantum mechanics of two *distinguishable* particles.

Section 4.1 presents the basic quantum theory of a system of two distinguishable particles. We start with spatial wave functions of two particles and then show how to combine this with a representation of their spin to obtain a *total* wave function. Section 4.2 introduces a new and uniquely quantum feature: the fact that all particles of a specific kind are absolutely identical. It turns out that microscopic particles fall into two distinct categories: fermions and bosons. You will see that identical bosons must be described by a *symmetric* total wave function, and identical fermions by an *antisymmetric* total wave function. Finally, Section 4.3 contrasts the behaviour of fermions and bosons in real systems. You will see how the fermion nature of electrons contributes to the rigidity of metals, and how the boson nature of some atoms leads to a remarkable quantum phenomenon called *Bose–Einstein condensation.*

## 4.1 Systems of two distinguishable particles

In previous chapters we have presented the quantum mechanics of a single particle, such as a particle in a box. Here, we take the first steps toward describing systems of more than one particle. We shall not solve Schrödinger's equation for particular systems, but rather extract some very important general properties of wave functions for any system of more than one particle. Many of these features already occur with systems of just two particles, and we focus on two-particle systems in this section. All the ideas extend straightforwardly to the general case of $N$ particles.

In this section we impose further temporary simplifications: we deal only with *distinguishable particles* and restrict ourselves to the case in which each particle is confined to *one dimension*, the $x$-axis. We also assume the particles do not interact with each other, although they may be subject to external forces. In fact, there are few physical situations in which particles do not interact. However, working with non-interacting particles greatly simplifies the points we wish to make in this chapter. Even in the cases where the particles do interact, the non-interacting case is a useful starting point for more elaborate calculations.

### 4.1.1 Schrödinger's equation and wave functions

The system we shall initially consider has two *distinguishable* particles, 1 and 2, confined to the $x$-axis. The particles have masses $m_1$ and $m_2$ and coordinates $x_1$ and $x_2$. The external forces acting on the particles are expressed in terms of potential energy functions $V_1(x_1)$ and $V_2(x_2)$. The wave function describing the system depends on $x_1$ and $x_2$ and on time $t$, and is written as $\Psi(x_1, x_2, t)$. It satisfies Schrödinger's equation for the system in question.

The first step in writing down Schrödinger's equation is to find the classical Hamiltonian function. This is the sum of the two kinetic energies, written in terms of momenta, and the two potential energies:

To simplify notation, we write $p_{x_i}$ as $p_i$.

$$H = \frac{p_1^2}{2m_1} + \frac{p_2^2}{2m_2} + V_1(x_1) + V_2(x_2). \tag{4.1}$$

Since the particles do not interact with each other there is no mutual potential energy term, $V(x_1 - x_2)$, and $H$ is simply a sum of terms, $H_1 + H_2$, associated with the individual particles.

To convert the Hamiltonian function $H$ into a Hamiltonian operator $\widehat{\mathrm{H}}$, we replace the momenta of the two particles by momentum operators

$$p_i \Longrightarrow \widehat{\mathrm{p}}_i = -\mathrm{i}\hbar \frac{\partial}{\partial x_i}, \tag{4.2}$$

where the index $i$ can be 1 or 2. With this substitution, the Hamiltonian function becomes the Hamiltonian operator:

$$H \Longrightarrow \widehat{\mathrm{H}} = -\frac{\hbar^2}{2m_1}\frac{\partial^2}{\partial x_1^2} - \frac{\hbar^2}{2m_2}\frac{\partial^2}{\partial x_2^2} + V_1(x_1) + V_2(x_2). \tag{4.3}$$

The wave function $\Psi(x_1, x_2, t)$ is then a solution of Schrödinger's equation:

$$\mathrm{i}\hbar \frac{\partial \Psi(x_1, x_2, t)}{\partial t} = \widehat{\mathrm{H}}\,\Psi(x_1, x_2, t). \tag{4.4}$$

Before Schrödinger's equation can be solved, we need to know the Hamiltonian operator $\widehat{\mathrm{H}}$ for the specific system we are studying. The following exercise illustrates the process of finding $\widehat{\mathrm{H}}$.

**Exercise 4.1** A one-dimensional two-particle system consists of particle 1 of mass $m_1$ and particle 2 of mass $m_2$. Particle 1 is subject to a force whose potential energy function is $\frac{1}{2}C_1x_1^2$, and particle 2 is subject to a force whose potential energy function is $\frac{1}{2}C_2x_2^2$, where $C_1$ and $C_2$ are force constants. Find the Hamiltonian function and Hamiltonian operator for this system. Write down the explicit form of Schrödinger's equation for this system. ■

It is not difficult to write down Schrödinger's equation for a specific system of more than one particle, but we still have to solve the equation and interpret its solutions. The first step is to look for *stationary-state solutions*, which are the product of two functions:

$$\Psi(x_1, x_2, t) = \psi(x_1, x_2)\,T(t). \tag{4.5}$$

These two functions are:

- a time-dependent part, $T(t) = \mathrm{e}^{-\mathrm{i}Et/\hbar}$, the solution of

$$\mathrm{i}\hbar\frac{\mathrm{d}}{\mathrm{d}t}T(t) = E\,T(t); \tag{4.6}$$

- a spatial eigenfunction, the solution of

$$\left[-\frac{\hbar^2}{2m_1}\frac{\partial^2}{\partial x_1^2} - \frac{\hbar^2}{2m_2}\frac{\partial^2}{\partial x_2^2} + V_1(x_1) + V_2(x_2)\right]\psi(x_1, x_2) = E\,\psi(x_1, x_2). \tag{4.7}$$

Equation 4.7 is the *time-independent Schrödinger equation* for the two-particle system with total energy $E$. Its solutions give the energy eigenfunctions and eigenvalues of the two-particle system. Before looking at the solutions in more detail, we shall pause to consider the meaning of the wave function $\Psi(x_1, x_2, t)$.

For distinguishable particles, a two-particle wave function is interpreted using the following extension of **Born's rule**:

**Born's rule for two distinguishable particles**

The probability of finding particle 1 in a small interval $\delta x_1$ centred on $x_1$ *and* particle 2 in a small interval $\delta x_2$ centred on $x_2$ is given by

$$|\Psi(x_1, x_2, t)|^2\,\delta x_1\,\delta x_2. \tag{4.8}$$

This probability depends on the coordinates of both particles. For Equation 4.8 to make sense, we must ensure that $\Psi(x_1, x_2, t)$ is normalized so that the probability of finding both particles somewhere in all space is equal to 1:

**Normalizing the wave function of a two-particle system**

$$\int_{-\infty}^{\infty}\int_{-\infty}^{\infty}|\Psi(x_1, x_2, t)|^2\,\mathrm{d}x_1\,\mathrm{d}x_2 = 1. \tag{4.9}$$

In this chapter we shall almost always deal with stationary state solutions. In this case the probability is time-independent since $|\Psi(x_1, x_2, t)|^2 = |\psi(x_1, x_2)|^2$, where $\psi(x_1, x_2)$ is the eigenfunction in Equation 4.7. Thus, for stationary states, $\psi(x_1, x_2)$ can replace $\Psi(x_1, x_2, t)$ in Equation 4.9.

Sometimes, we are interested in knowing the probability of finding particle $i$ within a small interval $\delta x_i$ regardless of where the other particle is. In this case we need to integrate over the coordinates of the other particle. For example, the probability of finding particle 1 ($i = 1$) in a small interval $\delta x_1$, centred on $x_1$, regardless of the whereabouts of particle 2, is

$$\left[\int_{-\infty}^{\infty} |\Psi(x_1, x_2, t)|^2 \, \mathrm{d}x_2\right] \delta x_1. \tag{4.10}$$

Based on this, the following example shows how to calculate the expectation value of the position of one of the particles.

**Essential skill**

Evaluating the expectation value of an observable in a state described by a two-particle wave function

**Worked Example 4.1**

Consider a one-dimensional two-particle system whose wave function at $t = 0$ is

$$\psi(x_1, x_2) = \left(\frac{1}{\pi a_1 a_2}\right)^{1/2} \mathrm{e}^{-x_1^2/2a_1^2} \, \mathrm{e}^{-x_2^2/2a_2^2}.$$

(a) Verify that the wave function is normalized.

(b) Find the expectation value of $x_2$, the coordinate of the second particle. (The integrals you need are inside the back cover of the book.)

**Solution**

(a) The wave function will be normalized if it satisfies Equation 4.9. We therefore need to evaluate

$$\begin{aligned} I &= \int_{-\infty}^{\infty}\int_{-\infty}^{\infty} \psi^*(x_1, x_2)\, \psi(x_1, x_2) \, \mathrm{d}x_1 \, \mathrm{d}x_2 \\ &= \frac{1}{\pi a_1 a_2}\int_{-\infty}^{\infty}\int_{-\infty}^{\infty} \mathrm{e}^{-x_1^2/a_1^2} \, \mathrm{e}^{-x_2^2/a_2^2} \, \mathrm{d}x_1 \, \mathrm{d}x_2 \\ &= \frac{1}{\pi a_1 a_2}\int_{-\infty}^{\infty} \mathrm{e}^{-x_1^2/a_1^2} \, \mathrm{d}x_1 \times \int_{-\infty}^{\infty} \mathrm{e}^{-x_2^2/a_2^2} \, \mathrm{d}x_2. \end{aligned}$$

Using integrals from the back cover, we obtain

$$I = \frac{1}{\pi a_1 a_2} a_1\sqrt{\pi} \times a_2\sqrt{\pi} = 1.$$

(b) The expectation value of $x_2$ is given by the sandwich integral

$$\begin{aligned} \langle x_2 \rangle &= \int_{-\infty}^{\infty}\int_{-\infty}^{\infty} \psi^*(x_1, x_2)\, x_2\, \psi(x_1, x_2) \, \mathrm{d}x_1 \, \mathrm{d}x_2 \\ &= \frac{1}{\pi a_1 a_2}\int_{-\infty}^{\infty}\int_{-\infty}^{\infty} x_2 \, \mathrm{e}^{-x_1^2/a_1^2} \, \mathrm{e}^{-x_2^2/a_2^2} \, \mathrm{d}x_1 \, \mathrm{d}x_2 \end{aligned}$$

$$= \frac{1}{\pi a_1 a_2} \int_{-\infty}^{\infty} \mathrm{e}^{-x_1^2/a_1^2}\,\mathrm{d}x_1 \times \int_{-\infty}^{\infty} x_2\,\mathrm{e}^{-x_2^2/a_2^2}\,\mathrm{d}x_2$$

$$= \frac{1}{\pi a_1 a_2} \times a_1\sqrt{\pi} \times \int_{-\infty}^{\infty} x_2\,\mathrm{e}^{-x_2^2/a_2^2}\,\mathrm{d}x_2 = 0.$$

The last integral is zero because the integrand is an odd function of $x_2$, integrated over a range that is centred on $x_2 = 0$.

In general, the expectation value of any observable $A$ in a system of two particles described by the wave function $\Psi(x_1, x_2, t)$ is given by the sandwich integral

$$\langle A\rangle = \int_{-\infty}^{\infty}\int_{-\infty}^{\infty} \Psi^*(x_1, x_2, t)\,\widehat{\mathrm{A}}\,\Psi(x_1, x_2, t)\,\mathrm{d}x_1\,\mathrm{d}x_2. \qquad (4.11)$$

**Exercise 4.2** For the wave function in Worked Example 4.1:

(a) Find the expectation value of $p_1$, the momentum of the first particle.

(b) Find the expectation value of $(x_1 - x_2)^2$. What is the physical significance of this expectation value? ■

We now consider the energy eigenfunction $\psi(x_1, x_2)$ in more detail. In order to prepare the way for the case of identical particles, we shall specialize somewhat. We now assume that both particles are in the same potential energy well, $V(x)$, so that particle 1 has potential energy $V(x_1)$ and particle 2 has potential energy $V(x_2)$; however, we continue to assume there is no interaction between the particles (so there is no $V(x_1 - x_2)$ term). We assume that both particles have the same mass $m_1 = m_2 = m$, but that they are distinguishable by some other means. With these simplifications, Equation 4.7 becomes

$$\left[-\frac{\hbar^2}{2m}\frac{\partial^2}{\partial x_1^2} - \frac{\hbar^2}{2m}\frac{\partial^2}{\partial x_2^2} + V(x_1) + V(x_2)\right]\psi(x_1, x_2) = E\,\psi(x_1, x_2). \quad (4.12)$$

We shall look for solutions that can be written in the product form

$$\psi(x_1, x_2) = \psi_n(x_1)\,\psi_k(x_2), \qquad (4.13)$$

where $\psi_n(x_1)$ and $\psi_k(x_2)$ are single-particle energy eigenfunctions describing the states of particles 1 and 2, respectively.

Introducing this form for $\psi(x_1, x_2)$ into Equation 4.12 gives

$$\left[-\frac{\hbar^2}{2m}\frac{\partial^2}{\partial x_1^2} - \frac{\hbar^2}{2m}\frac{\partial^2}{\partial x_2^2} + V(x_1) + V(x_2)\right]\psi_n(x_1)\,\psi_k(x_2) = E\,\psi_n(x_1)\,\psi_k(x_2).$$

Now, $\partial^2/\partial x_1^2$ and $V(x_1)$ do not do anything to $\psi_k(x_2)$, and similarly $\partial^2/\partial x_2^2$ and $V(x_2)$ do not affect $\psi_n(x_1)$. We can therefore re-write the above equation as

$$\psi_k(x_2)\left[-\frac{\hbar^2}{2m}\frac{\partial^2}{\partial x_1^2} + V(x_1)\right]\psi_n(x_1)$$
$$+\,\psi_n(x_1)\left[-\frac{\hbar^2}{2m}\frac{\partial^2}{\partial x_2^2} + V(x_2)\right]\psi_k(x_2) = E\,\psi_n(x_1)\,\psi_k(x_2).$$

Dividing both sides of this equation by $\psi_n(x_1)\,\psi_k(x_2)$, we arrive at

$$\frac{1}{\psi_n(x_1)}\left[-\frac{\hbar^2}{2m}\frac{\partial^2}{\partial x_1^2}+V(x_1)\right]\psi_n(x_1)$$
$$+\frac{1}{\psi_k(x_2)}\left[-\frac{\hbar^2}{2m}\frac{\partial^2}{\partial x_2^2}+V(x_2)\right]\psi_k(x_2)=E.$$

In order for this equation to hold for all values of $x_1$ and $x_2$, we require that

$$\frac{1}{\psi_n(x_1)}\left[-\frac{\hbar^2}{2m}\frac{\partial^2}{\partial x_1^2}+V(x_1)\right]\psi_n(x_1)=E_n$$

and

$$\frac{1}{\psi_k(x_2)}\left[-\frac{\hbar^2}{2m}\frac{\partial^2}{\partial x_2^2}+V(x_2)\right]\psi_k(x_2)=E_k,$$

where $E_n$ and $E_k$ are constants satisfying $E_n+E_k=E$. These two equations can be rewritten as individual eigenvalue equations for each particle:

$$\left[-\frac{\hbar^2}{2m}\frac{\partial^2}{\partial x_1^2}+V(x_1)\right]\psi_n(x_1)=E_n\,\psi_n(x_1), \tag{4.14}$$

$$\left[-\frac{\hbar^2}{2m}\frac{\partial^2}{\partial x_2^2}+V(x_2)\right]\psi_k(x_2)=E_k\,\psi_k(x_2). \tag{4.15}$$

We now see that the subscripts $n$ and $k$ signify the $n$th and $k$th energy eigenfunctions and eigenvalues for a particle in the potential energy well $V(x)$. Because Equations 4.14 and 4.15 have the same form, we can say that the two particles have the same set of energies in the well.

The time-dependent phase factor that satisfies Equation 4.6 is

$$T(t)=\mathrm{e}^{-\mathrm{i}Et/\hbar}=\mathrm{e}^{-\mathrm{i}(E_n+E_k)t/\hbar},$$

where $E$ is the total energy of the system. In an energy eigenstate of the two-particle system, each particle has a definite energy and the total energy of the system is the sum of the energies of the two particles; this is a consequence of having no interaction term $V(x_1-x_2)$ in the Hamiltonian operator. The ground state (i.e. the state of lowest energy) is that in which both particles are in the single-particle state of lowest energy. The first excited state of the two-particle system is that in which one particle has this lowest energy, and the other has the next-to-lowest energy.

In this chapter we focus on stationary states, which have time-independent probability densities. For this reason, we can calculate all probability densities directly from the eigenfunctions. For the product eigenfunction $\psi(x_1,x_2)=\psi_n(x_1)\,\psi_k(x_2)$, Born's rule tells us that the probability of finding particle 1 in a small interval $\delta x_1$, centred on $x_1$, and particle 2 in a small interval $\delta x_2$, centred on $x_2$, is

$$|\psi(x_1,x_2)|^2\,\delta x_1\,\delta x_2=|\psi_n(x_1)|^2\,\delta x_1\times|\psi_k(x_2)|^2\,\delta x_2. \tag{4.16}$$

This is reasonable: in a non-interacting system we would expect the probability densities for the two particles to be independent of one another, and independent probabilities are multiplied together. It is a general property of systems of *non-interacting, distinguishable* particles that the total probability density for the whole system is the product of independent probability densities for the individual particles.

### Two particles in an infinite square well

It is not easy to visualize $\psi(x_1, x_2)$ or the probability density $|\psi(x_1, x_2)|^2$, and the simplest way to represent them is with contour plots. The case we consider is that of two non-interacting distinguishable particles, 1 and 2, trapped in a one-dimensional infinite square well, described by the potential energy function

$$V(x) = \begin{cases} 0 & \text{for } 0 \leq x \leq L, \\ \infty & \text{elsewhere,} \end{cases} \tag{4.17}$$

where we take $x = x_1$ for particle 1 and $x = x_2$ for particle 2. From Book 1 Chapter 3, we know the energy eigenfunctions for a single particle in such a well. Let us suppose that the first particle is in the lowest state, $n = 1$, with eigenfunction

$$\psi_1(x_1) = \sqrt{\frac{2}{L}} \sin\left(\frac{\pi x_1}{L}\right), \tag{4.18}$$

while the second particle is in the first excited state, $n = 2$, with eigenfunction

$$\psi_2(x_2) = \sqrt{\frac{2}{L}} \sin\left(\frac{2\pi x_2}{L}\right). \tag{4.19}$$

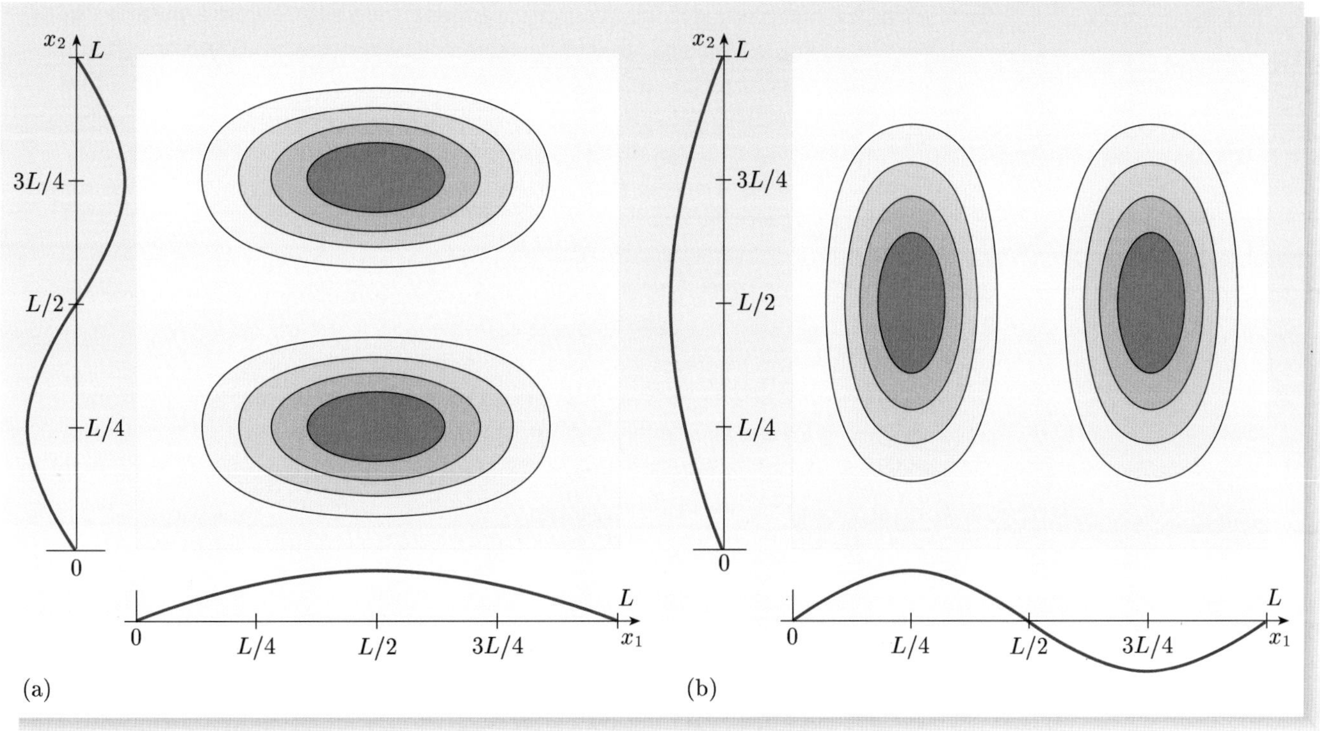


**Figure 4.1** Contour plots of the probability density as a function of the coordinates $x_1$ and $x_2$ of two distinguishable particles trapped in a one-dimensional infinite square well of length $L$: (a) particle 1 in the ground state and particle 2 in the first excited state; (b) the two states reversed. In both panels, the bottom left-hand corner corresponds to $x_1 = x_2 = 0$.

Now refer to Figure 4.1a. Below the main figure we show $\psi_1(x_1)$, and on the left-hand side we show $\psi_2(x_2)$, which has a node at $x_2 = L/2$. The main figure is a contour plot of the probability density $|\psi_1(x_1)\,\psi_2(x_2)|^2$. This probability density is zero along the $x_2 = L/2$ line, where $\psi_2(x_2)$ has a node, and it has ridges along $x_2 = L/4$ and $x_2 = 3L/4$. The ridges are highest at $x_1 = L/2$.

Figure 4.1b shows a similar contour plot of the probability density $|\psi_2(x_1)\,\psi_1(x_2)|^2$, which describes the case where particle 1 is in the first excited state, $n = 2$, and particle 2 is in the lowest state, $n = 1$.

The two parts of Figure 4.1 differ substantially from one another because of our assumption that the particles are distinguishable; it matters *which* particle is in *which* state. You will see that such distinctions disappear later in this chapter when we consider identical particles – in which case the probability densities are very different.

**Exercise 4.3** (a) For the case shown in Figure 4.1a, write down an explicit expression for the probability density of finding particle 1 in a small interval around $x_1$ and particle 2 in a small interval around $x_2$.

(b) Confirm that the probability density in part (a) reaches its maximum value at $(x_1, x_2) = (L/2, L/4)$ and at $(x_1, x_2) = (L/2, 3L/4)$. ■

## 4.1.2 Including spin in the wave function

So far, we have neglected the spin of the particles. However, many particles (including electrons, protons and neutrons) have spin. Here we consider how to take spin into account for two distinguishable spin-$\frac{1}{2}$ particles.

First, we shall consider the description of spin for a single spin-$\frac{1}{2}$ particle. In the previous chapter, we specified spin states with respect to a variety of different reference directions (as in $|\uparrow_x\rangle$, $|\downarrow_y\rangle$ or $|\uparrow_{\mathbf{n}}\rangle$). Here, however, we can adopt a simpler convention: all spin states will be specified with respect to the $z$-direction. There is no loss of generality because we can choose the $z$-axis to be in any direction we like. Bearing this convention in mind, we shall omit unnecessary subscripts by writing

$$\text{spin-up} = |\uparrow\rangle = |\uparrow_z\rangle \quad \text{and} \quad \text{spin-down} = |\downarrow\rangle = |\downarrow_z\rangle.$$

There is an alternative way of specifying the spin state of a spin-$\frac{1}{2}$ particle, based on the quantum numbers $s$ and $m_s$. By definition, the *spin quantum number* of a spin-$\frac{1}{2}$ particle is $s = \frac{1}{2}$, which means that, in any state, the square of the magnitude of the spin angular momentum is $S^2 = s(s+1)\hbar^2 = 3\hbar^2/4$. The *spin magnetic quantum number*, $m_s$, is equal to $\pm\frac{1}{2}$. This defines the $z$-component of the spin angular momentum via the equation $S_z = m_s\hbar = \pm\hbar/2$. Thus we can specify a spin state by giving $s$ and $m_s$. We have

$$|s = \tfrac{1}{2}, m_s = +\tfrac{1}{2}\rangle = |\uparrow\rangle \quad \text{and} \quad |s = \tfrac{1}{2}, m_s = -\tfrac{1}{2}\rangle = |\downarrow\rangle.$$

We can abbreviate this notation by omitting $s = \frac{1}{2}$, since we know that we are dealing with spin-$\frac{1}{2}$ particles. We also omit the '$m_s =$', so the spin states are labelled unambiguously by

$$|{+\tfrac{1}{2}}\rangle = |\uparrow\rangle = |\uparrow_z\rangle \quad \text{and} \quad |{-\tfrac{1}{2}}\rangle = |\downarrow\rangle = |\downarrow_z\rangle.$$

Now let's consider the description of spin for two distinguishable particles. To each spin ket, and to all spin observables and quantum numbers, we attach the subscript $i$, where $i$ can be equal to 1 or 2 depending on the particle under consideration. We then have the eigenvalue equations

$$\widehat{\mathrm{S}}_i^2 \,|\uparrow\rangle_i = \tfrac{3}{4}\hbar^2 \,|\uparrow\rangle_i, \tag{4.20}$$

$$\widehat{\mathrm{S}}_i^2 \,|\downarrow\rangle_i = \tfrac{3}{4}\hbar^2 \,|\downarrow\rangle_i, \tag{4.21}$$

$$\widehat{\mathrm{S}}_{zi} \,|\uparrow\rangle_i = +\tfrac{1}{2}\hbar \,|\uparrow\rangle_i, \tag{4.22}$$

$$\widehat{\mathrm{S}}_{zi} \,|\downarrow\rangle_i = -\tfrac{1}{2}\hbar \,|\downarrow\rangle_i. \tag{4.23}$$

In our alternative notation, the last two equations can be combined to give

$$\widehat{\mathrm{S}}_{zi} \,|\pm\tfrac{1}{2}\rangle_i = \pm\tfrac{1}{2}\hbar \,|\pm\tfrac{1}{2}\rangle_i. \tag{4.24}$$

Just as the spatial eigenfunctions $\psi(x_1, x_2) = \psi_n(x_1)\,\psi_k(x_2)$ of a two-particle system are products of single-particle functions, so the spin state of the system can be expressed in terms of 'products' of spin kets. For example, if particle 1 has spin up, and particle 2 has spin down, we can represent the spin of the two-particle system as

$$|\uparrow\rangle_1 \,|\downarrow\rangle_2 = |+\tfrac{1}{2}\rangle_1 \,|-\tfrac{1}{2}\rangle_2. \tag{4.25}$$

The meaning of this product will be discussed shortly; for the moment, you can simply regard it as a notation that indicates the spins of the particles, with the subscripts on the kets making it clear *which* particle has *which* spin. It is also possible to indicate the spins of the particles using a single ket, for example, as

$$|+\tfrac{1}{2}, -\tfrac{1}{2}\rangle = |\uparrow\downarrow\rangle, \tag{4.26}$$

or more generally as $|m_{s1}, m_{s2}\rangle$, but here a very important convention applies: the first entry in the ket *always* refers to particle 1 and the second entry to particle 2. We call this the **positional convention** for spin states. It means that $|\uparrow\downarrow\rangle$ does *not* represent the same spin state as $|\downarrow\uparrow\rangle$.

**Exercise 4.4** Express the following spin states in $|m_{s1}, m_{s2}\rangle$ form:
(a) $|\downarrow\rangle_1 \,|\uparrow\rangle_2$, (b) $|\downarrow\rangle_1 \,|\downarrow\rangle_2$. ■

The meaning of an expression like $|\uparrow\rangle_1 \,|\downarrow\rangle_2$ becomes clearer when we consider the effect that a spin operator has on it. The rule is that any spin operator for particle 1 acts only on the spin ket of particle 1, and any spin operator for particle 2 acts only on the spin ket of particle 2. We therefore have

$$\widehat{\mathrm{S}}_{z1} \,|\uparrow\rangle_1 \,|\downarrow\rangle_2 = \left(\widehat{\mathrm{S}}_{z1} \,|\uparrow\rangle_1\right) |\downarrow\rangle_2 = +\tfrac{1}{2}\hbar \,|\uparrow\rangle_1 \,|\downarrow\rangle_2,$$

$$\widehat{\mathrm{S}}_{z2} \,|\uparrow\rangle_1 \,|\downarrow\rangle_2 = |\uparrow\rangle_1 \left(\widehat{\mathrm{S}}_{z2} \,|\downarrow\rangle_2\right) = -\tfrac{1}{2}\hbar \,|\uparrow\rangle_1 \,|\downarrow\rangle_2,$$

and we can add these two equations to give

$$\left(\widehat{\mathrm{S}}_{z1} + \widehat{\mathrm{S}}_{z2}\right) |\uparrow\rangle_1 \,|\downarrow\rangle_2 = 0. \tag{4.27}$$

The operator on the left-hand side represents the total $z$-component of spin for the system. This acts on $|\uparrow\rangle_1 \,|\downarrow\rangle_2$ to give zero, as you might expect for a two-particle system in which one particle has spin up and the other has spin down.

The final step is to combine information about the coordinates and spin of the particles. This is done by introducing a quantity called the **total wave function** of the system, $\Psi_{1,2}$. The total wave function is written as a product of the **spatial**

**wave function** $\Psi(x_1, x_2, t)$ and the spin ket $|m_{s_1}, m_{s_2}\rangle$ that describes the spin state of the system. Thus

$$\Psi_{1,2}(t) = \Psi(x_1, x_2, t)\,|m_{s_1}, m_{s_2}\rangle. \tag{4.28}$$

This chapter deals only with stationary states, and is not concerned with time-development. We shall therefore simplify matters by setting $t = 0$, at which time the stationary-state wave function $\Psi(x_1, x_2, t)$ is equal to the corresponding energy eigenfunction $\psi(x_1, x_2)$. We therefore consider

$$\psi_{1,2} = \psi(x_1, x_2)\,|m_{s_1}, m_{s_2}\rangle, \tag{4.29}$$

and will also call this the *total wave function.*

Total wave functions can be acted on by any type of operator. Spin operators act only on the spin part, while operators involving coordinates or momenta act only on the spatial part. For example, consider a state described by the total wave function

$$\psi_{1,2} = \psi_n(x_1)\,\psi_k(x_2)\,|\uparrow\rangle_1\,|\downarrow\rangle_2 \tag{4.30}$$

in a system where the Hamiltonian operator is that in Equation 4.12:

$$\widehat{\mathrm{H}} = -\frac{\hbar^2}{2m_1}\frac{\partial^2}{\partial x_1^2} - \frac{\hbar^2}{2m_2}\frac{\partial^2}{\partial x_2^2} + V(x_1) + V(x_2).$$

The argument leading up to Equation 4.15 showed that $\psi_n(x_1)\,\psi_k(x_2)$ is an eigenfunction of $\widehat{\mathrm{H}}$ with eigenvalues $(E_n + E_k)$.

This operator does not contain any spin matrices, so it acts only on the spatial part of the wave function. We obtain

$$\begin{aligned}
\widehat{\mathrm{H}}\,\psi_{1,2} &= \widehat{\mathrm{H}}\,\psi_n(x_1)\,\psi_k(x_2)\,|\uparrow\rangle_1\,|\downarrow\rangle_2 \\
&= \Big(\widehat{\mathrm{H}}\,\psi_n(x_1)\,\psi_k(x_2)\Big)\,|\uparrow\rangle_1\,|\downarrow\rangle_2 \\
&= \Big((E_n + E_k)\,\psi_n(x_1)\,\psi_k(x_2)\Big)\,|\uparrow\rangle_1\,|\downarrow\rangle_2 \\
&= (E_n + E_k)\psi_{1,2}.
\end{aligned}$$

So the total wave function $\psi_{1,2}$ is an eigenfunction of $\widehat{\mathrm{H}}$, with eigenvalue $E_n + E_k$; this is interpreted as the total energy of the system.

**Essential skill**

Applying operators to total wave functions

**Worked Example 4.2**

A system of two distinguishable particles has the total wave function

$$\psi_{1,2} = \psi_n(x_1)\,\psi_k(x_2)\,|\uparrow\rangle_1\,|\uparrow\rangle_2,$$

where $\psi_n(x_1)$ and $\psi_k(x_2)$ are the eigenfunctions in Equations 4.14 and 4.15. Show that this total wave function is an eigenfunction of $\widehat{\mathrm{S}}_{z1}$, and find the corresponding eigenvalue.

**Solution**

Applying $\widehat{\mathrm{S}}_{z1}$ to the total wave function, we note that $\psi_n(x_1)$ and $\psi_k(x_2)$ do not depend on spin, so the spin operator does not 'see' them. Hence

$$\widehat{\mathrm{S}}_{z1}\,\psi_{1,2} = \psi_n(x_1)\,\psi_k(x_2)\,\widehat{\mathrm{S}}_{z1}\,|\uparrow\rangle_1\,|\uparrow\rangle_2.$$

In addition, $\widehat{S}_{z1}$ does not act on the spin ket of particle 2, so

$$\begin{aligned}\widehat{S}_{z1}\,\psi_{1,2} &= \psi_n(x_1)\,\psi_k(x_2)\Big(\widehat{S}_{z1}\,|\uparrow\rangle_1\Big)\,|\uparrow\rangle_2\\ &= \psi_n(x_1)\,\psi_k(x_2)\Big(+\tfrac{1}{2}\hbar\,|\uparrow\rangle_1\Big)\,|\uparrow\rangle_2\\ &= +\tfrac{1}{2}\hbar\psi_{1,2}.\end{aligned}$$

Hence $\psi_{1,2}$ is an eigenfunction of the spin operator $\widehat{S}_{z1}$, with eigenvalue $+\frac{1}{2}\hbar$.

In general, the total wave function gives a complete description of the system, including spin.

**Exercise 4.5** (a) Is $|\uparrow\uparrow\rangle$ an eigenvector of the operator $(\widehat{S}_{z1} + \widehat{S}_{z2})$?

(b) Is $|\uparrow\downarrow\rangle + |\downarrow\uparrow\rangle$ an eigenvector of $(\widehat{S}_{z1} + \widehat{S}_{z2})$?

(c) Is $|\uparrow\downarrow\rangle - |\downarrow\uparrow\rangle$ an eigenvector of $(\widehat{S}_{z1} + \widehat{S}_{z2})$? ■

## 4.2 Identical particles

We now encounter a profound difference between the world of everyday things and the quantum world: the existence of **identical particles**. However similar two ball bearings may appear, they are not identical. It is effectively impossible for two individual balls, each made of a vast number of atoms, to be identical. By contrast, all electrons are absolutely identical, as are all protons and all alpha particles. Two particles are said to be identical if all their unalterable attributes (such as charge and mass) are the same. The difference between 'extremely similar' (as snooker balls may be) and 'identical', as electrons are, is profound, and is a crucial ingredient in determining the nature of the world.

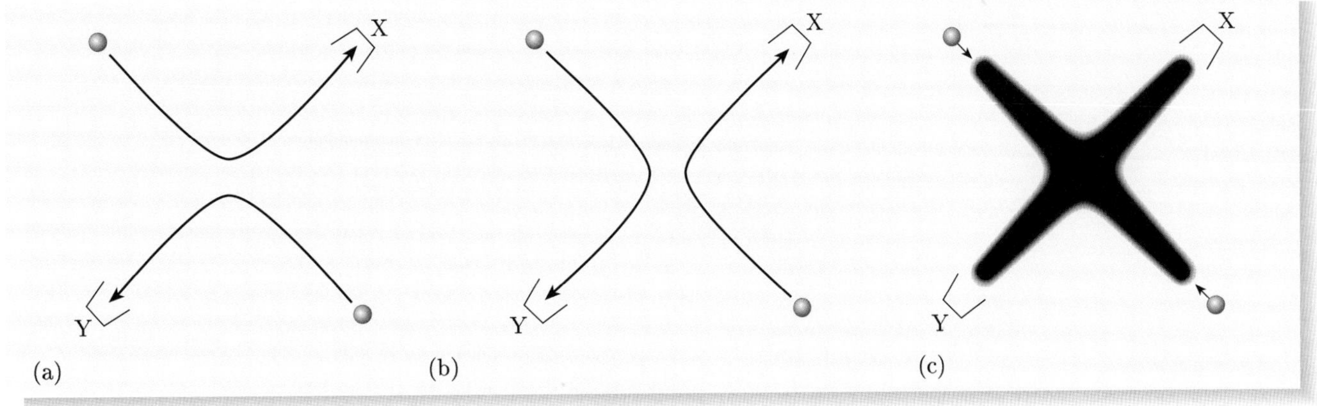


**Figure 4.2** (a) and (b) A collision between two seemingly identical particles in classical physics. The trajectories can be followed at all times: two different cases are shown, in which different particles enter detector X. (c) A collision between two identical particles in quantum physics. The trajectories cannot be followed and it is impossible to say which particle enters detector X.

Let us explore the vital difference between similar particles in classical physics and identical particles in quantum physics. Figure 4.2 shows the collision between two seemingly identical balls in classical physics. In Figure 4.2a, the ball originally in the top left-hand corner reaches detector X. In Figure 4.2b, the ball originally in the bottom right-hand corner reaches detector X. We have no doubt about which of these outcomes has occurred because we can follow the trajectories of the balls. We could also predict, on the basis of Newtonian mechanics, which ball will end up in which detector.

A very different situation applies in quantum physics. In quantum physics, particles cannot be said to follow well-defined trajectories because the uncertainty principle prevents us from knowing both the position and the momentum of a particle at any given time. If two identical particles originate in well-separated regions, they may initially be distinguished from one another by virtue of their locations, but as soon as their wave functions overlap, we lose track of which particle is which, and the particles become *indistinguishable*. This idea is represented in Figure 4.2c where, instead of thin lines representing well-defined trajectories, we use fuzzy regions because the positions of the particles are not well-defined. In quantum physics we cannot say which of the particles enters detector X because there is no way to distinguish between the particles once they have arrived, and the trajectories of the particles are ill-defined. All we can say is that a particle has arrived at this detector. There are two ways in which this might happen, since either of the particles could have triggered the detector. When a given event can happen in two different ways, the possibility of interference arises; this is what happens when a particle can reach a screen via two different slits, for example. A similar thing happens here. When beams of identical particles scatter from one another, the intensity of scattered particles displays peaks and troughs when plotted as a function of the scattering angle (Figure 4.3). Such an interference pattern is not found for distinguishable particles, so the identity of particles makes a profound difference; it leads to completely new phenomena!

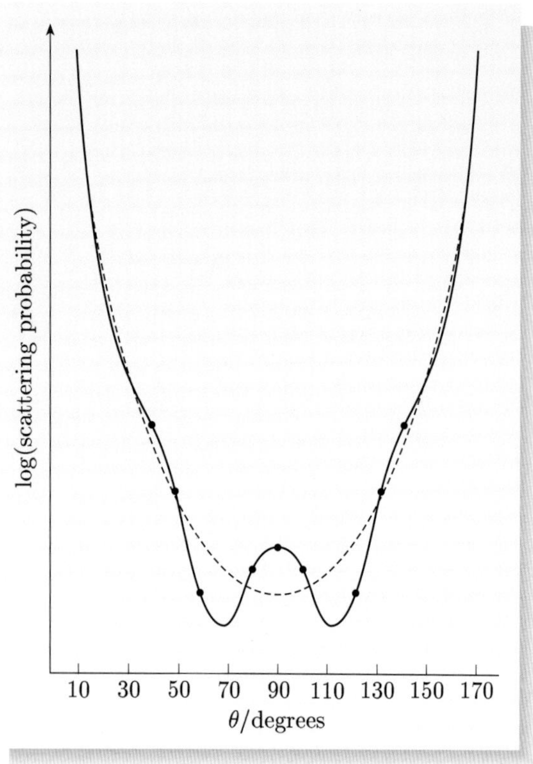


**Figure 4.3** The scattering probability of two particles as a function of their scattering angle, $\theta$. The solid line is for two identical alpha particles, and shows the peaks and troughs characteristic of an interference pattern; the dashed line shows what would be observed for two similar but distinguishable particles.

We cannot give all the details at this stage, but it may be useful to survey the main ideas, so that you can see the route that lies ahead. When we describe a system of two identical particles in quantum mechanics, we generally start by labelling the particles: 1 and 2. This may seem contradictory, but it is necessary for book-keeping purposes, as it provides a consistent way of indicating 'this particle' and 'the other particle'. However, the whole point about having a system of identical particles in quantum mechanics is that we are unable to distinguish between the particles in any way. Therefore alternative ways of labelling the particles (with the labels swapped over) must describe exactly the same state. To pretend otherwise would be to pretend that we know more about the system than is knowable, which is against the rules in quantum mechanics — comparable to pretending that we know which slit an electron passes through in a two-slit interference experiment.

A full description of the state of a two-particle system in quantum mechanics is provided by the *total wave function*, $\psi_{1,2}$. If we label the particles the other way around, this becomes $\psi_{2,1}$ which must describe precisely the same state as $\psi_{1,2}$. Remembering that a wave function can be multiplied by an arbitrary phase factor

$e^{i\alpha}$ without changing the state being described, we can say that $\psi_{2,1}$ must be equal to $\psi_{1,2}$, possibly multiplied by a phase factor.

- Does the total wave function of Equation 4.30 provide an adequate description of a system containing two identical particles?
- No, this total wave function will not do. We have

$$\psi_{1,2} = \psi_n(x_1)\,\psi_k(x_2)\,|\uparrow\rangle_1\,|\downarrow\rangle_2,$$

so reversing the labelling gives

$$\psi_{2,1} = \psi_n(x_2)\,\psi_k(x_1)\,|\uparrow\rangle_2\,|\downarrow\rangle_1.$$

Clearly $\psi_{2,1}$ is not equal to a phase factor times $\psi_{1,2}$, so neither $\psi_{1,2}$ nor $\psi_{2,1}$ gives a correct description of a system containing two identical particles.

It turns out that Nature allows only two possibilities. The first possibility is that swapping the particle labels leaves the total wave function unchanged; in this case $\psi_{2,1} = \psi_{1,2}$, and the total wave function is said to be *symmetric*. The alternative is that swapping the particle labels reverses the sign of the total wave function; in this case $\psi_{2,1} = -\psi_{1,2}$, and the total wave function is said to be *antisymmetric*.

How do we know which of these possibilities applies in any given case? It turns out that all the particles in Nature fall into two categories, called *bosons* and *fermions*. For example, alpha particles are bosons, and electrons are fermions. The basic rule can then be stated as follows: systems of identical bosons have *symmetric* total wave functions, while systems of identical fermions have *antisymmetric* total wave functions.

We must now fill in the details of constructing symmetric and antisymmetric total wave functions. The total wave function is a product of a spatial wave part and a spin part, and we consider each of these parts in turn. The next two subsections will do this, before putting everything back together to arrive at satisfactory total wave functions, suitable for systems of identical bosons or fermions.

### 4.2.1 The spatial wave function for identical particles

In this section we examine the spatial wave function of a pair of *identical* particles of mass $m_1 = m_2 = m$. As before, we assume that both particles are in the same potential energy well, $V(x)$, and that they do not interact with one another ($V(x_1 - x_2) = 0$). The Hamiltonian operator is then

$$\widehat{\mathrm{H}} = -\frac{\hbar^2}{2m}\frac{\partial^2}{\partial x_1^2} - \frac{\hbar^2}{2m}\frac{\partial^2}{\partial x_2^2} + V(x_1) + V(x_2). \tag{4.31}$$

Following the discussion in Section 4.1, we will assume that the spatial energy eigenfunctions of the Hamiltonian operator have the form

$$\psi(x_1, x_2) = \psi_n(x_1)\,\psi_k(x_2), \tag{4.32}$$

where $\psi_n(x)$ and $\psi_k(x)$ are the $n$th and $k$th energy eigenfunctions of the single-particle Hamiltonian operator

$$\widehat{\mathrm{H}}_{\text{single}} = -\frac{\hbar^2}{2m}\frac{\partial^2}{\partial x^2} + V(x). \tag{4.33}$$

The product function in Equation 4.32 describes a state in which the particle labelled 1 is in state $n$ and the particle labelled 2 is in state $k$. We have labelled the particles, 1 and 2, since this is needed to write down explicit expressions for $\widehat{\mathrm{H}}$ and $\psi(x_1, x_2)$, but we do not expect any measurable property to depend on these labels. We therefore insist that the eigenfunction with the labels reversed,

$$\psi(x_2, x_1) = \psi_n(x_2)\,\psi_k(x_1), \tag{4.34}$$

describes exactly the same state of the system. Both functions are equally valid eigenfunctions of the Hamiltonian operator in Equation 4.31, and both have the same energy eigenvalue, $E = E_n + E_k$, the total energy of the two-particle system. We therefore have no reason to prefer Equation 4.32 over Equation 4.34.

If the particles are identical, the probability density (linked to what we can measure) *must have the same values for all $x_1$ and $x_2$, regardless of whether particle 1 is in state $n$ and particle 2 in state $k$ or the other way round.* Therefore the indistinguishability of the particles imposes the following condition on the spatial functions:

$$|\psi(x_1, x_2)|^2 = |\psi(x_2, x_1)|^2, \tag{4.35}$$

that is, the probability density does not change when the particle labels are exchanged. This requirement is fulfilled if

$$\psi(x_1, x_2) = \pm\psi(x_2, x_1). \tag{4.36}$$

Any function $f(x_1, x_2)$ of two variables is said to be **symmetric** if $f(x_1, x_2) = +f(x_2, x_1)$ and is said to be **antisymmetric** if $f(x_1, x_2) = -f(x_2, x_1)$.

The plus sign corresponds to a symmetric eigenfunction, and the minus sign corresponds to an antisymmetric eigenfunction. However, a simple product of one-particle eigenfunctions is neither symmetric nor antisymmetric since, in general,

$$\psi_n(x_1)\,\psi_k(x_2) \neq \pm\psi_n(x_2)\,\psi_k(x_1).$$

To obtain satisfactory eigenfunctions, suitable for describing a system of two identical particles, we shall make use of the facts that $\psi(x_1, x_2)$ and $\psi(x_2, x_1)$ have the same energy and that $\widehat{\mathrm{H}}$ is a linear operator. In general, if $\psi_A$ and $\psi_B$ are two eigenfunctions of $\widehat{\mathrm{H}}$ with the same energy eigenvalue $E$ (so that $\widehat{\mathrm{H}}\psi_A = E\psi_A$ and $\widehat{\mathrm{H}}\psi_B = E\psi_B$), then the fact that $\widehat{\mathrm{H}}$ is a linear operator guarantees that

$$\widehat{\mathrm{H}}(a\psi_A + b\psi_B) = a\widehat{\mathrm{H}}\psi_A + b\widehat{\mathrm{H}}\psi_B = aE\psi_A + bE\psi_B = E(a\psi_A + b\psi_B),$$

for any constants $a$ and $b$. In other words: any linear superposition of two solutions of the time-independent Schrödinger equation *with the same energy eigenvalue $E$* is also a solution with eigenvalue $E$. This is the **principle of superposition** for the time-independent Schrödinger equation. Applying this result to $\psi(x_1, x_2)$ and $\psi(x_2, x_1)$, which *do* have the same energy eigenvalue, we can write two alternative linear combinations of products,

Note that the principle of superposition *always* applies to the full Schrödinger equation. It applies to the time-independent Schrödinger equation *only* for eigenfunctions with the same eigenvalue.

$$\psi^{\pm}(x_1, x_2) = \frac{1}{\sqrt{2}}\left[\psi_n(x_1)\,\psi_k(x_2) \pm \psi_k(x_1)\,\psi_n(x_2)\right], \tag{4.37}$$

which both satisfy the condition stated in Equation 4.35. The $\pm$ signs on the left of Equation 4.37 match the $\pm$ signs on the right: $\psi^+$ obeys $\psi^+(x_1, x_2) = +\psi^+(x_2, x_1)$, while $\psi^-$ obeys $\psi^-(x_1, x_2) = -\psi^-(x_2, x_1)$. The constant $1/\sqrt{2}$ normalizes the eigenfunction, provided that $\psi_n$ and $\psi_k$ are themselves normalized, as you can verify in Exercise 4.6 below.

### Worked Example 4.3

Prove that the eigenfunction $\psi^-$ in Equation 4.37 satisfies the condition stated in Equation 4.35.

**Solution**

To prove this, we only need to prove Equation 4.36. We know that

$$\psi^-(x_1, x_2) = \frac{1}{\sqrt{2}}\big[\psi_n(x_1)\,\psi_k(x_2) - \psi_k(x_1)\,\psi_n(x_2)\big],$$

so what we need to do is to write out $\psi^-(x_2, x_1)$ explicitly.

Exchanging the particle labels:

$$\psi^-(x_2, x_1) = \frac{1}{\sqrt{2}}\big[\psi_n(x_2)\,\psi_k(x_1) - \psi_k(x_2)\,\psi_n(x_1)\big].$$

A simple rearrangement then gives

$$\begin{aligned}\psi^-(x_2, x_1) &= \frac{1}{\sqrt{2}}\big[-\psi_k(x_2)\,\psi_n(x_1) + \psi_n(x_2)\,\psi_k(x_1)\big]\\ &= -\psi^-(x_1, x_2),\end{aligned}$$

so the condition $|\psi(x_1, x_2)|^2 = |\psi(x_2, x_1)|^2$ is satisfied.

**Essential skill**

Verifying that a spatial function is symmetric or antisymmetric with respect to particle exchange

The above worked example reveals that $\psi^-(x_1, x_2)$ changes sign when the particle labels are exchanged. A similar argument shows that $\psi^+(x_1, x_2)$ remains unchanged when the particle labels are exchanged. Both $\psi^+$ and $\psi^-$ are satisfactory energy eigenfunctions for a system of two identical particles; the former is symmetric and the latter antisymmetric.

**Exercise 4.6** (a) Verify that $\psi^+(x_1, x_2)$ given by Equation 4.37 is a symmetric function.

(b) Show that if $\psi_n(x)$ and $\psi_k(x)$ are two different normalized orthogonal single-particle eigenfunctions, then the two-particle eigenfunction $\psi^+(x_1, x_2)$ is itself normalized, so that the total probability of there being two particles in the whole of space is unity.

**Exercise 4.7** Show that the antisymmetric two-particle eigenfunction given by Equation 4.37 is everywhere equal to zero if $\psi_n(x) = \psi_k(x)$. ■

Exercise 4.7 tells us something important: that we cannot find an antisymmetric eigenfunction corresponding to both particles being in the *same* spatial state. This is something that has profound consequences, as you will see later. By contrast, we can construct the *symmetric* eigenfunctions $\psi_n(x_1)\,\psi_n(x_2)$ and $\psi_k(x_1)\,\psi_k(x_2)$. These two product eigenfunctions, together with the symmetric and antisymmetric combinations $\frac{1}{\sqrt{2}}\big[\psi_n(x_1)\,\psi_k(x_2) \pm \psi_k(x_1)\,\psi_n(x_2)\big]$, are the only possible symmetric or antisymmetric eigenfunctions that can be constructed from the single-particle eigenfunctions $\psi_n$ and $\psi_k$.

The following exercise concerns two identical particles in a harmonic oscillator potential energy well. As in our previous discussion, there is no interaction between the particles, so the total Hamiltonian operator $\widehat{\mathrm{H}}$ is the sum of the

Hamiltonian operators $\widehat{\text{H}}_1 + \widehat{\text{H}}_2$ for particles 1 and 2. This would not be the case if the particles interacted with each other, in which case there would be an additional potential energy term $V(x_1 - x_2)$.

**Exercise 4.8** (a) Find the symmetric and antisymmetric two-particle spatial energy eigenfunctions $\psi^{\pm}(x_1, x_2)$ for two identical non-interacting particles of mass $m$, one in the ground state and the other in the first excited state of a one-dimensional harmonic oscillator. The first two single-particle harmonic oscillator eigenfunctions and eigenvalues are

$$\psi_0(x) = \left(\frac{1}{a\sqrt{\pi}}\right)^{1/2} \mathrm{e}^{-x^2/2a^2}, \qquad E_0 = \tfrac{1}{2}\hbar\omega_0,$$

$$\psi_1(x) = \left(\frac{1}{2a\sqrt{\pi}}\right)^{1/2} \frac{2x}{a}\,\mathrm{e}^{-x^2/2a^2}, \quad E_1 = \tfrac{3}{2}\hbar\omega_0,$$

where $a = \sqrt{\hbar/m\omega_0}$ is the length parameter of the oscillator, and $\omega_0$ is the classical angular frequency.

(b) Confirm that the functions $\psi^{\pm}(x_1, x_2)$ found in part (a) are eigenfunctions of the Hamiltonian operator describing the two-particle system, and find their eigenvalues. ■

### 4.2.2 Spin states of a system of two electrons

We now consider the spin state of a pair of identical particles. Different descriptions apply depending on the types of particle involved, but we shall deal only with spin-$\frac{1}{2}$ particles, such as electrons. This is the most important case for most applications, given the central role that electrons play in atoms, molecules, metals and so on.

We know that the total wave function must be symmetric or antisymmetric, which implies that the space and spin parts must also be symmetric or antisymmetric. We have seen how to construct symmetric and antisymmetric spatial functions, $\psi^{\pm}(x_1, x_2)$. We shall now construct symmetric and antisymmetric combinations of spin kets.

Our starting point is the set of four possible product spin kets:

$$|\uparrow\uparrow\rangle = |\uparrow\rangle_1\,|\uparrow\rangle_2, \qquad |\downarrow\downarrow\rangle = |\downarrow\rangle_1\,|\downarrow\rangle_2,$$
$$|\uparrow\downarrow\rangle = |\uparrow\rangle_1\,|\downarrow\rangle_2, \qquad |\downarrow\uparrow\rangle = |\downarrow\rangle_1\,|\uparrow\rangle_2.$$

The two entries in the first row remain unchanged when the labels 1 and 2 are swapped, so they are symmetric. The entries in the second row are changed by swapping the labels, and they are neither symmetric nor antisymmetric. However, adding and subtracting them produces symmetric and antisymmetric combinations. The complete set of symmetric and antisymmetric two-particle spin kets is:

**symmetric:** $$\frac{1}{\sqrt{2}}\left(|\uparrow\downarrow\rangle + |\downarrow\uparrow\rangle\right), \quad |\uparrow\uparrow\rangle, \quad |\downarrow\downarrow\rangle, \tag{4.38}$$

**antisymmetric:** $$\frac{1}{\sqrt{2}}\left(|\uparrow\downarrow\rangle - |\downarrow\uparrow\rangle\right), \tag{4.39}$$

where $1/\sqrt{2}$ is a normalization factor. Following the method of Worked Example 4.3, you can easily check that the '+' combination is symmetric with respect to particle exchange, and the '−' combination is antisymmetric.

**Exercise 4.9** Verify that the three spin kets in 4.38 are symmetric with respect to swapping the labels of the particles. ■

The four symmetric and antisymmetric spin states for two spin-$\frac{1}{2}$ particles listed in Equations 4.38 and 4.39 are the main output of this subsection. They play the same role for the spin part of the wave function as the symmetric and antisymmetric eigenfunctions did for the spatial part. Before putting the space and spin parts together to form the total wave function, we shall characterize the properties of these spin states more fully.

In the same way that we constructed the Hamiltonian operator for a system of two particles in Section 4.1, we can introduce operators for the total spin of the system. We define

$$\widehat{\mathbf{S}} = \widehat{\mathbf{S}}_1 + \widehat{\mathbf{S}}_2 \qquad \text{and} \qquad \widehat{S}_z = \widehat{S}_{z1} + \widehat{S}_{z2}. \tag{4.40}$$

In both cases, the operator for the whole system is the sum of the corresponding operators for the two particles. Notice, however, that it follows from the definition of $\widehat{\mathbf{S}}$ that the operator for the square of the total spin is $\widehat{S}^2 = \widehat{S}_1^2 + 2\widehat{\mathbf{S}}_1 \cdot \widehat{\mathbf{S}}_2 + \widehat{S}_2^2$, which is *not* the same as $\widehat{S}_1^2 + \widehat{S}_2^2$.

Now it is easy to show that the symmetric and antisymmetric spin kets in Equations 4.38 and 4.39 are all eigenvectors of the spin operator $\widehat{S}_z$, and that their eigenvalues can be expressed as $M_S\hbar$, where $M_S = 1$ for $|\uparrow\uparrow\rangle$, $M_S = 0$ for $\frac{1}{\sqrt{2}}(|\uparrow\downarrow\rangle \pm |\downarrow\uparrow\rangle)$, and $M_S = -1$ for $|\downarrow\downarrow\rangle$. These results are demonstrated in Exercise 4.5 and in Exercise 4.10 below.

Capital letters are used to denote $S$ and $M_S$, the total spin and total spin magnetic quantum numbers for the two-particle system; this is to distinguish them from $s$ and $m_s$ which refer to single particles.

The four spin kets in Equations 4.38 and 4.39 also turn out to be eigenvectors of $\widehat{S}^2$ with eigenvalues $S(S+1)\hbar^2$, where $S = 1$ for the three symmetric states and $S = 0$ for the antisymmetric state. They are therefore simultaneous eigenvectors of $\widehat{S}^2$ and $\widehat{S}_z$; this is allowed because the operators $\widehat{S}^2$ and $\widehat{S}_z$ can be shown to commute with one another – a detail we shall take on trust to avoid a lengthy proof.

These facts give us an alternative way of describing the spin states of a pair of identical spin-$\frac{1}{2}$ particles such as electrons. We introduce the notation $|S, M_S\rangle$ for simultaneous eigenvectors of the total spin operators $\widehat{S}^2$ and $\widehat{S}_z$, where

$$\widehat{S}^2\,|S, M_S\rangle = S(S+1)\hbar^2\,|S, M_S\rangle \tag{4.41}$$

and

$$\widehat{S}_z\,|S, M_S\rangle = M_S\hbar\,|S, M_S\rangle. \tag{4.42}$$

Then we can classify the four symmetric and antisymmetric spin states as follows. First we have the symmetric spin states. There are three of these, so they are called **triplet states**:

**Triplet spin states for two identical spin-$\frac{1}{2}$ particles**

$$|\uparrow\uparrow\rangle = |1,\, 1\rangle,$$
$$\frac{1}{\sqrt{2}}(|\uparrow\downarrow\rangle + |\downarrow\uparrow\rangle) = |1,\, 0\rangle,$$
$$|\downarrow\downarrow\rangle = |1,\, -1\rangle.$$

In the kets on the right-hand sides, the first number is the value of $S$ and the second number is the value of $M_S$. For example, $|1, 1\rangle$ is $|S = 1, M_S = 1\rangle$, written in full, and so on.

There is also an antisymmetric spin state. There is only one of these, so it is called the **singlet state**:

**Singlet spin state for two identical spin-$\frac{1}{2}$ particles**

$$\frac{1}{\sqrt{2}}(|\uparrow\downarrow\rangle - |\downarrow\uparrow\rangle) = |0, 0\rangle.$$

Here $|0, 0\rangle$ is $|S = 0, M_S = 0\rangle$, written in full. We sometimes say that electron spins in the singlet state are opposite but, strictly speaking, it is not correct to think of either of the electrons as 'having' a definite value of $S_z$ since we cannot say which electron is 'spin up' and which is 'spin down'. This is a point we shall refer to again when we discuss entanglement in the next chapter.

We emphasize that the $|S,\, M_S\rangle$ notation is just an alternative way of specifying the symmetric and antisymmetric spin states that are needed to describe particles like electrons. When using this notation, you must remember that the symmetric (triplet) states have $S = 1$, while the antisymmetric (singlet) state has $S = 0$.

**Exercise 4.10** Show that $|\downarrow\downarrow\rangle$ is an eigenvector of the total spin operator $\widehat{S}_z = \widehat{S}_{z1} + \widehat{S}_{z2}$. Find the eigenvalue of $\widehat{S}_z$ and the quantum number $M_S$. ■

## 4.2.3 Putting the spatial and spin functions together

We now have all the ingredients needed for constructing the total wave function of a system of two identical spin-$\frac{1}{2}$ particles. Section 4.2.1 gave us symmetric and antisymmetric energy eigenfunctions, which are functions of the particle coordinates. Section 4.2.2 gave us symmetric and antisymmetric spin ket vectors describing the spin states of two identical spin-$\frac{1}{2}$ particles. We are less concerned here with other types of particle (with, say, spin-1) but, for completeness, we note that their spin states can also be represented by appropriate $|S,\, M_S\rangle$ ket vectors.

Now, the total wave function of the system (depending on the spatial coordinates and spin) can be written as a product of a spatial eigenfunction depending on particle coordinates and a spin ket vector:

$$\psi_{1,2} = \psi(x_1, x_2)\, |S,\, M_S\rangle.$$

As we stated earlier, this total wave function *must be either symmetric or antisymmetric* with respect to exchange of the particle labels, 1 and 2. There are four ways in which this can be achieved:

- spatial symmetric $\times$ spin symmetric = total symmetric,
- spatial antisymmetric $\times$ spin antisymmetric = total symmetric,
- spatial symmetric $\times$ spin antisymmetric = total antisymmetric,
- spatial antisymmetric $\times$ spin symmetric = total antisymmetric.

The first two ways produce a *symmetric* total wave function, and the last two ways produce an *antisymmetric* total wave function.

In the introduction to Section 4.2, we mentioned that all particles can be classified as either *bosons* or *fermions*. Systems composed of identical bosons are described by *symmetric* total wave functions, while systems composed of identical fermions are described by *antisymmetric* total wave functions. Electrons are spin-$\frac{1}{2}$ fermions, so the total wave function describing a pair of electrons takes one of the following antisymmetric forms.

**Triplet states**:

$$\psi^-(x_1,x_2)|1,1\rangle = \frac{1}{\sqrt{2}}\big[\psi_n(x_1)\,\psi_k(x_2) - \psi_k(x_1)\,\psi_n(x_2)\big]\,|\uparrow\uparrow\rangle$$

$$\psi^-(x_1,x_2)|1,0\rangle = \frac{1}{2}\big[\psi_n(x_1)\,\psi_k(x_2) - \psi_k(x_1)\,\psi_n(x_2)\big]\big(|\uparrow\downarrow\rangle + |\downarrow\uparrow\rangle\big)$$

$$\psi^-(x_1,x_2)|1,-1\rangle = \frac{1}{\sqrt{2}}\big[\psi_n(x_1)\,\psi_k(x_2) - \psi_k(x_1)\,\psi_n(x_2)\big]\,|\downarrow\downarrow\rangle$$

**Singlet state**:

$$\psi^+(x_1,x_2)|0,0\rangle = \frac{1}{2}\big[\psi_n(x_1)\,\psi_k(x_2) + \psi_k(x_1)\,\psi_n(x_2)\big]\big(|\uparrow\downarrow\rangle - |\downarrow\uparrow\rangle\big)$$

It is also worth noting that identical spinless particles are counted as being bosons with symmetric spin states, so the first possibility listed above is always realized for them, with a symmetric spatial wave function.

**Exercise 4.11** Two identical non-interacting spinless bosons occupy the single-particle energy eigenfunctions $\psi_n(x)$ and $\psi_k(x)$. Write down an appropriate two-particle spatial eigenfunction describing this pair of bosons.

**Exercise 4.12** Construct the four possible total wave functions for the first excited level of two identical, non-interacting, spin-$\frac{1}{2}$ fermions of mass $m$ in the one-dimensional harmonic oscillator well of Exercise 4.8. What are the energies of these two-particle states? ■

### 4.2.4 Fermions and bosons

Although we have touched on the point previously, we are now ready to explore the crucial fact that all particles can be classified as being either bosons or fermions. How do we know whether a given particle is a boson or a fermion? The following definition makes the classification straightforward.

We say a particle has spin-$x$ if its spin quantum number $s = x$.

### Bosons and fermions

**Bosons** are particles with integer spin ($s = 0, 1, 2, \ldots$).

**Fermions** are particles with half-integer spin ($s = 1/2, 3/2, 5/2, \ldots$).

For example, we know that an electron has spin-$\frac{1}{2}$ so it is a fermion, and so are other spin-$\frac{1}{2}$ particles such as protons and neutrons. Photons (light quanta) have spin 1, and alpha particles ($^4_2$He nuclei) have zero spin, so these are both bosons. More bosons and fermions are listed in Table 4.1. You will see from the table that a nucleus that is composed of fermions may be a boson, for example $^4_2$He. The general rule (established by Ehrenfest and Oppenheimer in 1930) is that a composite particle containing an *odd* number of fermions is a fermion, while one containing an *even* number of fermions is a boson. For example, a neutral $^{85}_{37}$Rb atom is a boson, formed from 37 protons, $85 - 37 = 48$ neutrons and 37 electrons (122 fermions in all). Composite particles composed exclusively of bosons are bosons.

**Table 4.1** Some bosons and fermions. The symbol $^A_Z$X represents an atom or nucleus of element X with atomic number $Z$ and mass number $A$; $Z$ is the number of protons and $A$ is the total number of protons plus neutrons.

| Bosons | Fermions |
|---|---|
| photon | electron |
| pion | proton |
| deuteron, $^2_1$H | neutron |
| $^4_2$He atom | $^3_2$He atom |
| $^{85}_{37}$Rb atom | $^{85}_{37}$Rb nucleus |
| alpha particle | all quarks |
| $^{23}_{11}$Na atom | $^{23}_{11}$Na nucleus |
| $N_2$ molecule | |
| $O_2$ molecule | |

**Exercise 4.13** Classify the following as fermions or bosons: a hydrogen atom; a deuterium atom (with $^2_1$H nucleus); a singly-ionized helium atom (with $^4_2$He nucleus); a $^{238}_{92}$U nucleus; a $^{235}_{92}$U nucleus; a $^{235}_{92}$U atom. ■

When we consider collections of identical particles, it is the boson or fermion nature of the particles that determines the symmetry of the total wave function.

### The symmetry of the total wave function

The total wave function describing any system of identical *bosons* is *symmetric* with respect to particle exchange.

The total wave function describing any system of identical *fermions* is *antisymmetric* with respect to particle exchange.

The first question that we need to consider when writing the total wave function for a system of identical particles is: are the particles bosons or fermions? If they are bosons, the total wave function must be symmetric; if they are fermions, it must be antisymmetric. You have seen this principle used for pairs of particles, but it is true for systems containing any number of particles. The link between the boson or fermion nature of particles and symmetric or antisymmetric total wave functions can be regarded as a fundamental fact about the world we live in. It has actually been derived from other principles, including special relativity, but the proof (published by Wolfgang Pauli in 1940) is far beyond the scope of this course.

A dramatic difference between bosons and fermions appears if we consider a state in which all the particles have the same $z$-component of spin, so that the spin part of the total wave function is symmetric. If the particles are identical bosons, the total wave function is symmetric, so the spatial part of the wave function must also be symmetric. This does not prevent the particles from all being in the same single-particle spatial state, since the product function $\psi_n(x_1)\,\psi_n(x_2)\ldots$ is a perfectly valid normalized symmetric function. There is no restriction on the number of bosons, with the same spin, that can occupy a given spatial state represented by $\psi_n(x)$. In particular, it is possible for all particles in a system of identical bosons to be in the lowest single-particle energy level.

The situation for identical fermions is profoundly different. If two fermions have the same $z$-component of spin, they must be in one of the *symmetric* spin states $|\uparrow\uparrow\rangle$ or $|\downarrow\downarrow\rangle$. The total wave function of two identical fermions is antisymmetric, so the spatial part of the wave function must take the antisymmetric form $\psi^-(x_1, x_2) = \frac{1}{\sqrt{2}}\big[\psi_n(x_1)\,\psi_k(x_2) - \psi_k(x_1)\,\psi_n(x_2)\big]$, where $n$ and $k$ denote the spatial states occupied by the particles. Now, if we set $n = k$, we see that the spatial part of the wave function vanishes everywhere, from which we conclude that two fermions with the same $z$-component of spin, $S_z$, *cannot* be in the same spatial state. Electrons only have two different values of $S_z$, so the number of electrons in a given spatial state is limited to two. This is the origin of the 'classically non-describable two-valuedness' discovered by Pauli and mentioned in Section 3.1.2 of Chapter 3.

**Figure 4.4** Satyendranath Bose (1894–1974), after whom bosons are named.

This restriction on the number of electrons per spatial state has important consequences for systems containing many electrons. If we imagine the electrons being added progressively to the system, they cannot all go into the lowest single-particle energy level, but are forced into higher and higher energy levels. We will return to this point in the final section of this chapter.

Finally, we mention the reason for the names 'boson' and 'fermion'. Bosons are named after the Indian physicist Satyendranath Bose (Figure 4.4), and fermions after the Italian physicist Enrico Fermi (Figure 4.5). The discovery of this way of categorizing particles had a complicated history involving many people, including Einstein and Dirac. It involved evidence coming from the thermal behaviour of macroscopic systems containing vast numbers of particles. The way that particles tend to occupy the various energy levels of macroscopic systems at different temperatures is described in the branch of physics known as *statistical mechanics*. Bose found rules appropriate for photons and Einstein generalized them to atoms and molecules that are bosons, producing what is known as *Bose–Einstein statistics*. Fermi and Dirac presented the corresponding rules for fermions, leading to *Fermi–Dirac statistics*. We shall not concern ourselves with the details here, but it is interesting to note that many properties of matter can be explained by combining the quantum-mechanical concepts of bosons and fermions with the classical idea of temperature.

**Figure 4.5** Enrico Fermi (1901–1954), after whom fermions are named. Fermi received the Nobel prize for physics in 1937.

**Exercise 4.14** The two protons within a helium nucleus have the same spatial eigenfunction. What is the total spin of the two-proton state in this nucleus? ■

## 4.2.5 Spatial distribution of bosons and fermions

The indistinguishability of identical particles in quantum mechanics gives rise to a remarkable effect for which there is no classical analogue. We return to the case illustrated for distinguishable particles in Figure 4.1 — the probability density for a system of two particles in a one-dimensional infinite square well of width $L$, with one particle in the ground state and the other in the first excited state.

We now consider the same situation *except* that the particles will be taken to be identical. The single-particle eigenfunctions that we need are, as before,

$$\psi_1(x) = \sqrt{\frac{2}{L}}\sin\left(\frac{\pi x}{L}\right) \quad \text{and} \quad \psi_2(x) = \sqrt{\frac{2}{L}}\sin\left(\frac{2\pi x}{L}\right).$$

The appropriate symmetric and antisymmetric combinations are

$$\psi^+(x_1,x_2) = \frac{1}{\sqrt{2}}\big[\psi_1(x_1)\,\psi_2(x_2) + \psi_2(x_1)\,\psi_1(x_2)\big],$$

$$\psi^-(x_1,x_2) = \frac{1}{\sqrt{2}}\big[\psi_1(x_1)\,\psi_2(x_2) - \psi_2(x_1)\,\psi_1(x_2)\big].$$

These are possible spatial wave functions for pairs of identical particles.

Born's rule continues to apply to identical particles, but now in the following form:

$\Psi^\pm$ is the symmetrical $(+)$ or antisymmetrical $(-)$ spatial wave function for the system. Notice the subtle difference in wording between this box and the one containing Equation 4.8.

**Born's rule for two identical particles**

The probability of finding one particle in a small interval $\delta x_1$ centred on $x_1$ and the other particle in a small interval $\delta x_2$ centred on $x_2$ is given by

$$|\Psi^\pm(x_1,x_2,t)|^2\,\delta x_1\,\delta x_2.$$

Contour plots of $|\psi^\pm(x_1,x_2)|^2$ are shown in Figure 4.6. They look nothing like the unsymmetrized probability densities of Figure 4.1.

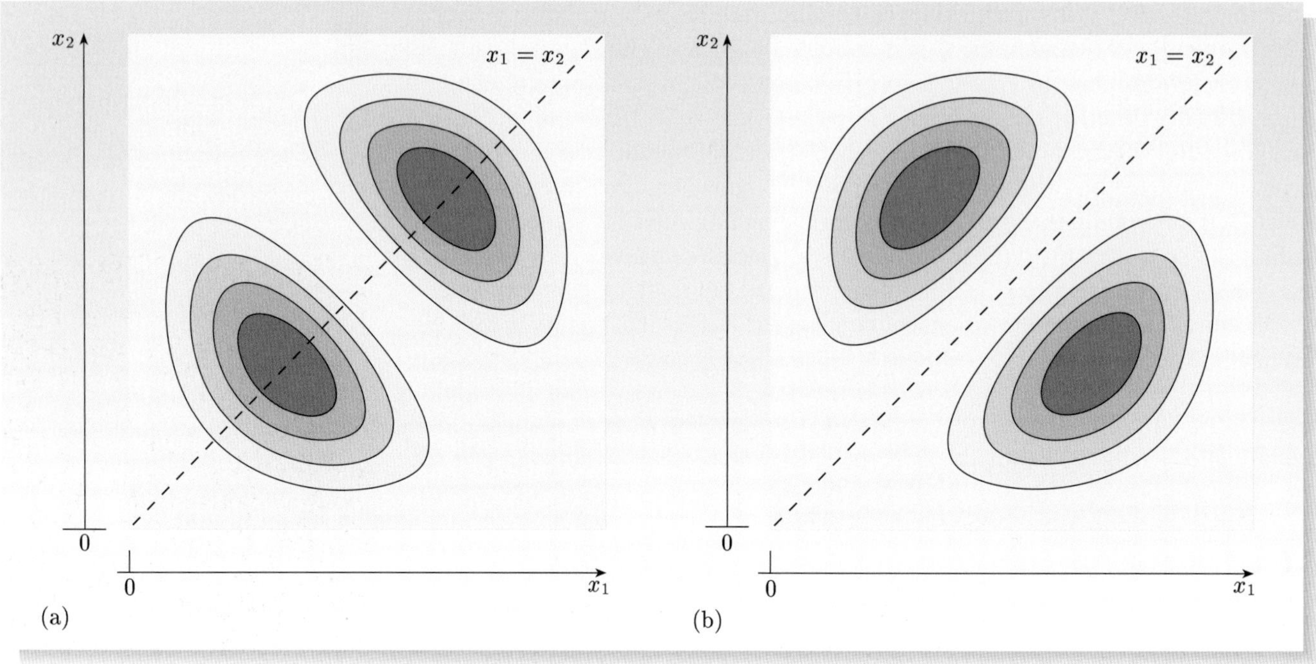


**Figure 4.6** The probability density for two non-interacting identical particles in an infinite square well: (a) symmetric spatial wave function; (b) antisymmetric spatial wave function. In both panels, the bottom left-hand corner has coordinates $x_1 = x_2 = 0$.

For the symmetric spatial wave function (Figure 4.6a), the probability density has two maxima (at $x_1 = x_2 = L/4$) lying on the $x_1 = x_2$ line. As we move away from this line, the probability density decreases. It is *as if* the particles were mysteriously attracted to one another, although there is no force between them. We might say that the particles described by $\psi^+(x_1, x_2)$ 'prefer' to crowd together in places where $x_1 = x_2$.

Figure 4.6b shows the probability density for the antisymmetric spatial wave function. By contrast, this is equal to *zero* along the $x_1 = x_2$ line. The maxima of this probability distribution occur when $x_1$ and $x_2$ have very different values. It is *as if* the particles were mysteriously repelled, although there is no force between them. We might say that particles described by $\psi^-(x_1, x_2)$ 'prefer' to avoid each other.

We emphasize again that the 'crowding' and 'avoidance' of particles displayed in Figure 4.6 are purely quantum-mechanical effects resulting from the identity of the particles. It has nothing to do with forces because the Hamiltonian operator of the system contains no term $V(x_1 - x_2)$ that would describe a mutual interaction between the particles.

Both Figures 4.6a and 4.6b apply to bosons and fermions. Figure 4.6a assumes a symmetric spatial wave function. Since identical bosons have a symmetric total wave function, this case applies to identical bosons in a symmetric spin state (or to spinless bosons). Since identical fermions have an antisymmetric total wave function, it also applies to identical fermions in an antisymmetric spin state. For a pair of electrons, this implies a triplet spin state. By contrast, Figure 4.6b assumes an antisymmetric spatial wave function; this is found for identical bosons in an antisymmetric spin state, or identical fermions in an symmetric spin state. For a pair of electrons, this implies a singlet spin state.

# 4.3 Consequences of particle indistinguishability

## 4.3.1 The Pauli exclusion principle

The rules applying to fermions, stated in the previous section, have a momentous consequence: the Pauli exclusion principle, proposed by Wolfgang Pauli in 1925. Initially formulated in terms of electrons, this principle applies to all fermions and can be stated as follows:

**Pauli exclusion principle**

No two identical fermions can exist in the same quantum state.

This is equivalent to saying that no two fermions in a system can ever have exactly the same set of quantum numbers. It is understood that both the state, and the set of quantum numbers, include a specification of spin. As you will see in Book 3, the Pauli exclusion principle is crucial for explaining atomic spectra, the Periodic Table, and the bonding of atoms to form molecules. It also helps to explain the behaviour of nuclei, white dwarf stars and neutron stars, and determines many of the properties of the matter around us.

**Figure 4.7** Wolfgang Pauli (1900–1958). Pauli was awarded the Nobel prize for physics in 1945 for his discovery of the exclusion principle.

The Pauli exclusion principle follows from the fact that identical fermions must be described by an antisymmetric total wave function. As you saw in the previous section, this implies that two electrons with the same $z$-component of spin, $S_z$, *cannot* be in the same spatial state $\psi_n(x)$. This is because two electrons with the same value of $S_z$ are in a *symmetric* spin state, so the spatial part must be *antisymmetric*. However, there is no (non-zero) antisymmetric spatial wave function having both particles in the same spatial state, $\psi_n(x)$. The label $n$ here could represent a single quantum number or several quantum numbers in the three-dimensional case. We therefore conclude that not all the quantum numbers can be the same. There is no such restriction if the pair of electrons is in an antisymmetric spin state but, in this case, the two spin quantum numbers, $m_{s_1}$ and $m_{s_2}$ are different, so the two electrons never have exactly the same set of quantum numbers. This property, described here for electrons, applies to any number of identical fermions: it is the Pauli exclusion principle.

### 4.3.2 Rigidity of metals

The Pauli exclusion principle applies to all systems of identical fermions. The electrons in a metal provide an example of such a system. The atoms in a metal lose one or more electrons, becoming positively-charged ions. The 'free' electrons then move through the whole body of the metal. Although the electrons are subject to the mutual repulsion and attractive forces of the ions, various properties of metals can be explained by treating the electrons as free particles.

We can model the behaviour of free electrons in a metal as follows. The electrons are treated as non-interacting particles of mass $m$ within a metal cube having sides of length $L$. Within this cube, the potential energy of the electrons can be taken to be zero, with the sides of the cube constituting an infinite barrier. The energy levels of an electron are therefore just those of a particle in a three-dimensional infinite square well:

$$E = \frac{(n_x^2 + n_y^2 + n_z^2)\pi^2\hbar^2}{2mL^2}. \tag{4.43}$$

Here $n_x$, $n_y$ and $n_z$ are the quantum numbers associated with the coordinates $x$, $y$ and $z$, respectively. Due to the Pauli exclusion principle, no more than two electrons can have the same value for these three quantum numbers. (If all three spatial quantum numbers are the same, then the electrons must have different spin quantum numbers: $m_s = 1/2$ and $m_s = -1/2$). Hence the quantum states in the box are filled in a very specific way: electrons cannot all go to the lowest spatial state (defined by $n_x = n_y = n_z = 1$). A maximum of two electrons will occupy this spatial state. The next two electrons must occupy a different spatial state (with at least one of the quantum numbers being different from 1); the electrons therefore pile up into higher and higher levels. As a result, no matter how much we try to lower the energy of the electrons in the metal, there will always be electrons with large energies.

This is one reason why metals resist being compressed. If we try to compress the metal, and therefore make $L$ in Equation 4.43 smaller, the energies of all the electrons increase. The electrons cannot lose energy by dropping down into lower energy levels because these are all full. The increase in energy requires work done by the compressing force — so much work, in fact, that it is hard to achieve an appreciable decrease in volume. The same mechanism is responsible for the stability of white dwarf stars. A white dwarf star is rather like a huge piece of metal, with all the electrons in a giant potential energy well the size of a star. There is a tendency for gravity to compress the star, but a significant compression would be accompanied by a huge increase in the energy of the star, more than is available from the loss of gravitational potential energy, so the white dwarf star resists compression and remains in near-equilibrium.

**Exercise 4.15** Consider a three-dimensional box containing many electrons. Is it correct to say that the Pauli exclusion principle implies that there can only be a maximum of two electrons with the same energy? ■

### 4.3.3 Bose–Einstein condensation

In Chapter 4 of Book 1 we mentioned an experiment in which about 2000 rubidium atoms were trapped by a magnetic field and cooled down so that a large number of them occupied the ground state of the well in which they were confined. The resulting 'substance' is a new phase of matter called a **Bose–Einstein condensate** (BEC). What is this phase of matter? Why and how is it formed? And more importantly, why is it interesting?

The existence of Bose–Einstein condensates was predicted by Einstein in the 1920s. His prediction concerns the low-temperature behaviour of a gas of atoms that are bosons. When such a gas is so cold that the de Broglie wavelength $\lambda_{\text{dB}}$ of the atoms is comparable to the spacing between them, the atoms behave in a collective way, and the whole gas can be described by a single wave function. In this sense, the atoms lose their individuality.

We define the atom number density, $N$, as the number of atoms per unit volume. Then, if we call the mean inter-atom separation $d$, we can set $d = N^{-1/3}$ because there will, on average, be one atom within a volume $d^3$. The criterion for the formation of a Bose–Einstein condensate is that

$$N\lambda_{\text{dB}}^3 \gtrsim 2.612. \qquad (4.44)$$

Consider what happens to atoms that are bosons trapped in a small box. We assume that every atom is in its *internal* ground state, an accurate assumption at very low temperatures. The kinetic energy of the atoms is quantized since the box acts as a three-dimensional infinite square well. At room temperature, there is a distribution of particles over all the possible energy levels. But, as the temperature falls, the atoms move from higher energy levels to lower energy levels; their average speed decreases and their average de Broglie wavelength increases. Now the fact that the atoms are bosons comes into play. There is no reason why the bosons should not all be in the same quantum state. In fact, it can be shown that bosons 'prefer' to be in the same state (much as they 'prefer' to crowd together). It turns out that at some (very low) critical temperature, a phase transition takes place in which many of the atoms 'condense' into the lowest energy single-particle state. These atoms form the Bose–Einstein condensate, which behaves in many respects like a single entity, described by a so-called **macroscopic wave function** $\Psi(\mathbf{r}, t)$. The remarkable point about this wave function is that it depends only on a single position vector $\mathbf{r}$, not on the position vectors of all the particles in the condensate. It turns out that the number density of particles in the condensate is given by $|\Psi(\mathbf{r},t)|^2$. The process of Bose–Einstein condensation is represented schematically in Figure 4.8.

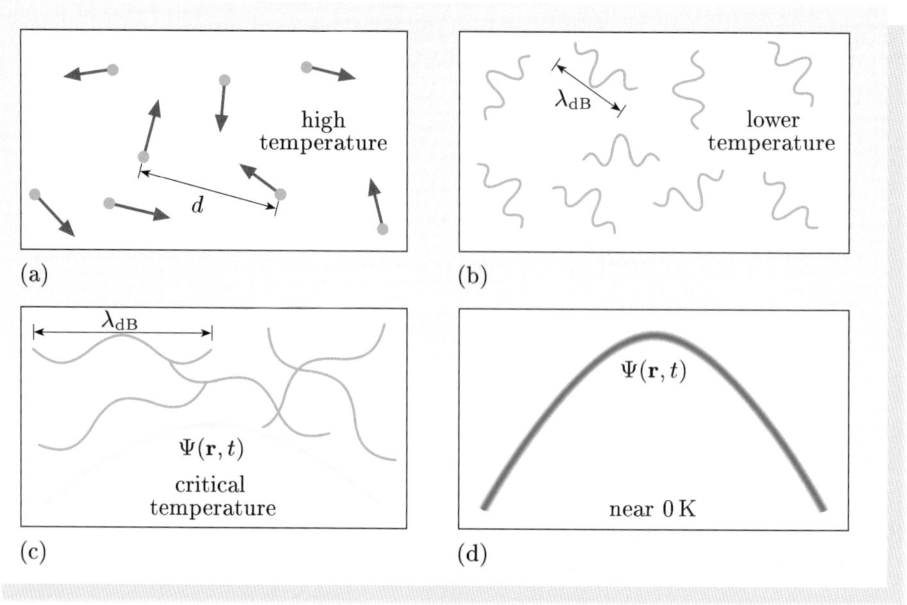


**Figure 4.8** The formation of a Bose–Einstein condensate. (a) At high temperatures, the average distance between atoms is larger than their typical de Broglie wavelength and the atoms behave like individual particles. (b) As the temperature decreases, the de Broglie wavelength increases. (c) At a critical temperature, the de Broglie wavelength becomes comparable to the distance between atoms, and a Bose–Einstein condensate, described by a macroscopic wave function $\Psi(\mathbf{r},t)$, starts to form. (d) At a temperature close to absolute zero, practically all the atoms belong to the condensate. (Adapted from Wolfgang Ketterle's Nobel lecture (2001).)

It was not until 1995 that a gaseous Bose–Einstein condensate was finally realized experimentally. We can say a few words about how this was done. A gas of atoms that are bosons will undergo a phase transition to a Bose–Einstein condensate if Equation 4.44 is satisfied, which suggests high number densities and long de Broglie wavelengths. However, there is an upper limit to the number density: when atoms are very close, they start to interact with one another and form molecules or undergo other phase transitions. This puts a limit on the minimum distance $d$ between the atoms. Since $d = N^{-1/3}$, there is an upper limit to the number densities $N$ that we can use. We are left with increasing the de Broglie wavelength. Since $\lambda_{\text{dB}}$ increases as the atomic speed falls, the temperature must be very low, close to absolute zero.

At temperatures much higher than those required for Bose–Einstein condensation, most gases suffer a phase transition into a liquid, and then solid, state. To produce a Bose–Einstein condensate, these 'normal' transitions must be avoided.

In 1995, Eric Cornell and Carl Wieman cooled $^{87}_{37}\text{Rb}$ atoms down to around $1.7 \times 10^{-7}$ K by using lasers and a technique called evaporative cooling. Soon afterwards, Wolfgang Ketterle produced a condensate of sodium atoms. Because Ketterle's condensate contained more atoms, he was able to split it into two and then let the two parts interact to form an interference pattern (Figure 4.9), rather like the pattern found when light passes through a double slit. This pattern is evidence that the Bose–Einstein condensate can be described by a single macroscopic wave function. Cornell, Wieman and Ketterle won the Nobel prize for physics in 2001 for the achievement of Bose–Einstein condensation.

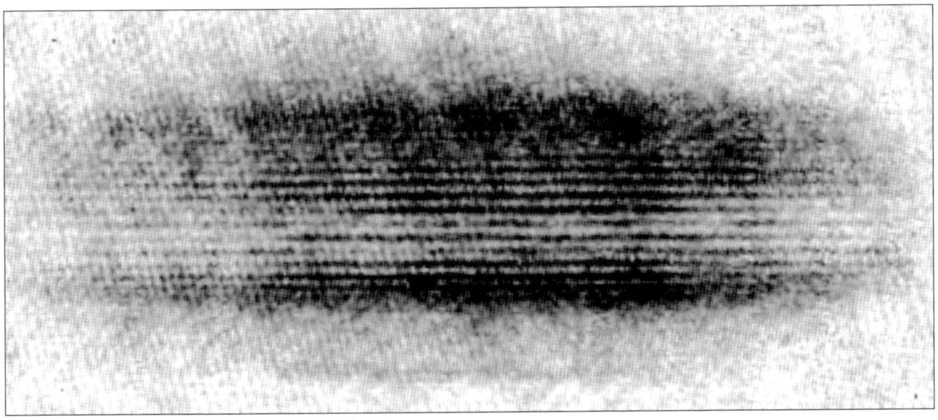

**Figure 4.9** Interference fringes produced by the superposition of two Bose–Einstein condensates consisting of sodium atoms. The fringes represent variations in the density of the gas due to the interference of the wave functions representing each condensate.

Much research has been devoted to ultra-cold atoms since the first Bose–Einstein condensate was created. Remarkably, condensates containing atoms that are fermions have also been produced. How is this possible? The Pauli exclusion principle prevents fermions from condensing into the lowest energy state. The trick is that pairs of fermion-type atoms can join to produce molecules that are *bosons*, and it is these molecules that form the condensate.

# Summary of Chapter 4

**Section 4.1** The Hamiltonian operator $\widehat{\mathrm{H}} = \widehat{\mathrm{H}}_1 + \widehat{\mathrm{H}}_2$ for a system of two non-interacting particles is a sum of Hamiltonian operators associated with the individual particles. It acts on a wave function $\Psi(x_1, x_2, t)$ that depends on the coordinates of both particles.

For two distinguishable particles, Born's rule states that the probability of finding particle 1 in a small interval $\delta x_1$, centred on $x_1$, *and* particle 2 in a small interval $\delta x_2$, centred on $x_2$, is $|\Psi(x_1, x_2, t)|^2\, \delta x_1\, \delta x_2$.

Separating the space and time variables in Schrödinger's equation, we obtain stationary state solutions which are the product of an energy eigenfunction $\psi(x_1, x_2)$ and a time-dependent phase factor, $\mathrm{e}^{-\mathrm{i}Et/\hbar}$. Solving the time-independent Schrödinger equation for a system of two non-interacting *distinguishable* particles gives energy eigenfunctions of the form $\psi(x_1, x_2) = \psi_n(x_1)\, \psi_k(x_2)$, where $n$ and $k$ are quantum numbers of single-particle states with eigenvalues $E_n$ and $E_k$, and $E_n + E_k = E$. For distinguishable spin-$\frac{1}{2}$ particles, a more complete description is provided by the total wave function $\psi_{1,2} = \psi(x_1, x_2)\, |m_{s1}, m_{s2}\rangle$. Operators that depend on coordinates and momenta act on the spatial part of the total wave function, while spin operators act on the spin part.

**Section 4.2** In the quantum world, all particles sharing the same set of unalterable attributes are *identical*. All electrons are identical, for example. Any particle can be classified as being either a boson or a fermion. For identical bosons, the total wave function is always *symmetric* (unchanged by swapping a pair of particle labels); for identical fermions, the total wave function is always *antisymmetric* (reversed in sign by swapping the particle labels).

The spatial part of the total wave function must either be symmetric ($\psi^+(x_1, x_2)$) or antisymmetric ($\psi^-(x_1, x_2)$), where

$$\psi^{\pm}(x_1, x_2) = \frac{1}{\sqrt{2}}\big[\psi_n(x_1)\,\psi_k(x_2) \pm \psi_k(x_1)\,\psi_n(x_2)\big].$$

Both these possibilities are consistent with the fact that the probability density is independent of the scheme used to label the particles.

The spin part of the total wave function must also be symmetric or antisymmetric. For identical spin-$\frac{1}{2}$ particles, the possibilities are:

**symmetric:** $\dfrac{1}{\sqrt{2}}(|\uparrow\downarrow\rangle + |\downarrow\uparrow\rangle),\quad |\uparrow\uparrow\rangle,\quad |\downarrow\downarrow\rangle,$

**antisymmetric:** $\dfrac{1}{\sqrt{2}}(|\uparrow\downarrow\rangle - |\downarrow\uparrow\rangle).$

These spin states are eigenfunctions of the total spin operators $\widehat{\mathrm{S}}^2$ and $\widehat{\mathrm{S}}_z$, and they can be classified in terms of the eigenvalues $S(S+1)\hbar^2$ and $M_S\hbar$ of these operators. Writing them in the same order as before, we have:

**symmetric:** $|1, 0\rangle,\quad |1, 1\rangle,\quad |1, -1\rangle,$
**antisymmetric:** $|0, 0\rangle.$

The three symmetric states are called *triplet states* and have $S = 1$, and the antisymmetric state is called the *singlet state* and has $S = 0$.

Bosons are particles of integer spin ($s = 0, 1, 2, \ldots$). Fermions are particles of half-integer spin ($s = 1/2, 3/2, 5/2, \ldots$). For example, photons are bosons, and electrons, protons and neutrons are fermions. Composite particles made up of an odd number of fermions are fermions; those made up of an even number of fermions are bosons. Composite particles made up exclusively of bosons are bosons.

Systems of bosons are represented by symmetric total wave functions, so the spin and spatial parts have the same symmetry (both symmetric or both antisymmetric). Systems of identical fermions are represented by antisymmetric total wave functions, so the spin and spatial parts have opposite symmetries. A pair of electrons in a symmetric (i.e. triplet) spin state is represented by an antisymmetric spatial wave function $\psi^-(x_1, x_2)$. A pair of electrons in the antisymmetric (i.e. singlet) spin state is represented by a symmetric spatial wave function $\psi^+(x_1, x_2)$.

The probability densities for systems of identical particles differ markedly from those for non-identical particles. Both the overall spin state and the boson/fermion nature of the particles matter. Identical bosons in a symmetric spin state show a marked tendency to 'crowd together', as do identical fermions in an antisymmetric spin state. However, identical bosons in an antisymmetric spin state and identical fermions in a symmetric spin state show the contrary tendency: they avoid each other. These effects arise from the symmetry or antisymmetry of the wave function and are not connected with forces acting between the particles.

**Section 4.3** As a result of the antisymmetry of their total wave function, identical fermions obey the Pauli exclusion principle: no two identical fermions can be in the same quantum state, with the same set of quantum numbers (including those associated with spin). The Pauli exclusion principle has profound effects on the chemical and physical properties of matter. For example, it explains the incompressibility of metals and the stability of white dwarf stars.

A Bose–Einstein condensate is a phase of matter formed by boson-type atoms at extremely low temperatures, when their de Broglie wavelengths become comparable to the inter-atomic spacing. At a critical temperature, a phase transition takes place in which many of the atoms 'condense' into the lowest energy single-particle state. These atoms form the Bose–Eintein condensate, which behaves in many respects like a single entity, described by a macroscopic wave function, $\Psi(\mathbf{r}, t)$.

## Achievements from Chapter 4

*After studying this chapter, you should be able to:*

**4.1** Explain the meanings of the newly defined (emboldened) terms and symbols, and use them appropriately.

**4.2** Write down the Hamiltonian operator for a system of two particles, and the corresponding Schrödinger equation.

**4.3** Explain why solutions of the time-independent Schrödinger equation for a system of two non-interacting distinguishable particles can be written as products of two single-particle eigenfunctions, each depending only on the coordinate of one of the particles.

**4.4** Find the effects of operators acting on the spatial and spin parts of total wave functions.

**4.5** Write down possible spatial wave functions for a system of two identical fermions or bosons.

**4.6** Write down possible state vectors for a system of two identical spin-$\frac{1}{2}$ particles using ket notation. Assign the associated quantum numbers $S$ and $M_S$, and identify the spin states as being singlet or triplet.

**4.7** Combine spatial wave functions and spin kets to produce the total wave function of a system of two identical spin-$\frac{1}{2}$ particles.

**4.8** Identify whether particles are bosons or fermions, given information about their spin or composition.

**4.9** Relate the symmetry of the total wave function describing a system of identical particles to the boson or fermion nature of its particles.

**4.10** Explain how the probability density of a pair of identical particles is affected by the symmetry or antisymmetry of their spatial wave function.

**4.11** State the Pauli exclusion principle and describe some of its consequences.

**4.12** Describe the formation and behaviour of a Bose–Einstein condensate.

# Chapter 5 The principles of quantum mechanics: a review

## Introduction

Chapter 2 of Book 1 presented a list of statements described as '*Preliminary principles of wave mechanics*'. You have seen a great deal of quantum mechanics since then, including additional principles, new notation and many examples of quantum mechanics in action. Now is a good time to pause and take stock.

This chapter contains little that is new; much of it will draw together ideas introduced in Book 1 and the first four chapters of this book. However, there will also be some deeper discussion of what happens when we make a measurement in quantum mechanics and how we deal with continuous ranges of possible values. The aim is to arrive at an updated list of the principles of quantum mechanics, and to prepare the way for the remarkable physics in the last two chapters of this book.

We begin by reproducing the list of preliminary principles of wave mechanics, exactly as they appeared in Chapter 2 of Book 1.

**Box 1: Preliminary principles of wave mechanics**

1. The state of a system at time $t$ is represented by a wave function $\Psi(x,t)$.
2. An observable, such as energy or momentum, is represented by a linear operator, such as $-i\hbar\,\partial/\partial x$ for the momentum component $p_x$.
3. As a general rule, the only possible outcomes of a measurement of an observable are the eigenvalues of the associated operator.
4. The time-evolution of a system in a given state is governed by Schrödinger's equation.
5. A measurement will cause the collapse of the wave function — a sudden and abrupt change that is not described by Schrödinger's equation.

Now it is clear that these principles need to be overhauled and extended. Take the first principle, for example, which refers to a wave function $\Psi(x,t)$. Such a function may describe the state of a single spinless particle travelling along the $x$-axis, but it cannot describe the state of a system of many particles in three dimensions, or even the state of a single particle with spin. It is also clear that some key quantum-mechanical ideas are missing, including the rules needed to predict the probabilities of particular experimental outcomes and the rules describing the special properties of systems of identical particles.

We will go through these principles, reviewing and extending them in Sections 5.1–5.5. Finally, in Section 5.6, we will draw together a revised list of *principles of quantum mechanics*. The change in title is significant: the list will no longer be preliminary, and it will encompass the whole of quantum mechanics, not just the wave mechanics of Book 1.

## 5.1 Describing the state of a system

In the context of wave mechanics, the state of an isolated system is described by a *wave function*. The variables in the wave function depend on the type of system under study:

- For a particle in one dimension, the wave function can be written as $\Psi(x, t)$, a complex-valued function of a single position coordinate, $x$, and time, $t$.
- For two particles in three dimensions, the wave function can be written as $\Psi(\mathbf{r}_1, \mathbf{r}_2, t)$ or as $\Psi(x_1, y_1, z_1, x_2, y_2, z_2, t)$.

The wave function for an atom with many electrons depends on the position vectors of all the electrons as well as time: $\Psi(\mathbf{r}_1, \mathbf{r}_2, \ldots, \mathbf{r}_n, t)$. The wave function therefore does not have a (complex) value at each point in space, $\mathbf{r}$. This is unlike an electric field, for example, which has the value $\mathbf{E}(\mathbf{r}, t)$ at position $\mathbf{r}$ and time $t$.

In order to be consistent with Born's rule, each wave function must be normalized: the square of its modulus, integrated over all the coordinates of all the particles must be equal to 1. For a single particle in three dimensions, this means that

$$\int_{-\infty}^{\infty} |\Psi(\mathbf{r}, t)|^2 \, \mathrm{d}V = 1. \tag{5.1}$$

For a pair of particles in one dimension, it means that

$$\int_{-\infty}^{\infty} \int_{-\infty}^{\infty} |\Psi(x_1, x_2, t)|^2 \, \mathrm{d}x_1 \, \mathrm{d}x_2 = 1, \tag{5.2}$$

where $\mathrm{d}x_1$ and $\mathrm{d}x_2$ are infinitesimal intervals associated with the positions of particles 1 and 2, and both integrals extend over the whole of the $x$-axis. As the number of particles increases, the normalization integrals become more complicated to write down, but the principle remains the same.

Given a wave function, we can extract information from it and make (generally probabilistic) predictions. However, there is some redundancy in the way a wave function is specified. Any two wave functions that differ by an overall multiplicative factor $\mathrm{e}^{\mathrm{i}\alpha}$, where $\alpha$ is real, represent the same state. A factor like $\mathrm{e}^{\mathrm{i}\alpha}$ (a complex number of unit modulus) is called a *phase factor*. When normalizing a wave function, any phase factor can be chosen.

**Exercise 5.1** For given functions $f(x)$ and $g(x)$, which of the following wave functions represent the same state at $t = 0$?

$$\Psi_1 = f(x) + \mathrm{i}\,g(x), \quad \Psi_2 = \mathrm{i}f(x) + g(x), \quad \Psi_3 = \mathrm{i}f(x) - g(x).$$ ■

The notation of wave functions is explicit but cumbersome. At the beginning of this book we introduced a shorthand notation, due to Dirac, which represents states by vectors in an abstract vector space. The state of a system is then represented by a state vector, written as $|\Psi\rangle$. Along with this notation comes the idea of defining an inner product between vectors. In one-dimensional wave mechanics, the inner product is defined by

$$\langle\phi|\psi\rangle = \int_{-\infty}^{\infty} \phi^*(x)\, \psi(x) \, \mathrm{d}x, \tag{5.3}$$

where the symbol $\langle\phi|\psi\rangle$ is called the Dirac bracket of the functions $\phi(x)$ and $\psi(x)$. Using this shorthand notation, the normalization integrals in Equations 5.1 and 5.2 can be written simply as

$$\langle\Psi|\Psi\rangle = 1. \tag{5.4}$$

The irrelevance of phase factors means that $e^{i\alpha}|\Psi\rangle$ represents the same state as $|\Psi\rangle$. We can immediately see, for example, that the phase factor has no effect on the normalization:

$$\langle e^{i\alpha}\Psi|e^{i\alpha}\Psi\rangle = e^{-i\alpha}e^{i\alpha}\langle\Psi|\Psi\rangle = \langle\Psi|\Psi\rangle = 1.$$

Obviously, much detail is omitted, but this is a strength of Dirac notation, allowing us to see the wood for the trees. The concept of a vector space also fits in naturally with the principle of superposition: if $|\Psi_1\rangle$ and $|\Psi_2\rangle$ represent two possible states of a system, then so does any properly-normalized linear combination

$$|\Psi\rangle = a_1\,|\Psi_1\rangle + a_2\,|\Psi_2\rangle. \tag{5.5}$$

This principle explains all types of interference in quantum mechanics, including the famous two-slit interference of electrons.

Moving beyond wave mechanics, particles can have spin, and the spin state of a spin-$\frac{1}{2}$ particle is described not by a wave function but by a two-component matrix, called a *spinor*. Each spinor represents a vector in a complex two-dimensional space (spin space). For example, the spinors for spin-up and spin-down along the $z$-axis are written as

$$|\uparrow_z\rangle = \begin{bmatrix}1\\0\end{bmatrix} \quad\text{and}\quad |\downarrow_z\rangle = \begin{bmatrix}0\\1\end{bmatrix},$$

and any spin state $|A\rangle$ of a spin-$\frac{1}{2}$ particle can be written as

$$|A\rangle = a_1\,|\uparrow_z\rangle + a_2\,|\downarrow_z\rangle = \begin{bmatrix}a_1\\a_2\end{bmatrix}. \tag{5.6}$$

This means that vector space ideas, introduced as a shorthand in wave mechanics, carry over directly into spin space. The main difference is in the definition of the inner product. For a spin-$\frac{1}{2}$ particle, this is defined as

$$\langle A|B\rangle = \begin{bmatrix}a_1^* & a_2^*\end{bmatrix}\begin{bmatrix}b_1\\b_2\end{bmatrix} = a_1^*b_1 + a_2^*b_2. \tag{5.7}$$

So bra and ket vectors provide a general notation for quantum mechanics, which can be interpreted using either wave functions or spinors, according to context (Table 5.1). But, no matter what kind of system is being considered, bra and ket vectors always obey the same rules. For example, the inner product always satisfies

$$\langle A|B\rangle = \langle B|A\rangle^*. \tag{5.8}$$

**Table 5.1** General notation, wave mechanics notation for a particle in one dimension, and spinor notation for the spin state of a spin-$\frac{1}{2}$ particle.

| Property | General | Wave mechanics | Spin |
|---|---|---|---|
| Ket vector | $\lvert A\rangle$ | $\Psi_A(x,t)$ | $\begin{bmatrix} a_1 \\ a_2 \end{bmatrix}$ |
| Bra vector | $\langle A\rvert$ | $\Psi_A^*(x,t)$ | $\begin{bmatrix} a_1^* & a_2^* \end{bmatrix}$ |
| Inner product | $\langle A\vert B\rangle$ | $\int \Psi_A^*(x,t)\,\Psi_B(x,t)\,\mathrm{d}x$ | $\begin{bmatrix} a_1^* & a_2^* \end{bmatrix}\begin{bmatrix} b_1 \\ b_2 \end{bmatrix}$ |
| Normalization | $\langle A\vert A\rangle = 1$ | $\int \Psi_A^*(x,t)\,\Psi_A(x,t)\,\mathrm{d}x = 1$ | $\begin{bmatrix} a_1^* & a_2^* \end{bmatrix}\begin{bmatrix} a_1 \\ a_2 \end{bmatrix} = 1$ |

In general, we need to describe both the spatial variation of a wave function *and* the spin state of a system. In Chapter 4, this was done by writing down a *total wave function* — the product of a spatial wave function and a ket vector describing the spin. However, we could also use a single ket vector such as $\lvert\Psi, S, M_S\rangle$, where $\Psi$ labels the spatial behaviour, and $S$ and $M_S$ label the spin. So Dirac notation is flexible enough to describe any state in quantum mechanics.

### Identical particles

Chapter 4 of this book introduced a remarkable feature of the quantum world: identical particles. All particles of a given kind (e.g. all electrons) are identical, and the effect on the description of states is profound.

It turns out that all particles in Nature fall into two categories: *fermions* and *bosons*. Fermions have a spin quantum number $s$ that is equal to an odd number times $1/2$, while bosons have $s$ equal to an integer (which may be zero). Any composite particle built up of an odd number of fermions is a fermion, while any particle built up of an even number of fermions is a boson.

If a system is made up of identical fermions, its total wave function (including both space and spin parts) is *antisymmetric* with respect to interchange of particle labels. A consequence of this antisymmetry is the *Pauli exclusion principle*, which prevents more than one fermion from occupying the same quantum state and has a decisive effect on the properties and stability of matter.

If a system is made up of identical bosons, its total wave function is *symmetric* with respect to interchange of particle labels. At low temperatures, this can lead to the phenomenon of *Bose–Einstein condensation*, which results in many atoms occupying the same quantum state; all of these atoms can be described by a single macroscopic wave function, dependent on a single position vector.

**Exercise 5.2** Is a silver atom a fermion or a boson? The two stable isotopes are $^{107}$Ag and $^{109}$Ag, and silver has atomic number $Z = 47$. ■

## 5.2 Describing observables

The second principle in Box 1 tells us that each observable quantity $A$ in quantum mechanics is represented by a *linear operator* $\widehat{\mathrm{A}}$. The word 'observable' is used for any physical quantity that can be measured. Its use highlights the fact that the formalism of quantum mechanics includes some things that cannot be measured — the phase factor of a wave function, for example.

The third principle in Box 1 highlights the key role played by operators in quantum mechanics: they determine the possible values of measurements. You may wonder why we included the phrase 'As a general rule' at the beginning of Principle 3. The reason is that there are some technical issues associated with the continuum which are best avoided in a first reading of the subject. We will finally confront these issues in Section 5.5 of this chapter, but can safely ignore them for the moment.

In wave mechanics, operators act on functions to produce new functions. These operators typically involve the act of differentiating the function, or multiplying it by a constant or by some other function. For example, the operator that represents the $x$-component of momentum is

$$\widehat{\mathrm{p}}_x = -\mathrm{i}\hbar\,\frac{\partial}{\partial x}. \tag{5.9}$$

By contrast, the operators that describe spin observables are square matrices. For a spin-$\frac{1}{2}$ particle, the operator representing the spin component in the direction of the unit vector $\mathbf{n}$, defined by the spherical coordinates $\theta$ and $\phi$, is

$$\widehat{\mathrm{S}}_{\mathbf{n}} = \frac{\hbar}{2}\begin{bmatrix} \cos\theta & \mathrm{e}^{-\mathrm{i}\phi}\sin\theta \\ \mathrm{e}^{\mathrm{i}\phi}\sin\theta & -\cos\theta \end{bmatrix}, \tag{5.10}$$

and this acts on column spinors through ordinary matrix multiplication to produce new column spinors.

Although $\widehat{\mathrm{S}}_{\mathbf{n}}$ looks very different to $\widehat{\mathrm{p}}_x$, both operators are linear, with the general feature that

$$\widehat{\mathrm{A}}\Big(\sum_i a_i\,|\Psi_i\rangle\Big) = \sum_i a_i\,(\widehat{\mathrm{A}}\,|\Psi_i\rangle) \tag{5.11}$$

for any constant coefficients $a_i$.

We can now add a further requirement for the operators that represent observables in quantum mechanics: they must be *Hermitian* as well as linear. This fits in with Principle 3, which tells us that the possible values of an observable are given by the eigenvalues of the corresponding operator. Measured values are always real (rather than complex), and this is guaranteed by the fact that Hermitian operators have real eigenvalues.

In Dirac notation, an operator $\widehat{\mathrm{A}}$ is said to be Hermitian if

$$\langle\psi_1|\widehat{\mathrm{A}}\psi_2\rangle = \langle\widehat{\mathrm{A}}\psi_1|\psi_2\rangle \tag{5.12}$$

for any normalizable functions $\psi_1$ and $\psi_2$. In the context of one-dimensional wave mechanics, this means that

$$\int_{-\infty}^{\infty} \psi_1^*(x)\left[\widehat{\mathrm{A}}\,\psi_2(x)\right]\mathrm{d}x = \int_{-\infty}^{\infty}\left[\widehat{\mathrm{A}}\,\psi_1(x)\right]^*\psi_2(x)\,\mathrm{d}x, \tag{5.13}$$

for all normalizable functions $\psi_1(x)$ and $\psi_2(x)$. In Chapter 1, we proved that the momentum operator is indeed Hermitian, using this definition.

In the context of spin, we note that the *Mathematical toolkit* shows that any $2 \times 2$ matrix that behaves as a Hermitian operator must be of the form

$$A = \begin{bmatrix} A_{11} & A_{12} \\ A_{21} & A_{22} \end{bmatrix} \quad \text{with } A_{ij} = A^*_{ji}. \tag{5.14}$$

Such matrices are said to be Hermitian. The general spin matrix $\widehat{\mathrm{S}}_{\mathbf{n}}$ in Equation 5.10 is Hermitian because its diagonal elements are real and its off-diagonal elements are complex conjugates of one another.

But how do we find the quantum-mechanical operator $\widehat{\mathrm{A}}$ that describes a given observable $A$? It is generally a good plan to write down a classical expression for the observable $A$ in terms of Cartesian position and momentum components, and then make replacements such as

$$p_x \Longrightarrow \widehat{\mathrm{p}}_x = -i\hbar \frac{\partial}{\partial x} \qquad \text{and} \qquad x \Longrightarrow \widehat{\mathrm{x}} = x.$$

For example, the $x$-component of orbital angular momentum is represented by the operator

$$\widehat{\mathrm{L}}_x = \widehat{\mathrm{y}}\,\widehat{\mathrm{p}}_z - \widehat{\mathrm{z}}\,\widehat{\mathrm{p}}_y = -i\hbar \left( y\frac{\partial}{\partial z} - z\frac{\partial}{\partial y} \right).$$

We cannot use this procedure for the spin components of spin-$\frac{1}{2}$ particles because there is no classical starting point in this case: spin is an entirely quantum property. Instead, we impose constraints based on the experimentally observed values ($\pm\hbar/2$), the need for spin matrices to be Hermitian, and the assumption that they obey commutation relations similar to those of the orbital angular momentum operators $\widehat{\mathrm{L}}_x$, $\widehat{\mathrm{L}}_y$ and $\widehat{\mathrm{L}}_z$. With appropriate conventions, these assumptions lead to the matrix in Equation 5.10, but of course the ultimate justification of this matrix is that it leads to results that agree with experiment.

**Exercise 5.3** Given that $\widehat{\mathrm{y}}$, $\widehat{\mathrm{z}}$, $\widehat{\mathrm{p}}_y$ and $\widehat{\mathrm{p}}_z$ are all Hermitian operators, show that $\widehat{\mathrm{L}}_x = \widehat{\mathrm{y}}\,\widehat{\mathrm{p}}_z - \widehat{\mathrm{z}}\,\widehat{\mathrm{p}}_y$ is also Hermitian. ■

## 5.3 Predicting the probabilities of outcomes

Box 1 contains a very significant omission which goes right to the heart of quantum mechanics. It is generally impossible to predict the result of an individual measurement, but if we know the state of a system, quantum mechanics allows us to predict the *probabilities* of different outcomes. The principles covering this aspect of quantum mechanics were first discussed in Chapter 4 of Book 1 and were illustrated again in the context of spin. These developments are important enough to be included in our revised list of the principles of quantum mechanics.

To begin with, let us restrict attention to any observable $A$ with a discrete set of possible values. The corresponding operator $\widehat{\mathrm{A}}$ has eigenvalue equation

$$\widehat{\mathrm{A}}|a_i\rangle = a_i\,|a_i\rangle \quad \text{for } i = 1, 2, 3, \ldots,$$

where $|a_i\rangle$ is the normalized eigenvector corresponding to the eigenvalue $a_i$. We shall assume that each eigenvalue $a_i$ has only one eigenvector $|a_i\rangle$ (ignoring, as usual, the physically insignificant choice of overall phase factor).

Any measurement of $A$ gives one or other of the eigenvalues $a_1, a_2, \ldots$, but what can we say about the *probabilities* of these outcomes in any given state? Expressing the results of Book 1 Chapter 4 in terms of Dirac notation, we have:

**The overlap rule**

For a system in a state described by the state vector $|\Psi\rangle$, the probability that a measurement of $A$ will yield the result $a_i$ is

$$p_i = \left|\langle a_i|\Psi\rangle\right|^2, \tag{5.15}$$

where $|a_i\rangle$ is the eigenvector corresponding to the eigenvalue $a_i$.

In wave mechanics, the inner product in Equation 5.15 is found by integration. For example, in a harmonic oscillator, in a state described by the wave function $\Psi(x,t)$, the probability of getting the energy eigenvalue $E_i$ is

$$p_i = \left|\int_{-\infty}^{\infty} \psi_i^*(x)\,\Psi(x,t)\,\mathrm{d}x\right|^2,$$

where $\psi_i(x)$ is the energy eigenfunction corresponding to the eigenvalue $E_i$. For spin, by contrast, the inner product is found by matrix multiplication.

**Exercise 5.4** A spin-$\frac{1}{2}$ particle is in a spin state described by the spinor $|\uparrow_x\rangle$. If its spin is measured in the $y$-direction, what is the probability of measuring the value $+\hbar/2$, for which the eigenvector is $|\uparrow_y\rangle$? You may use the results

$$|\uparrow_x\rangle = \frac{1}{\sqrt{2}}\begin{bmatrix}1\\1\end{bmatrix} \quad \text{and} \quad |\uparrow_y\rangle = \frac{1}{\sqrt{2}}\begin{bmatrix}1\\\mathrm{i}\end{bmatrix}.$$

■

So far, we have assumed that each allowed value corresponds to a *unique* eigenvector. This is not always the case; for example, a particle in a three-dimensional box has degenerate energy levels, with several different eigenfunctions corresponding to the same energy.

Let us suppose that there are $n$ orthonormal eigenvectors corresponding to a single energy eigenvalue $E_i$. We denote these eigenvectors by $|\psi_{i,1}\rangle$, $|\psi_{i,2}\rangle$, $\ldots$, $|\psi_{i,n}\rangle$. Then the probability of getting the energy eigenvalue $E_i$ in a state described by the state vector $|\Psi\rangle$ is given by

$$p_i = \left|\langle\psi_{i,1}|\Psi\rangle\right|^2 + \left|\langle\psi_{i,2}|\Psi\rangle\right|^2 + \cdots + \left|\langle\psi_{i,n}|\Psi\rangle\right|^2.$$

Notice that we add the probabilities associated with different eigenvectors. You might wonder whether this is correct. At the very beginning of the course, we mentioned the *interference rule* which involves adding probability amplitudes *before* taking the square of the modulus. This rule applies when there is more than one way of going from a given initial state to a given final state, but it does not apply here because the eigenvectors $|\psi_{i,1}\rangle$, $|\psi_{i,2}\rangle$, $\ldots$, $|\psi_{i,n}\rangle$ all refer to *different* final states — not distinguished by their energy, but nevertheless different from one another in some other way. For example, electrons in the ground state of a three-dimensional box can be spin-up or spin-down.

So far, we have considered observables with discrete possible values. In wave mechanics, however, observables such as position and momentum have a continuum of allowed values, and this leads to difficulties with using Equation 5.15 directly. For example, it is futile to ask what the chances are of finding a particle at a single point in space; in practice, we measure positions only to within some finite resolution, so it is much more sensible to ask for the probability of finding a particle in a small range centred on a given point. Fortunately, Born's interpretation of the wave function tells us this probability. In one dimension, the probability that the particle at time $t$ is in a small interval $\delta x$, centred on $x$, is

$$\text{probability that position is in small range} = |\Psi(x,t)|^2\,\delta x. \tag{5.16}$$

Similarly, the probability that the momentum of the particle at time $t$ is in a small interval $\hbar\,\delta k$, centred on $\hbar k$, is

$$\text{probability that momentum is in small range} = |A(k,t)|^2\,\delta k, \tag{5.17}$$

where $A(k,t)$ is the Fourier transform of the wave function:

$$A(k,t) = \frac{1}{\sqrt{2\pi}}\int_{-\infty}^{\infty} \mathrm{e}^{-\mathrm{i}kx}\,\Psi(x,t)\,\mathrm{d}x. \tag{5.18}$$

These equations can be thought of as extensions of Equation 5.15, adapted for the continuum, as outlined in Sections 4.2 and 6.4 of Book 1.

#### Predictions made with certainty

If a system is in a state described by $|a_i\rangle$, an eigenvector of $\widehat{\mathrm{A}}$ with eigenvalue $a_i$, the overlap rule tells us that the probability of measuring the value $a_i$ is $\left|\langle a_i|a_i\rangle\right|^2 = 1$. The probability of measuring any other eigenvalue, $a_j \neq a_i$, in this state is therefore equal to zero. This agrees with the fact that any two eigenvectors of a Hermitian operator, corresponding to *different* eigenvalues, are orthogonal, so that $\left|\langle a_j|a_i\rangle\right|^2 = 0$ for $a_j \neq a_i$.

If two operators $\widehat{\mathrm{A}}$ and $\widehat{\mathrm{B}}$ commute with one another, so that

$$[\widehat{\mathrm{A}},\widehat{\mathrm{B}}] = \widehat{\mathrm{A}}\widehat{\mathrm{B}} - \widehat{\mathrm{B}}\widehat{\mathrm{A}} = 0,$$

it is possible to find a set of ket vectors that are simultaneous eigenvectors of both operators. These eigenvectors describe states in which both $A$ and $B$ have definite values, and the observables $A$ and $B$ are then said to be *compatible* with one another.

An example is given by the operators $\widehat{\mathrm{L}}^2$ and $\widehat{\mathrm{L}}_z$, which commute with one another and have a series of simultaneous eigenvectors labelled by the quantum numbers $l = 0, 1, 2, \ldots$ and $m = -l, \ldots, 0, \ldots, l$. We have

$$\widehat{\mathrm{L}}^2\,|l,m\rangle = l(l+1)\hbar^2\,|l,m\rangle,$$
$$\widehat{\mathrm{L}}_z\,|l,m\rangle = m\hbar\,|l,m\rangle.$$

By contrast, $\widehat{\mathrm{L}}_x$ and $\widehat{\mathrm{L}}_z$ do not commute. The corresponding observables $L_x$ and $L_z$ are not compatible, and it is impossible to find states with definite (non-zero) values of both these quantities.

### Expectation values

Once we know the probabilities of all the possible values, we can evaluate expectation values and uncertainties, and these can be compared with experimentally-measured average values and standard deviations.

For a discrete set of possible outcomes, the expectation value of an observable $A$ is defined by

$$\langle A \rangle = \sum_i p_i a_i, \tag{5.19}$$

where the value $a_i$ has probability $p_i$, and the sum runs over all the possible outcomes.

Fortunately, there is an alternative way of calculating expectation values, which is usually simpler to use and applies to all observables, whether their values are discrete or not. In the state represented by $|\Psi\rangle$, the expectation value of the observable $A$ is given by

$$\langle A \rangle = \langle \Psi | \widehat{\mathrm{A}} | \Psi \rangle \equiv \langle \Psi | \widehat{\mathrm{A}} \Psi \rangle. \tag{5.20}$$

For obvious reasons, this is called the **sandwich rule** for expectation values. As usual, the inner product must be interpreted according to context, using wave functions or spinors as appropriate; Table 5.2 shows some examples.

**Table 5.2** Expectation values of position $x$ and momentum $p_x$ in one-dimensional wave mechanics, and the expectation value of $S_z$ for a spin-$\frac{1}{2}$ particle in the spin state $|\uparrow_y\rangle$.

| Observable | General | Specific |
|---|---|---|
| $x$ | $\langle \Psi \vert \widehat{\mathrm{x}} \vert \Psi \rangle$ | $\displaystyle\int_{-\infty}^{\infty} \Psi^*(x,t)\, x\, \Psi(x,t)\, \mathrm{d}x$ |
| $p_x$ | $\langle \Psi \vert \widehat{\mathrm{p}}_x \vert \Psi \rangle$ | $\displaystyle\int_{-\infty}^{\infty} \Psi^*(x,t) \left( -\mathrm{i}\hbar \frac{\partial}{\partial x} \Psi(x,t) \right) \mathrm{d}x$ |
| $S_z$ | $\langle \uparrow_y \vert \widehat{\mathrm{S}}_z \vert \uparrow_y \rangle$ | $\displaystyle\frac{1}{\sqrt{2}} \begin{bmatrix} 1 & -\mathrm{i} \end{bmatrix} \frac{\hbar}{2} \begin{bmatrix} 1 & 0 \\ 0 & -1 \end{bmatrix} \frac{1}{\sqrt{2}} \begin{bmatrix} 1 \\ \mathrm{i} \end{bmatrix}$ |

**Exercise 5.5** Evaluate the matrix product in the last row of Table 5.2. What does your answer tell you about the individual probabilities of getting $S_z = +\hbar/2$ and $S_z = -\hbar/2$ in the state represented by $|\uparrow_y\rangle$? ■

## 5.4 Time-dependence of states and measurement

The last two principles in Box 1 describe the time-dependence of quantum states, contrasting two very different types of behaviour.

### Schrödinger's equation

First, let us review the time-dependence predicted by Schrödinger's equation. Expressed in bra-ket notation, this states that

$$\mathrm{i}\hbar\,\frac{\mathrm{d}}{\mathrm{d}t}|\Psi\rangle = \widehat{\mathrm{H}}\,|\Psi\rangle, \tag{5.21}$$

where $\widehat{\mathrm{H}}$ is the Hamiltonian operator for the system. An ordinary (rather than partial) time derivative is used on the left-hand side because the ket vector $|\Psi\rangle$ contains no explicit variables.

In wave mechanics, Schrödinger's equation is a partial differential equation, involving a first-order derivative with respect to time, and second-order derivative(s) with respect to position coordinate(s). You saw many examples of this in Book 1.

In the context of a spin-$\frac{1}{2}$ particle in a magnetic field $\mathbf{B} = B\mathbf{n}$, the Hamiltonian operator is a $2 \times 2$ matrix

$$\widehat{\mathrm{H}} = -\gamma_{\mathrm{s}} B \widehat{\mathrm{S}}_{\mathbf{n}} = -\frac{\gamma_{\mathrm{s}} B\hbar}{2}\begin{bmatrix}\cos\theta & \mathrm{e}^{-\mathrm{i}\phi}\sin\theta \\ \mathrm{e}^{\mathrm{i}\phi}\sin\theta & -\cos\theta\end{bmatrix}, \tag{5.22}$$

where $\gamma_{\mathrm{s}}$ is the spin gyromagnetic ratio for the particle. In this case, Schrödinger's equation is a matrix equation giving the rates of change of the components of the spinor that describes the spin state of the particle.

For any isolated system, Schrödinger's equation determines the time-development of the state vector. Given the state vector at time $t = 0$, we can use Schrödinger's equation to predict the state vector at a later time.

A procedure for this was outlined in Book 1 in the context of wave packets. In a harmonic oscillator, for example, we write the initial wave function as a linear combination of energy eigenfunctions:

$$\Psi(x,0) = \sum_{i=0}^{\infty} c_i\,\psi_i(x). \tag{5.23}$$

The coefficients $c_i$ are determined using the fact that the energy eigenfunctions are orthonormal. Finally, we insert appropriate time-dependent factors into each term of the sum, to obtain

$$\Psi(x,t) = \sum_{i=0}^{\infty} c_i\,\psi_i(x)\,\mathrm{e}^{-\mathrm{i}E_i t/\hbar}, \tag{5.24}$$

where $E_i$ is the energy eigenvalue corresponding to the eigenfunction $\psi_i(x)$. Exactly the same procedure applies to spin, except that the eigenfunctions are now eigenvectors, and there are only two of these for any given direction of the magnetic field.

Schrödinger's equation is *linear*. This means that if $|\Psi_1\rangle$, $|\Psi_2\rangle$, ... are solutions of Schrödinger's equation, then so is the linear combination

$$|\Psi\rangle = c_1\,|\Psi_1\rangle + c_2\,|\Psi_2\rangle + \cdots,$$

where the $c_i$ are constants. This property ensures that the right-hand side of Equation 5.24 satisfies Schrödinger's equation, because it is a linear combination of stationary-state wave functions which are themselves solutions of the equation.

Schrödinger's equation also has the property of preserving the normalization of the state vector (whether this is a wave function or a spinor). If the state vector is normalized at $t = 0$, it will remain normalized as the system evolves in time. One way of establishing this result was given in Exercise 1.12 of Chapter 1, where the Hermitian character of the Hamiltonian operator was used to show that

$$\frac{\mathrm{d}}{\mathrm{d}t}\langle\Psi|\Psi\rangle = 0.$$

This property is important because principles such as the overlap rule or Born's rule, which assign probabilities to possible experimental outcomes, rely on the state vector being normalized at the instant of measurement.

### Measurement and collapse of the state vector

So long as Schrödinger's equation applies, the time-development of the wave function is completely deterministic: given $\Psi(x, 0)$, we can predict what $\Psi(x, t)$ will be. However, we know that quantum physics as a whole is indeterministic: in most cases, it is impossible to predict the result of a measurement carried on a system. We can predict the *probabilities* of various possible outcomes, but we cannot say which outcome will occur on any given occasion. How can we reconcile the determinism of Schrödinger's equation with the indeterminism of quantum measurements? The answer is that we cannot; the act of measurement causes the wave function to change uncontrollably and unpredictably, in a way that is not governed by Schrödinger's equation.

The word 'measurement' never appears in a list of principles of classical physics; it appears in laboratory procedures but not in the fundamentals of the theory. In quantum mechanics, however, the concept of measurement plays a key role in the theory itself. In classical physics, measurement is thought of as revealing some pre-existing property of a system, but quantum objects do not have properties until they have been measured, and, furthermore, the values returned by a quantum measurement are those of the system *after* the measurement, not before.

**Figure 5.1** John von Neumann, 1903–1957.

You can think of a **quantum measurement** as an interaction or communication of information between a quantum system and a measuring device *which is treated classically*. If we use a meter with a pointer, for example, we ignore the fact that the uncertainty principle implies some uncertainty in the position of the pointer. The measuring device is supposed to be sufficiently large for its own quantum fluctuations to be neglected. We will treat the measuring device as a sort of black box, and not ask too closely what happens inside it. We can say, however, that a measurement occurs when a quantum system causes some sort of *irreversible change* in the measuring device, and possibly in its surroundings. For example, a Geiger counter may click, causing a sound wave to travel outwards in the surrounding air, which heats up very slightly. This process cannot be undone; it is irreversible.

As a result of the measurement, two things happen, First, we get an experimental result — a reading on a meter or a click in a counter. Secondly, the state of the system changes abruptly and drastically. This process is called the collapse of the wave function or, more generally, the **collapse of the state vector**. It seems to have been first introduced in lectures given by Heisenberg in 1929, but is also associated with Dirac and, especially, von Neumann (Figure 5.1), who gave the first rigorous mathematical treatment of quantum mechanics.

Consider an observable $A$, represented by the operator $\widehat{\mathrm{A}}$ with a discrete set of eigenvalues $a_i$ and eigenvectors $|a_i\rangle$. Suppose that we measure $A$ in a state represented by the linear combination

$$|\Psi\rangle = c_1\,|a_1\rangle + c_2\,|a_2\rangle + \cdots . \tag{5.25}$$

We cannot predict the value of $A$ that will be obtained in such a measurement, but we can say that the probability of getting the value $a_i$ is $|c_i|^2$. David Bohm has described this situation by saying that a quantum state has within it a set of *potentialities* (things which might come into being), and that the act of measurement actualizes one of these.

But what does the measurement do to the state of the system? The general rule is as follows:

The state of the system immediately after the measurement is represented by the normalized eigenvector $|a_i\rangle$ that corresponds to the eigenvalue $a_i$ that was obtained in the measurement.

If we happened to get the value $a_2$, for example, then the state of the system immediately after the measurement would be $|a_2\rangle$. The transition

$$|\Psi\rangle = c_1\,|a_1\rangle + c_2\,|a_2\rangle + \cdots \quad \Longrightarrow \quad |a_2\rangle \tag{5.26}$$

is what constitutes the collapse of the state vector.

The collapse can be pictured as a combination of the two processes shown in Figure 5.2: a *projection* of the state vector $|\Psi\rangle$ onto the direction of one of the eigenvectors $|a_i\rangle$ of $\widehat{\mathrm{A}}$, and a *re-scaling* to produce the normalized eigenvector $|a_i\rangle$. Knowledge of the initial state $|\Psi\rangle$ has been lost once the measurement has been made and the collapse onto $|a_i\rangle$ has taken place. The collapse is not described by Schrödinger's equation. Not unnaturally, some physicists are concerned about this and are actively seeking a clearer understanding of the measurement process.

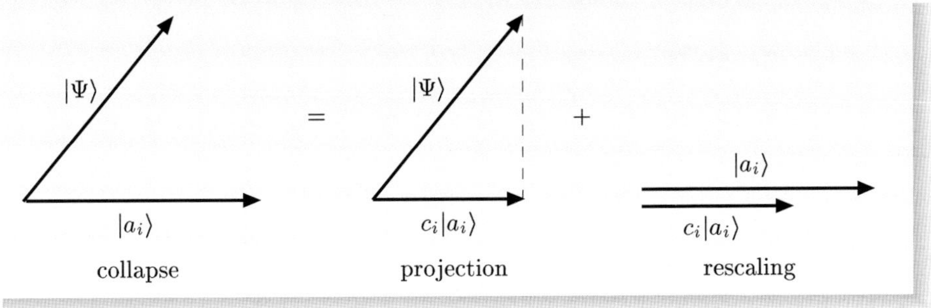


**Figure 5.2** The collapse of a state vector can be pictured as the combination of a projection and a re-scaling.

So far, we have considered an observable with a discrete set of possible values. As usual, modifications are needed for observables, such as position, with a continuous range of possible values. Modern instruments can measure quite accurately the position of a particle emerging from a nuclear experiment, but the recorded position $x, y, z$, say, is *always* within some finite region $\delta x\,\delta y\,\delta z$.

Figure 5.3 illustrates how the wave function of a particle in one dimension collapses when a position measurement is made. Figure 5.3a shows the real part of the wave function prior to the measurement. Let us suppose that the position of the particle is measured to be between $x_0 - \Delta x$ and $x_0 + \Delta x$; then the wave function immediately after the measurement is of the form shown in Figure 5.3b. This is equal to zero outside the region where the particle has been located, and is similar in shape to the original wave function inside that region, but is normalized to unity.

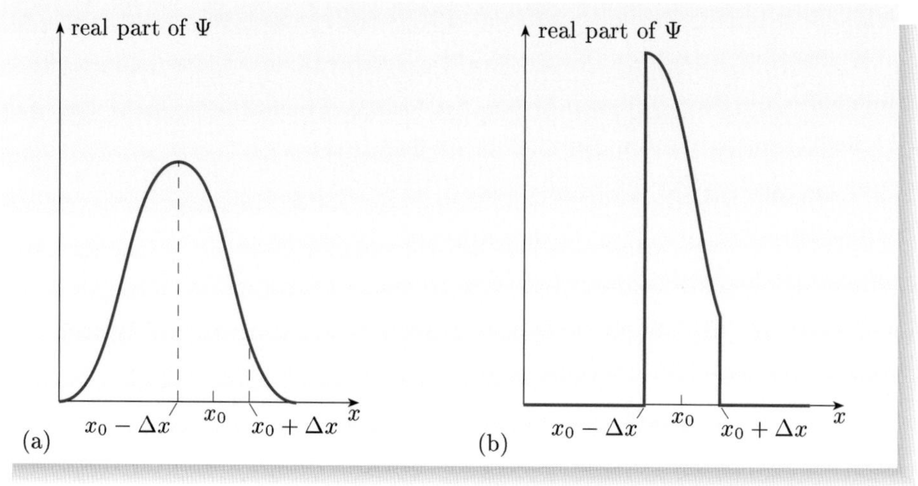


**Figure 5.3** The position of a particle is determined to be between $x_0 - \Delta x$ and $x_0 + \Delta x$. The real part of the wave function is shown (a) before the measurement and (b) after the measurement.

### Successive measurements

If we measure $A$ once and get the value $a_2$, and then measure $A$ again *immediately afterwards* on the same system, we are bound to get the same value again. This is because the first measurement has caused the state of the system to collapse to $|a_2\rangle$, and we are certain to get the value $a_2$ in this state. Of course, this makes good sense, since the second measurement simply corroborates the first. But what happens if we wait a while between the two measurements? There are two cases to consider.

1. If $A$ is a conserved quantity, the operator $\widehat{\mathrm{A}}$ will commute with the Hamiltonian $\widehat{\mathrm{H}}$, and these two operators will share a common set of eigenfunctions. Now, if the eigenvector $|a_2\rangle$ is also an eigenvector of $\widehat{\mathrm{H}}$, it will evolve as a stationary state and will therefore remain unchanged apart from an unimportant phase factor $\mathrm{e}^{-\mathrm{i}E_2t/\hbar}$. It will therefore *remain* an eigenvector of $\widehat{\mathrm{A}}$ with eigenvalue $a_2$, and we can afford to wait a considerable time before making the second measurement; provided that the system is isolated, the value $a_2$ will be certain, even after a considerable delay.

2. More generally, however, if $|a_2\rangle$ is not an eigenvector of $\widehat{\mathrm{H}}$, it will evolve as a linear combination of stationary states, and this implies significant changes. After a short time, the state of the system will no longer be described by $|a_2\rangle$, but will be some linear combination of eigenvectors of $\widehat{\mathrm{A}}$. The second measurement of $A$ may then give a value different from $a_2$, and it may even give a value that would not have been possible in the original state, before any measurements were made.

One consequence of the collapse of the state vector is that we end up with states that are quite different from those we started out with. This means that we cannot readily check the predictions of quantum mechanics by taking successive measurements on a *single* system. To confirm that a quantum-mechanical prediction for an expectation value is accurate, we really need to prepare a large number of systems in identical states, and take measurements on each of them. The average value of all these measurements should approach the predicted expectation value as the number of measurements becomes very large.

**Exercise 5.6** A particle is in the ground state of a simple harmonic well with energy $E_0$. Its position is measured to be $x_0$ to within a small resolution. The energy of the particle is then measured, and the particle is found to have an energy $E_{10}$, corresponding to the tenth excited state of the oscillator. The energy is then measured again after some delay, and the particle is still found to have energy $E_{10}$. Explain these results. ■

### Superposition matters

When a photon is incident on a half-silvered mirror (Figure 5.4), we might suppose that interaction with the mirror would cause the state of the photon to collapse, either into a state that passes through the mirror, or into a state that is reflected by it. This, however, can be shown to be false.

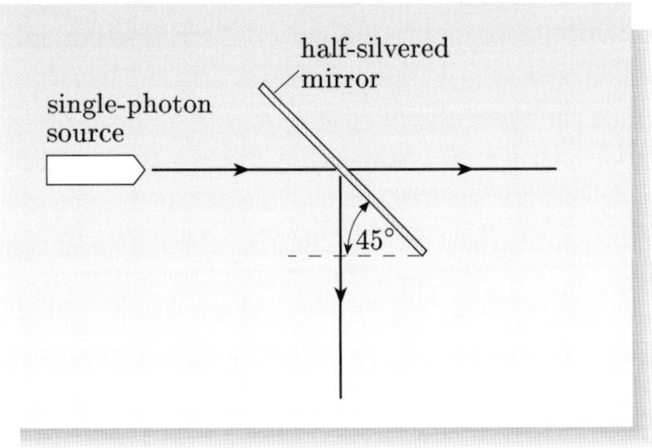


**Figure 5.4** A photon incident on a half-silvered mirror.

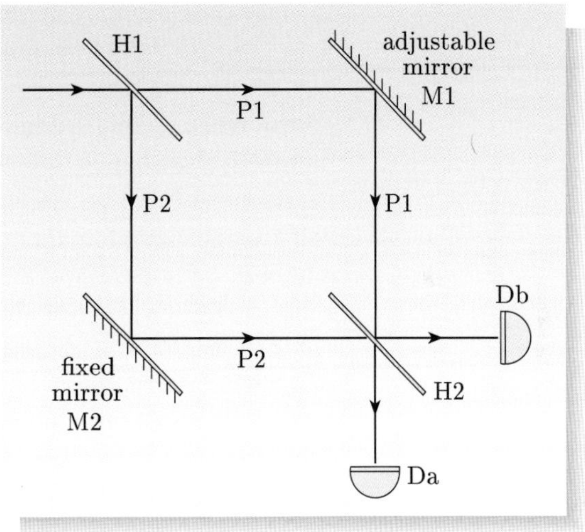


**Figure 5.5** A Mach–Zehnder interferometer.

Figure 5.5 shows a more complicated device called a *Mach–Zehnder interferometer*; this consists of two half-silvered mirrors, H1 and H2, two ordinary mirrors, M1 and M2, and two detectors, Da and Db. You met this device in Chapter 1 of Book 1.

The important point to note is that a suitable choice of path lengths can ensure that a photon arrives at detector Da with certainty. This cannot be understood if the photon travels along just one of the paths P1 or P2, because the half-silvered mirror H2 would then give only a 50% chance of arrival at detector Da. The photon must therefore emerge from the half-silvered mirror H1 in a superposition of states, and these states interfere with one another in such a way as to completely suppress any chance of detection by Db. This example shows that we must be very careful when claiming that a measurement, and the accompanying state vector collapse, has taken place. In this case, the collapse occurs when one of the detectors counts a photon, and not before.

A second example of superposition is provided by a beam of spin-$\frac{1}{2}$ particles all in the same spin state

$$|A\rangle = \frac{1}{\sqrt{2}}(|\uparrow_z\rangle + |\downarrow_z\rangle). \tag{5.27}$$

If these particles enter a Stern–Gerlach analyzer oriented in the $z$-direction, half of them will be measured to be spin-up and the other half spin-down. You might suppose that this incident beam would be indistinguishable from a beam containing a random mixture of spin-$\frac{1}{2}$ particles, half of which are prepared to be in the state $|\uparrow_z\rangle$, and the other half in the state $|\downarrow_z\rangle$. If so, think again!

The state $|A\rangle$ in Equation 5.27 is actually equal to $|\uparrow_x\rangle$, a state that is certain to give $+\hbar/2$ when spin is measured in the $x$-direction. So, if a beam of particles in this state enters a Stern–Gerlach analyzer oriented in the $x$-direction, we will find that *every* particle is measured to be spin-up. The same cannot be said for a beam containing a random mixture of particles in $|\uparrow_z\rangle$ and $|\downarrow_z\rangle$ states; in this case, half the particles will be measured to be spin-up in the $x$-direction, and the other half will be measured to be spin-down.

We can now briefly discuss the **Schrödinger cat paradox**, concocted by Schrödinger in 1935. Schrödinger asked us to imagine a cat that is enclosed in a box, along with a tamper-proof 'diabolical device' which will release a lethal poison when a Geiger counter clicks. Also inside the box is a tiny amount of a radioactive substance, whose decay would trigger the Geiger counter, leading to the demise of the cat. Suppose that the amount of radioactive substance, and its half-life, are such that there is a fair chance that the poison would be released in a matter of an hour or so. Now, suppose that we close the lid of the box and wait. How should we describe the state of the cat after one hour? Schrödinger pointed out that, prior to any measurement, quantum mechanics describes the cat as being in a linear superposition of two states — one in which it is dead and another in which it is alive. Only on opening the box and 'making a measurement' do we cause the cat's state vector to collapse onto either a living cat or a dead cat!

Just as there is a difference between two types of Stern–Gerlach beam discussed above, so there is a difference between the quantum-mechanical description (a linear superposition of an alive and a dead cat) and the more common-sense description in which the cat is either dead or alive, but we do not know which until we open the box. Naturally enough, Schrödinger found the quantum description unpalatable.

Attempts to resolve this 'paradox' have been very fruitful, leading to a deeper understanding of the role of the environment in disturbing superposition states in macroscopic systems, and in suggesting experiments that explore the possibility of a boundary between the classical world and the quantum world. But, so far, there is no universally-agreed resolution of the paradox.

## 5.5 Dealing with the continuum

In the process of stating the basic principles of quantum mechanics, we have run into a number of problems concerning observables with a continuum of possible values. These problems can be resolved at the expense of considerable mathematical complexity, beyond the level of this course. We can, however, sketch the main ideas.

### The possible values of an observable

Box 1 stated that in a 'as a general rule', the only possible outcomes of a measurement of an observable are the eigenvalues of the associated operator. The 'general rule' covers all observables with discrete values (e.g. $L^2$ and $L_z$), but it does not cover observables with a continuous set of possible values. In particular, there are difficulties with both position and momentum.

The difficulty with position is the most severe, since the position operator $\widehat{\mathrm{x}}$ has no legitimate eigenvalues or eigenfunctions. This is because it is impossible to find a fixed constant $\lambda$ and a function $f(x)$ such that

$$\widehat{\mathrm{x}}\, f(x) = x f(x) = \lambda f(x) \quad \text{for all } x.$$

The difficulty with momentum is slightly more technical. In this case, the eigenvalue equation

$$\widehat{\mathrm{p}}_x f(x) = -\mathrm{i}\hbar \frac{\partial}{\partial x} f(x) = \lambda f(x)$$

can be solved: the eigenfunctions can be expressed as $f(x) = \mathrm{e}^{\mathrm{i}kx}$, and the corresponding eigenvalues are $\hbar k$. However, these eigenfunctions do not describe realistic states because they cannot be normalized. Moreover, a sharp value, $\hbar k$, of the momentum, implies an infinite uncertainty in position, via the uncertainty principle.

You might wonder whether this really matters. The answer is that it is not very important in non-rigorous treatments, but that rigorous treatments of quantum mechanics confine themselves to functions that can be normalized. One illustration of the need for this is the proof given in Chapter 1 that the momentum operator is Hermitian; this proof hinged on the use of normalizable functions. So if we really want to be rigorous, the momentum eigenfunctions are unsatisfactory too.

In the absence of suitable eigenfunctions, how can we find the allowed values of a given observable? For the sake of completeness we will briefly sketch one way of doing this, although the details will not be assessed. A clue is provided by rewriting the eigenvalue equation $\widehat{\mathrm{A}}\,|f\rangle = \lambda\,|f\rangle$ in the form

$$(\widehat{\mathrm{A}} - \lambda)\,|f\rangle = |0\rangle, \tag{5.28}$$

where $|0\rangle$ is the zero vector — a vector whose norm, $\sqrt{\langle 0|0\rangle}$, is equal to zero. The normalized vectors $|f\rangle$ that satisfy this equation are the eigenvectors of $\widehat{\mathrm{A}}$, and the corresponding constants $\lambda$ are the eigenvalues.

Our problem is that position, momentum, and other observables with a continuum of allowed values, do not have appropriate normalized eigenvectors satisfying Equation 5.28. The best we can do in such a case is to write down an equation like

$$(\widehat{\mathrm{A}} - \lambda)\,|f\rangle = |\eta\rangle, \tag{5.29}$$

where $\lambda$ is a constant, $|f\rangle$ is a normalized vector, and $|\eta\rangle$, although small, is not quite equal to the zero vector. However, by adjusting the choice of the normalized

Any eigenvalue is also a *generalized* eigenvalue since zero is infinitesimally close to itself.

vector $|f\rangle$, it may be possible to make the norm of $|\eta\rangle$ as small as we like — getting *infinitesimally close* to zero. If this is possible for a fixed $\lambda$, we shall say that $\lambda$ is a **generalized eigenvalue** of $\widehat{\mathrm{A}}$, and interpret it as being an allowed value of the observable $A$.

#### Probabilities of experimental outcomes

If an observable has discrete values, we can find the probability of any given value by using the overlap rule (Equation 5.15). However, this rule is inappropriate for observables with continuous values. From a practical point of view, experiments never resolve single values from a continuum — there is always some finite resolution. Moreover, the overlap rule is phrased in terms of normalized eigenvectors, which do not exist in the continuum.

However, we can replace the normalized eigenvectors with the vectors $|f\rangle$ that approximate them in the sense of Equation 5.29, with $\sqrt{\langle\eta|\eta\rangle}$ tending to zero. For a position measurement centred on $x_0$, for example, we can choose $|f\rangle$ to be an extremely narrow normalized top-hat function centred on $x_0$. This is precisely what was done in Section 4.2 of Book 1, and you saw that it led to Born's rule for position. A similar procedure leads to Born's rule for momentum, although we shall not go through the details.

#### Collapse of the state vector

We discussed this issue in the previous section, in the context of position measurements. We shall not attempt to generalize beyond this; in practice, the details of any collapse depend on details of the measuring device. We can say in general that a fine-resolution measurement of an observable with a continuum of possible values results in a narrow wave packet centred on the value obtained in the measurement, with a width determined by the resolution of the measurement.

## 5.6 The principles of quantum mechanics

Finally, as a summary, we can now give a more comprehensive list of the principles of quantum mechanics. We make no attempt to give a minimal list of axioms or postulates, from which the whole subject follows. Our aim is merely to collect together key principles which lie at the heart of the subject and inform many different aspects of it. It is convenient to depart slightly from the order of the principles listed at the outset of this chapter.

**States**

1a The state of a system is specified by a normalized state vector $|\Psi\rangle$.

1b The vector $e^{i\alpha}|\Psi\rangle$, where $\alpha$ is a real number, represents the same physical state as $|\Psi\rangle$.

1c If $|\Psi_1\rangle$ and $|\Psi_2\rangle$ represent possible states of a system, and $c_1$ and $c_2$ are complex constants, the normalized linear combination $c_1|\Psi_1\rangle + c_2|\Psi_2\rangle$ also represents a possible state of the system.

### States of identical particles

2a All particles in Nature fall into two categories: fermions and bosons. For fermions, the spin quantum number $s$ is equal to an odd multiple of $1/2$; for bosons, $s$ is equal to an integer (including zero).

2b Composite particles with an odd number of fermions are fermions; composite particles with an even number of fermions are bosons.

2c The total wave function of a collection of identical fermions is antisymmetric under exchange of particle labels; this leads to the Pauli exclusion principle. The total wave function of a collection of identical bosons is symmetric under exchange of particle labels; this leads to Bose–Einstein condensation at low temperatures.

### Observables

3 Observables are represented by linear Hermitian operators.

### Measurements and their results

*The next three principles apply to observables with discrete sets of values:*

4a The possible measured values of an observable $A$ are the eigenvalues of the corresponding quantum-mechanical operator, $\widehat{\mathrm{A}}$.

5a For a system in a state represented by the normalized state vector $|\Psi\rangle$, the probability that a measurement of $A$ will yield the result $a_i$ is $p_i = \left|\langle a_i|\Psi\rangle\right|^2$, where $|a_i\rangle$ is the normalized eigenvector corresponding to the eigenvalue $a_i$. This is the overlap rule.

6a The state of the system immediately after a measurement is represented by the normalized eigenvector $|a_i\rangle$ that corresponds to the eigenvalue $a_i$ that was obtained in the measurement. This collapse of the state vector, leading from the state on which the measurement is made to $|a_i\rangle$, cannot be described by Schrödinger's equation and is accompanied by an irreversible change in the measuring device.

*These principles can be extended to observables with continuous ranges of values:*

4b The possible measured values of any observable $A$ are the set of numbers that are generalized eigenvalues of the corresponding quantum-mechanical operator, $\widehat{\mathrm{A}}$.

5b The overlap rule can be generalized to an observable with a continuous set of values, leading to Born's rules for position and momentum.

6b A fine-resolution measurement of an observable with a continuum of possible values causes the state vector to collapse onto a narrow wave packet centred on the value obtained in the measurement, with a width determined by the resolution of the measurement.

**Time-development in the absence of measurement**

7 Provided that a system does not interact with a measuring device, its time-development is governed by Schrödinger's equation

$$\mathrm{i}\hbar\,\frac{\mathrm{d}}{\mathrm{d}t}|\Psi\rangle = \widehat{\mathrm{H}}\,|\Psi\rangle,$$

where $|\Psi\rangle$ represents the state of the system at time $t$, and $\widehat{\mathrm{H}}$ is the Hamiltonian operator of the system.

**Exercise 5.7** Referring to Principle 1c, if $|\Psi_1\rangle$ and $|\Psi_2\rangle$ are orthonormal, how must $c_1$ and $c_2$ be related?

**Exercise 5.8** (a) Consider a system in which the observable $B$ has a discrete set of possible eigenvalues $b_i$, each corresponding to a single eigenvector $|b_i\rangle$. Use Principle 5a to find the probability that a measurement of $B$ in a state represented by $|b_i\rangle$ will yield the eigenvalue $b_j$.

(b) Write down a formula for the probability that a measurement of an observable $A$ in the state $|b_i\rangle$ will give a particular eigenvalue, $a_j$, of $\widehat{\mathrm{A}}$. Which named rule of Chapter 3 was an exemplar of this situation? ■

## Achievements from Chapter 5

*After studying this chapter, you should be able to:*

**5.1** Explain the meanings of the newly defined (emboldened) terms and symbols, and use them appropriately.

**5.2** Make appropriate use of the general bra-ket notation, and interpret it in the contexts of wave mechanics and spin space.

**5.3** Outline the basic principles of quantum mechanics, referring appropriately to states, identical particles, observables, measurements and time-development, and using language and notation appropriate for both wave mechanics and spin.

**5.4** Give an account of measurement in quantum mechanics. The account could include the probabilities of outcomes, the collapse of the state vector, the role of the measuring device and the need to compare quantum-mechanical predictions with repeated measurements carried out on identically-prepared states.

**5.5** Describe, in general terms, the difficulties presented by the continuum in quantum mechanics, and describe some ways in which these difficulties are overcome.

# Chapter 6 Quantum entanglement and the EPR argument

## Introduction: stranger and stranger

> 'I would call it [entanglement] not *one* but rather *the* characteristic trait of quantum mechanics, the one that enforces its entire departure from classical lines of thought.'
>
> Erwin Schrödinger, 1935

**Figure 6.1** Albert Einstein (1879–1955), Nobel prize for physics in 1921.

Those words are from a paper by Schrödinger written partly in response to a paper by Einstein (Figure 6.1), Podolsky and Rosen, that had been published shortly before. For many years, neither of these papers had much impact, as physicists around the world busily applied quantum mechanics, with enormous success, to understanding the structure of matter. But those papers were a time bomb ticking away in the foundations of physics. A handful of papers by Bohm in the 1950s, by Bell and others in the 1960s, and more recently a great stream of papers (see Figure 6.2), all look back to those once almost forgotten papers of the 1930s. From this work has sprung a new field of 'quantum information', which includes such topics as *quantum cryptography*, *quantum teleportation* and *quantum computing*.

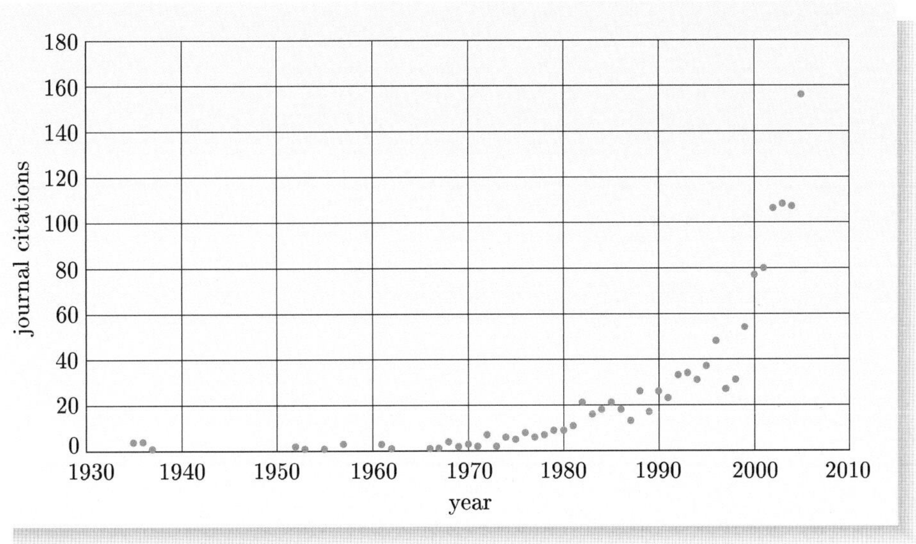


**Figure 6.2** The number of times that the paper by Einstein, Podolsky and Rosen was cited in other refereed journal articles for each year between its publication in 1935 until 2005.

These developments have also taken us deeper into understanding the meaning of quantum mechanics. For example, when we say that a particle does not *have* a position until its position is measured, how do we justify such a statement? The concept of *entanglement* introduced by Schrödinger is one key to addressing such issues. In this chapter we shall introduce the concept of entanglement, and explain how it has deeply affected our understanding of the world; the next chapter will describe some practical applications of entanglement.

Entanglement necessarily involves states of two or more particles (the particles that are 'entangled'), so this chapter will make essential use of results from Chapter 4 which explained how to describe spin states for more than one particle.

The first section of this chapter briefly discusses the fundamental question of the existence (or non-existence) of hidden variables. Section 6.2 explains what entanglement is, with some examples of entangled states. Section 6.3 explains the basic principles behind experiments that might test for entanglement. These 'in principle' experiments are based upon the properties of the singlet state of two spin-$\frac{1}{2}$ particles. Most actual experiments that have been done involve photons, and two key experiments are briefly described in Section 6.4. Section 6.5 very briefly discusses the general significance of entanglement, looking forward to Chapter 7 where technological applications are described.

## 6.1 Do hidden variables exist?

Does a particle *have* a position or momentum before these quantities are measured? In standard quantum mechanics, the answer is 'no', but what are the grounds for this assertion? It seems very natural to think that the probabilistic nature of quantum mechanics is, after all, rather like that of classical statistical physics. In classical physics, particles do have positions and momenta and so, given a sufficiently powerful computer, we could calculate the position and momentum of every gas molecule in a balloon, instead of making do with macroscopic quantities such as pressure. Are there hidden away, beyond the purview of the quantum formalism as we know it, markers or variables that determine exactly *when* a particular uranium nucleus will decay, or exactly *where* the electron is located within a hydrogen atom? Do the measured values exist before they are measured?

Here is the choice. One possibility is that quantum mechanics is a *complete theory*, giving a complete description of the state of any system. Since the formalism of quantum mechanics provides only a probability distribution for the position of a particle, we must then say that the particle does not have a position until a position measurement is made. The alternative possibility is that quantum mechanics — although highly successful — is an *incomplete theory*, giving only a partial description of the state of a system. In this case, the particle could have a definite position at all times, but this position is not part of the quantum-mechanical description. Any hypothetical variables that are supposed to determine the results of measurements with certainty, but are absent from the quantum-mechanical description, are called **hidden variables**. Many physicists (and this course) plump for the first alternative, asserting that quantum mechanics is a complete theory and that hidden variables do not exist. One aim of this chapter is to explain why this is so, in spite of the strange implications this has for the nature of reality.

Einstein did not accept the standard quantum-mechanical view, famously declaring that 'God does not play dice'. Already in 1927, he argued that quantum mechanics must be incomplete. He based his argument on the phenomenon of electron diffraction. We said in Book 1 that, when an electron passes through a tiny slit and is subsequently detected at some point on the screen, it instantaneously seems to 'know' *not* to be detected at any other point. This is an example of a **non-local effect**, meaning that what happens at some point appears to be affected by what happens at other points that are too far away for any communication of information, even at the speed of light. Einstein could not accept such non-locality, preferring to believe that the electron *does* have a position before a spot forms on the screen, and that quantum mechanics is incomplete since it does not include a representation of that 'hidden' position prior to measurement.

However, this argument is not at all conclusive. Supporters of quantum mechanics, such as Bohr and Heisenberg, could simply assert that non-local effects do occur in quantum mechanics, whether we like it or not. The question simply cannot be decided on the basis of the behaviour of a single particle. The paper by Einstein, Podolsky and Rosen (EPR) of 1935 provided a sharper argument for Einstein's point of view, based on the behaviour of *two* particles rather than one. It was Schrödinger who, in the article quoted in the Introduction, referred to the state of these two particles as being *entangled.* In 1952, David Bohm recast the EPR argument in a form that is easier for us to explain, and we prepare the way for Bohm's version of the EPR argument in Section 6.2.

It is interesting to note that John von Neumann (in 1932) claimed to prove that *any* theory based on hidden variables would be unable to reproduce the results of quantum mechanics. Since quantum mechanics is undeniably successful, this led many physicists to suppose that theories based on hidden variables would never be viable. However, it turned out that von Neumann's proof contained an oversight, and that it did not establish anything conclusive about hidden variables. In the 1950's David Bohm demonstrated that Schrödinger's equation for a single particle can be reinterpreted in terms of hidden variables. However Bohm's theory has features that lead most physicists to reject it; the price paid for particles having definite values of observables prior to measurement is such an extreme form of non-locality that the medicine seems worse than the cure. Bohm's theory even failed to enthuse Einstein, who had been hoping that hidden variables would one day be accepted, but it did open up the whole issue of hidden-variable alternatives to quantum mechanics.

Two more recent developments have transformed the subject. Firstly, John Bell showed that it is possible, in principle, to devise experiments that distinguish between quantum mechanics and the most plausible class of hidden-variable theory. Secondly, advances in experimental techniques, particularly with tunable lasers, have allowed some of these experiments to be carried out. But, before we can say how entanglement allows experimental tests of hidden variables, we must first explain entanglement itself.

## 6.2 Entanglement and spooky action at a distance

Consider the following statement: *A measurement of the properties of a particle can have an instantaneous effect on a measurement of properties of a second particle located indefinitely far from the first.* How could this possibly be? Einstein, in a letter to Max Born in 1947, referred to such 'spooky action at a distance' ('spukhafte Fernwirkungen' in German) as being contrary to our deep-rooted understanding of what it means for a body to have an individual existence. Surely what happens 'here' cannot be influenced by what happens 'there', when 'there' is too remote for light to travel 'here' in the timescale of the experiments. But, remarkably, that is just what happens; such non-locality is a fact of Nature.

The property of a pair (or more) of particles that makes this 'spookiness' possible, is *entanglement*. Two or more entangled particles may show non-local effects.

Most of the experiments that have actually demonstrated these non-local effects involve photons. However, much of the theoretical literature involves pairs of spin-$\frac{1}{2}$ particles; entanglement is most naturally introduced in terms of such pairs. Our first example of entanglement will therefore be in terms of entangled spin-$\frac{1}{2}$ particles, and we shall move on to more general cases later, especially entangled photons.

### 6.2.1 Entangled states of two spin-$\frac{1}{2}$ particles

Bohm's version of the EPR argument is based on the behaviour of the singlet state of two identical spin-$\frac{1}{2}$ particles. From Chapter 4, we recall that the *singlet state* of two spin-$\frac{1}{2}$ particles may be written

The last line of Equation 6.1 uses the *positional notation*, in which the first arrow is understood to apply to the particle labelled '1' in the first line. In this connection, 'particle 1' simply means 'the particle detected in detector 1'.

$$|S=0, M_S=0\rangle = \frac{1}{\sqrt{2}}(|\uparrow\rangle_1 |\downarrow\rangle_2 - |\downarrow\rangle_1 |\uparrow\rangle_2)$$
$$= \frac{1}{\sqrt{2}}(|\uparrow\downarrow\rangle - |\downarrow\uparrow\rangle). \quad (6.1)$$

In this expression, $|S=0, M_S=0\rangle$ represents the spin state of a two-particle system with total spin $S=0$ and $M_S=0$. The fact that a state with $S=0$ can only have $M_S=0$ is, of course, the reason for the term 'singlet state'. $|\uparrow\rangle_1$ represents particle 1 in a state with $m_s=+\frac{1}{2}$, and $|\downarrow\rangle_2$ represents particle 2 in a state with $m_s=-\frac{1}{2}$. The overall factor $\frac{1}{\sqrt{2}}$ normalizes the state to unity. Finally, note that $|\uparrow\rangle$and $|\downarrow\rangle$, without any directional indication on the arrows, refer to the spin-up and spin-down states *in the $z$-direction*.

Recall that the component of spin in the $z$-direction is $m_s\hbar$.

Now let us imagine that particles 1 and 2 have been prepared in such a singlet state while they are close together (this is perfectly reasonable), and that they then become separated. It doesn't really matter how far they separate, but let's say they are very far apart when particle 1 interacts with a detector (which you can think of as a Stern–Gerlach analyzer) that can measure particle 1 to be spin-up or spin-down in the $z$-direction. One or other of those results must be obtained; let us say particle 1 is found to be spin-up, i.e. with $m_s=+\frac{1}{2}$. That means that the state vector collapses onto the first part of the singlet state in Equation 6.1 to become a new state

$$|\text{collapsed}\rangle = |\uparrow\rangle_1 |\downarrow\rangle_2 = |\uparrow\downarrow\rangle, \quad (6.2)$$

which no longer requires the normalizing factor $\frac{1}{\sqrt{2}}$. The two particles are no longer in a singlet state, and, according to quantum mechanics, we believe that a measurement on particle 2, whether in Milton Keynes, Timbuktu or somewhere in the Andromeda galaxy, would reveal it to be spin-down, with $m_s=-\frac{1}{2}$.

On the other hand … *if* the measurement on particle 1 gave $m_s = -\frac{1}{2}$, *then* a measurement on particle 2 would reveal it to have $m_s = +\frac{1}{2}$, because the first measurement would have 'collapsed the state vector' onto the second term in Equation 6.1.

- Verify that the state represented by $|\text{collapsed}\rangle$ in Equation 6.2 is normalized to unity.

- We need to show that $\langle\text{collapsed}|\text{collapsed}\rangle = 1$. But this quantity is $\langle\uparrow\downarrow \mid \uparrow\downarrow\rangle$. In such expressions, the bra and ket for particle 1 go together, as do the bra and ket for particle 2, giving (departing briefly from positional notation) $\langle\uparrow \mid \uparrow\rangle_1 \times \langle\downarrow \mid \downarrow\rangle_2 = 1 \times 1 = 1$ since each state $\mid \uparrow\rangle_1$ and $\mid \downarrow\rangle_2$ is normalized.

In neither case can we predict what the results of a measurement on particle 1 would be. It's like tossing a perfectly balanced coin: over a sufficiently long interval there would be 50% heads up and 50% heads down. But, once $m_s$ for particle 1 has been measured, *we know that the result of a measurement of the spin of particle 2 will yield the opposite*. And, of course, it works both ways: the result 'there' whatever it was, would determine the result 'here' just as much as a measurement 'here' determines the result 'there'. Schrödinger referred to the particles as being subject to 'Verschränkung' (literally 'folding' or 'crossing over'), which is now translated into English as **entanglement**. A key point is that the results of the measurement 'there' are not directly communicated to the measurement 'here' by any possible signalling device; one measurement could be in the Andromeda galaxy and the other in Milton Keynes. Here indeed is Einstein's 'spooky action at a distance' and with this, 'spooky' entered the vocabulary of physics.

We stress the distance between the measurements in order to preclude the possibility of information from one measurement reaching the other measurement at the speed of light, the maximum speed at which information can travel.

At first sight, there is a simple classical description which avoids this spookiness. If we assume that the particles have opposite spin components in the $z$-direction when they are released, and that these values are definite even although we do not know them, it is not surprising that a measurement of spin-up for one particle will be accompanied by a measurement of spin-down for the other particle (and vice versa). However, you will soon see that this common-sense classical view itself runs into difficulties. Moreover, it is not the quantum-mechanical view, which denies that particles have definite spin components prior to measurement.

According to quantum mechanics, *everything* we know about the spins of the particles is encapsulated in the state vector given in Equation 6.1. Yet, as Einstein emphasized, the description seems incomplete: the particle 'there' may be too far away to know that a measurement 'here' has robbed it of the possibility enshrined in Equation 6.1 of being either spin-up or spin-down. This is similar to the diffraction of a single electron: the appearance of an electron at one point on the screen instantaneously makes its appearance at any other point impossible. In the spin-singlet case, if we measure one particle's spin 'here', we know what the result will be for the other particle's spin 'there'; the measurement 'here' *instantaneously* determines the result of the measurement 'there'. This is a manifestation of non-locality.

The mention of instantaneous effects over great distances naturally arouses the suspicions of anyone who is familiar with special relativity. In fact, it can be shown that such collapses cannot be used for transmitting information (the kind that sells newspapers) faster than light, so the predictions of special relativity are obeyed. Nevertheless, the result is extraordinary and underlies all of the phenomena connected with entanglement.

### 6.2.2 When is a state entangled?

**Entangled states**

A wave function or state vector representing the state of two particles is said to represent an **entangled state** if it cannot be expressed as a product of terms each specifying the state of a single particle. Entanglement does not depend upon the basis used to describe the state.

The singlet state given in Equation 6.1 represents an entangled state of two spin-$\frac{1}{2}$ particles, but entanglement is a general property that need not necessarily involve spin.

Product states exist for non-identical particles, so the spatial eigenfunction of two particles with coordinates $\mathbf{r}_1$ and $\mathbf{r}_2$,

$$\psi(\mathbf{r}_1, \mathbf{r}_2) = \psi_1(\mathbf{r}_1)\psi_2(\mathbf{r}_2), \tag{6.3}$$

is certainly not entangled. However, the spatially antisymmetric eigenfunction

$$\psi_{\rm A}(\mathbf{r}_1, \mathbf{r}_2) = \frac{1}{\sqrt{2}}[\psi_1(\mathbf{r}_1)\psi_2(\mathbf{r}_2) - \psi_2(\mathbf{r}_1)\psi_1(\mathbf{r}_2)] \tag{6.4}$$

cannot be written as such a product, and this *does* represent an entangled state.

Two non-entangled states involving spin are the $S = 1, M_S = \pm 1$ triplet states of two spin-$\frac{1}{2}$ particles that we write as

$$|S = 1, M_S = 1\rangle = |\uparrow\rangle_1 |\uparrow\rangle_2 = |\uparrow\uparrow\rangle$$

and

$$|S = 1, M_S = -1\rangle = |\downarrow\rangle_1 |\downarrow\rangle_2 = |\downarrow\downarrow\rangle.$$

However, one of the triplet states, that with $M_S = 0$, is entangled. This entangled state is like Equation 6.1 but with a plus sign:

$$|S = 1, M_S = 0\rangle = \frac{1}{\sqrt{2}}(|\uparrow\downarrow\rangle + |\downarrow\uparrow\rangle). \tag{6.5}$$

Equations 6.1 and 6.5 have a common feature:

A characteristic of entangled states is that the members of a system of entangled particles *do not each have their own quantum states* although the system as a whole does.

For example, in the case of the two spin-$\frac{1}{2}$ particles in a singlet state (Equation 6.1) there is no way to predict the outcome of a spin measurement on a single particle although the *pair* can be assigned quantum numbers $S = 0$ and $M_S = 0$ that determine the magnitude and $z$-component of the total spin.

We have said that entanglement does not depend on the choice of basis. As an example, consider the state:

$$|A\rangle = \tfrac{1}{2}\big(|\uparrow_x\rangle_1|\uparrow_x\rangle_2 - |\uparrow_x\rangle_1|\downarrow_x\rangle_2 - |\downarrow_x\rangle_1|\uparrow_x\rangle_2 + |\downarrow_x\rangle_1|\downarrow_x\rangle_2\big) \quad (6.6)$$

where $|\uparrow_x\rangle$ and $|\downarrow_x\rangle$ are spin-up and spin-down states in the $x$-direction. Although it is not be immediately obvious, this can be factored as follows:

$$|A\rangle = \frac{1}{\sqrt{2}}\big(|\uparrow_x\rangle_1 - |\downarrow_x\rangle_1\big) \times \frac{1}{\sqrt{2}}\big(|\uparrow_x\rangle_2 - |\downarrow_x\rangle_2\big). \quad (6.7)$$

You can multiply out the terms in this equation to check that it is equivalent to Equation 6.6.

This is a product of terms specifying the state of each particle, so $|A\rangle$ is *not* entangled. We have seen this in the basis of $|\uparrow_x\rangle$ and $|\downarrow_x\rangle$, but even if we change to a different basis, $|A\rangle$ will still be a product of terms specifying the states of particle 1 and particle 2, and so will not be entangled in the new basis.

For example, we know from Chapter 3 that the spin-up and spin-down states in the $x$-direction can be written as

$$|\uparrow_x\rangle = \frac{1}{\sqrt{2}}\big(|\uparrow_z\rangle + |\downarrow_z\rangle\big) \quad \text{and} \quad |\downarrow_x\rangle = \frac{1}{\sqrt{2}}\big(-|\uparrow_z\rangle + |\downarrow_z\rangle\big)$$

Combining these results, it is easy to see that Equation 6.7 can also be written as

$$|A\rangle = |\uparrow_z\rangle_1|\uparrow_z\rangle_2.$$

Non-entanglement is immediately obvious in the basis of $|\uparrow_z\rangle \equiv |\uparrow\rangle$ and $|\downarrow_z\rangle \equiv |\downarrow\rangle$, but the property of being entangled, or not entangled, has nothing to do with the choice of basis.

### 6.2.3 The singlet state from another angle

One property of the singlet state makes it particularly interesting from the point of view of entanglement. The singlet state $|S=0, M_S=0\rangle$ *looks the same from all directions*. To explain what this means, we recall that a single-particle state corresponding to spin-up in the $z$-direction is denoted by $|\uparrow\rangle$, which is written in spinor notation as $\begin{bmatrix}1\\0\end{bmatrix}$. We also know from Chapter 3 that a general spin state which is spin-up in the direction of unit vector $\mathbf{n}$, defined by the spherical coordinate angles $\theta$ and $\phi$, can be written in spinor and ket form as

$$|\uparrow_\mathbf{n}\rangle = \begin{bmatrix}\cos(\theta/2)\\ e^{i\phi}\sin(\theta/2)\end{bmatrix} = \cos(\theta/2)|\uparrow\rangle + e^{i\phi}\sin(\theta/2)|\downarrow\rangle, \quad (6.8)$$

with a similar equation for spin-down in the $\mathbf{n}$-direction:

$$|\downarrow_\mathbf{n}\rangle = \begin{bmatrix}-e^{-i\phi}\sin(\theta/2)\\ \cos(\theta/2)\end{bmatrix} = -e^{-i\phi}\sin(\theta/2)|\uparrow\rangle + \cos(\theta/2)|\downarrow\rangle. \quad (6.9)$$

As always, kets with arrows without subscripts, as in $|\uparrow\rangle$ and $|\downarrow\rangle$, signify states that are spin-up or spin-down with respect to the $z$-axis. Using Equations 6.8 and 6.9, it is not hard to show (see Worked Example 6.1 below) that, for *any direction* $\mathbf{n}$,

$$\begin{aligned}\frac{1}{\sqrt{2}}\big(|\uparrow_\mathbf{n}\downarrow_\mathbf{n}\rangle - |\downarrow_\mathbf{n}\uparrow_\mathbf{n}\rangle\big) &= \frac{1}{\sqrt{2}}\big(|\uparrow_z\downarrow_z\rangle - |\downarrow_z\uparrow_z\rangle\\ &= \frac{1}{\sqrt{2}}\big(|\uparrow\downarrow\rangle - |\downarrow\uparrow\rangle. \quad (6.10)\end{aligned}$$

**Essential skill**

Manipulating entangled spin states

### Worked Example 6.1

Use Equations 6.8 and 6.9 to verify Equation 6.10.

**Solution**

Substituting the expressions for $|\uparrow_{\mathbf{n}}\rangle$ and $|\downarrow_{\mathbf{n}}\rangle$ given in Equations 6.8 and 6.9 into the left-hand side of Equation 6.10, we obtain

$$\begin{aligned}\frac{1}{\sqrt{2}}\big(|\uparrow_{\mathbf{n}}\downarrow_{\mathbf{n}}\rangle - |\downarrow_{\mathbf{n}}\uparrow_{\mathbf{n}}\rangle\big) &= \frac{1}{\sqrt{2}}\big(|\uparrow_{\mathbf{n}}\rangle_1\,|\downarrow_{\mathbf{n}}\rangle_2 - |\downarrow_{\mathbf{n}}\rangle_1\,|\uparrow_{\mathbf{n}}\rangle_2\big)\\ &= \frac{1}{\sqrt{2}}\Big[\big(\cos(\theta/2)\,|\uparrow\rangle_1 + e^{i\phi}\sin(\theta/2)\,|\downarrow\rangle_1\big)\\ &\qquad\times\big(-e^{-i\phi}\sin(\theta/2)\,|\uparrow\rangle_2 + \cos(\theta/2)\,|\downarrow\rangle_2\big)\Big]\\ &\quad - \frac{1}{\sqrt{2}}\Big[\big(-e^{-i\phi}\sin(\theta/2)\,|\uparrow\rangle_1 + \cos(\theta/2)\,|\downarrow\rangle_1\big)\\ &\qquad\times\big(\cos(\theta/2)\,|\uparrow\rangle_2 + e^{i\phi}\sin(\theta/2)\,|\downarrow\rangle_2\big)\Big].\end{aligned}$$

Remember $\cos^2 x + \sin^2 x = 1$.

Collecting terms and multiplying out, noting that the terms involving $|\uparrow\rangle_1|\uparrow\rangle_2$ and $|\downarrow\rangle_1|\downarrow\rangle_2$ have cancelling coefficients, this gives

$$\begin{aligned}\frac{1}{\sqrt{2}}\big(|\uparrow_{\mathbf{n}}\downarrow_{\mathbf{n}}\rangle - |\downarrow_{\mathbf{n}}\uparrow_{\mathbf{n}}\rangle\big) &= \frac{1}{\sqrt{2}}\Big[\big(\cos^2(\theta/2) + \sin^2(\theta/2)\big)\,|\uparrow\rangle_1|\downarrow\rangle_2\\ &\qquad - \big(\cos^2(\theta/2) + \sin^2(\theta/2)\big)\,|\downarrow\rangle_1|\uparrow\rangle_2\Big],\\ &= \frac{1}{\sqrt{2}}\big(|\uparrow\rangle_1|\downarrow\rangle_2 - |\downarrow\rangle_1|\uparrow\rangle_2\big)\\ &\equiv \frac{1}{\sqrt{2}}\big(|\uparrow\downarrow\rangle - |\downarrow\uparrow\rangle\big),\end{aligned}$$

Reminder: with the positional notation, the first symbol refers to particle 1 and the second refers to particle 2.

which is the right-hand side of Equation 6.10, as required.

What this worked example tells us is that the singlet state $|S = 0, M_S = 0\rangle$ takes a similar form in any basis. Let us consider what this implies. Suppose that a singlet state of a pair of spin-$\frac{1}{2}$ particles, $|S = 0, M_S = 0\rangle$, is produced, and then a measurement of the spin of one of them is made with a Stern–Gerlach apparatus with its magnet oriented in an *arbitrary* direction $\mathbf{n}$. We have now seen that the singlet state can be represented by

$$|\text{singlet}\rangle = \frac{1}{\sqrt{2}}\big(|\uparrow_{\mathbf{n}}\rangle_1|\downarrow_{\mathbf{n}}\rangle_2 - |\downarrow_{\mathbf{n}}\rangle_1|\uparrow_{\mathbf{n}}\rangle_2\big).$$

The result of such a measurement at this new angle must be spin-up or spin-down in the direction of $\mathbf{n}$. Then we know with certainty what the result will be of a spin measurement of the other particle, also along the direction of $\mathbf{n}$, whatever the direction of $\mathbf{n}$. If the first measurement gave spin-up for particle 1, then the singlet state must have collapsed onto the first term, $|\uparrow_{\mathbf{n}}\rangle_1|\downarrow_{\mathbf{n}}\rangle_2$. It then follows that particle 2 would certainly be measured to be spin-down, i.e. having spin component $-\frac{1}{2}\hbar$ in the $\mathbf{n}$-direction. Even if the second measurement were light years distant, the measured spin would be the *opposite* of what was found for the first particle.

This is an extraordinary result. As Niels Bohr said, 'If you are not shocked by quantum mechanics, you don't understand it', and here is the touchstone of shocking! Consider: it is natural to think, as Einstein did to the end of his life, that a measurement of the spin of a nearby particle with a Stern–Gerlach analyzer, oriented as you wish, could in no way influence the outcome of a spin measurement on a distant particle. Moreover, just as one measurement in the $x$-direction tells you what the result of another, distant, measurement in the $x$-direction must yield, the same is true of $z$-direction measurements. So are both $x$- and $z$-components of spin simultaneously determined even before they are measured? Not according to quantum mechanics! We know that $\widehat{S}_x$ and $\widehat{S}_y$ do not commute with one another, so the observables $S_x$ and $S_y$ are incompatible. They do not both have definite values in the same state. If we measure $S_x$ for the first particle, the second particle collapses into a state with a definite value of $S_x$; if we measure $S_y$ for the first particle, the second particle collapses into a state with a definite value of $S_y$. The spooky influence of the first measurement on the state of the second particle is quite unnerving. We shall return to this discussion in Section 6.3.2.

**Exercise 6.1** A pair of spin-$\frac{1}{2}$ particles is created in the singlet state $|S = 0, M_S = 0\rangle$. The first particle is measured to have spin $+\frac{1}{2}\hbar$ in the direction $\mathbf{n}$ defined by $\theta = 60°$ and $\phi = 0°$. What is the probability that a subsequent spin measurement on the *second* particle, with the detector oriented along the $z$-axis, will yield $+\frac{1}{2}\hbar$? ■

## 6.2.4 Many phenomena involve entanglement

Entanglement is not just a property of singlet states of two electrons. It is involved in a huge range of phenomena; we describe two below.

### The optical beam splitter

An example of entanglement is provided by the optical beam splitter (implemented as a half-silvered mirror) of Book 1, Chapter 1. Such a beam splitter was at the heart of the quantum random number generator and also the Mach–Zehnder interferometer, in which there were two beam splitters. In that chapter we made the rather cryptic statement: '... each photon in some sense actually goes *both* straight through *and* is reflected at 90° ...'. The language of entanglement allows us to be a little clearer on this matter. In Figure 6.3 we show a beam splitter with detectors that can register the arrival of photons that are transmitted or reflected. We assume that the beam splitter is ideal in the sense that equal numbers of photons are detected in each detector. Notice that we do *not* say 'equal numbers of photons travel each route through the beam splitter'. In classical physics, we would know what such a statement meant, but this is not so in

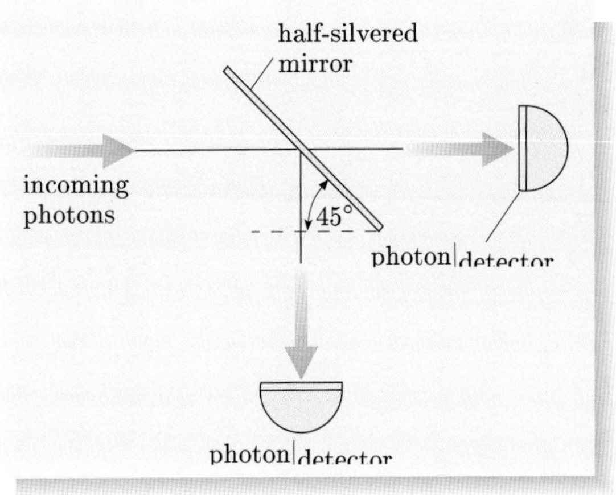


**Figure 6.3** Half of the photons arriving at the beam splitter from the left are detected at the 'transmitted straight through' detector, and half at the 'reflected downwards' detector.

quantum physics. However, we do have a clear idea of what it means to say that 'equal numbers of photons are detected in each detector.' We simply ask how many counts have been registered electronically.

In this context, $|0\rangle$ refers to a state with no photons. It might seem surprising to discuss states of no particles, but this is done in the quantum theory of fields. The $|0\rangle$ state for photons can be thought of as the state of zero-point motion of the electromagnetic field, analogous to the ground state $|n=0\rangle$ of a harmonic oscillator.

In order to clarify what is going on in the beam splitter, we must introduce some notation. We denote a state with a single photon in it as $|1\rangle$, and a state with zero photons as $|0\rangle$. We shall also use subscripts $\mathrm{T}$ and $\mathrm{R}$, respectively, to indicate transmitted and reflected photon states. We assert, without proof, that after a photon falls on the beam splitter, the state of the system can be written as

$$|\mathrm{BS}\rangle = a|0\rangle_\mathrm{R}|1\rangle_\mathrm{T} + b|1\rangle_\mathrm{R}|0\rangle_\mathrm{T}, \tag{6.11}$$

where the complex coefficients $a$ and $b$ satisfy $|a|^2 + |b|^2 = 1$ (to ensure normalization) and $|a|^2 = |b|^2$ (since equal numbers of photons are detected in each detector). We cannot say that $a = b = 1/\sqrt{2}$ because reflected and transmitted photons get different phases $\phi_\mathrm{R}$ and $\phi_\mathrm{T}$, giving $a = \mathrm{e}^{\mathrm{i}\phi_\mathrm{R}}/\sqrt{2}$ and $b = \mathrm{e}^{\mathrm{i}\phi_\mathrm{T}}/\sqrt{2}$; these phases have no effect on our argument here.

Equation 6.11 represents an entangled state. Neither the transmitted nor reflected channels of the beam splitter can be said to have one photon, neither can be said to have no photons, and there is definitely no such thing as half a photon. If the detector for transmitted photons fires, then the state vector $|\mathrm{BS}\rangle$ instantly loses the term $|1\rangle_\mathrm{R}|0\rangle_\mathrm{T}$ that represents a photon in the 'reflected' arm. Likewise, if the detector for reflected photons fires, the state vector $|\mathrm{BS}\rangle$ instantly loses its $|0\rangle_\mathrm{R}|1\rangle_\mathrm{T}$ term that represents a photon in the 'transmitted' arm. The behaviour of Mach–Zehnder interferometers discussed in Chapter 1 of Book 1 can be explained on the basis of these ideas.

Incidentally, Equation 6.11 allows us to illustrate what is meant by *partial entanglement*. If $|a|^2 = |b|^2 = \frac{1}{2}$, then the state is said to be fully entangled. If either $|a|^2 = 0$ or $|b|^2 = 0$, then the state is clearly not entangled. There is nothing to prevent intermediate cases, which are described as being **partially entangled**. In fact one has to have a very good beam splitter to make a fully entangled state.

All the extravagant examples presented in an earlier subsection for singlet states of spin-$\frac{1}{2}$ particles (one detector in Milton Keynes, one in Timbuktu, etc.) apply to the beam splitter. If the paths from the beam splitter could somehow be extended to these cities, then we could be sure that the detection of state $|1\rangle$ in Milton Keynes would instantaneously mean that the state in Timbuktu was $|0\rangle$, so no photon would be detected there.

Our picture of the output from a beam splitter as an entangled state is the reason for the vagueness in our account of the passage of photons through a Mach–Zehnder interferometer. None of the descriptions that would be appropriate for a macroscopic object apply: we cannot say a photon goes via one path, nor can we say that it goes the other way. Instead, the photon has complex probability amplitudes $a$ and $b$ for being detected on either path, with corresponding probabilities $|a|^2$ and $|b|^2$.

We have now given a mathematical description of a situation that might, with due circumspection, be described as the photon going both ways through a Mach–Zehnder interferometer. Finally, we remark that what we have said here for photons has also been verified experimentally for material particles such as neutrons, for which there are analogues of Mach–Zehnder interferometers.

### Entanglement in $\alpha$-decay

Let us suppose that we have an isolated nucleus of $^{238}$U in the far reaches of empty space. Let us also say that it emits an $\alpha$-particle by means of the tunnelling process described in Book 1. It turns out that $\alpha$-decay generally takes place with the emission of an $\alpha$-particle having an equal probability of being emitted in all directions. That is a deceptive statement; what it really means is that the $\alpha$-particle will have an equal probability of being *detected* coming out in all directions. The $\alpha$-particle does not have a direction until it has been detected coming out at some direction, any more than a particle described by $\Psi(x,t)$ is 'at' $x$ until it has been measured to be at $x$. But now for a complicating factor: momentum is conserved. In its rest frame, the original $^{238}$U nucleus has zero momentum, so the total momentum of the products, an $\alpha$-particle and the $^{234}$Th daughter nucleus, must also be zero, and this is achieved by an appropriate recoil of the daughter nucleus. But the $\alpha$-particle does not have a direction until it is detected, and so it does not have a momentum (a vector quantity) until it has been detected. So how does the daughter nucleus 'know' along which direction to recoil?

The resolution of this question is as follows: the decay process leaves the $\alpha$-particle and the $^{234}$Th daughter nucleus in an entangled state. The wave function contains all directions for the $\alpha$-particle and all directions for the recoiling daughter nucleus. If the $\alpha$-particle were to encounter a tiny piece of space dust, or even a planet, this would effectively measure its direction, i.e. its momentum vector. The daughter nucleus would at that instant, no matter how far away, assume a direction of motion such that its momentum vector would add to that of the $\alpha$-particle to give zero. Of course, if it were the nucleus that was first to encounter something like a spaceship or a star, then it would be the $\alpha$-particle that would, as a consequence, instantly acquire a corresponding well-determined momentum. The only limit to how far away the two particles would be before the detection of one would determine the momentum of the other would be the simple matter of how free of other particles the space surrounding the decaying nucleus is. For a uranium nucleus decaying in a lump of iron ore, the ore itself would probably very quickly register the recoiling nucleus, so that the $\alpha$-particle would very quickly attain a well-defined direction.

## 6.3 Quantifying the weirdness: testing for hidden variables

The entangled states of the last section have very surprising properties, but we do not yet have cast-iron evidence for quantum non-locality and against hidden variables. We shall approach this crucial issue in two steps.

**Step 1** In this section, we describe a hypothetical experiment for a pair of spin-$\frac{1}{2}$ particles and derive the predictions of quantum mechanics for measurements of the spins of the two particles, exploiting what we know for singlet states. You will see that any hidden-variable theory (in a wide class known as local hidden-variable theories) leads to results that differ from those of quantum mechanics.

**Step 2** In Section 6.4 we describe real experiments that decide between the predictions of local hidden-variable theories and the predictions of quantum

**Figure 6.4** (a) A schematic representation of an arrangement for spin measurements on a singlet state by Stern–Gerlach analyzers SG1 and SG2 (SG stands for Stern–Gerlach). The $y$-axis runs in the direction from the source to SG2. (b) This diagram shows the angle $\theta$ from a perspective of looking towards the central source of particles from SG2 (with the orientation of the pole pieces indicated).

mechanics. Most of the experiments have been done using photons rather than spin-$\frac{1}{2}$ particles, so Section 6.4 begins with an account of relevant aspects of the quantum theory of polarized photons and then describes the experiments.

### 6.3.1 Bohm's hypothetical experiment

It is helpful to have a definite experimental arrangement in mind when we consider the results of measurements on an entangled spin state. The particular arrangement described here was put forward by David Bohm in the early 1950s; the underlying physics is that of the experiment proposed by EPR in 1935. Figure 6.4 shows the arrangement.

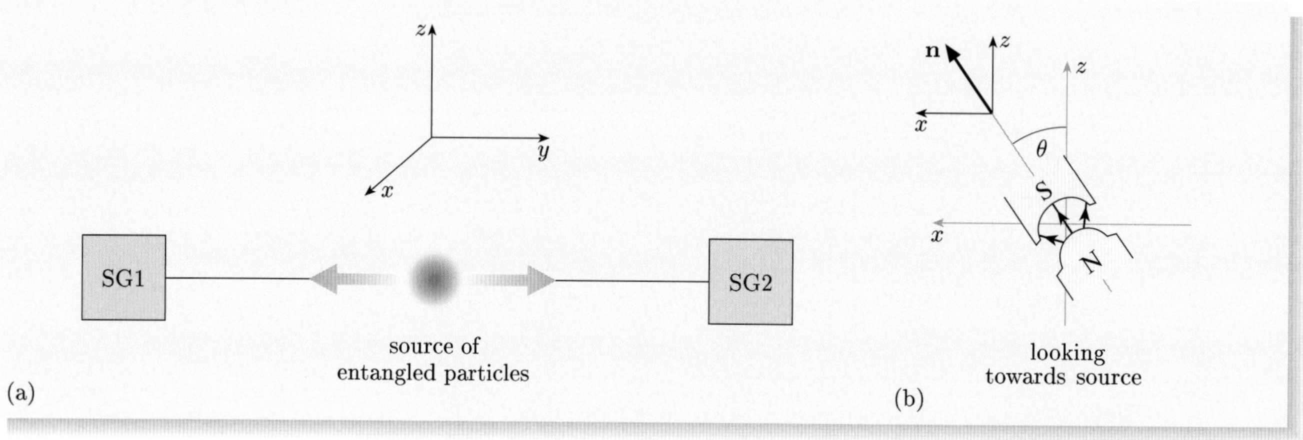


Pairs of particles are created in a singlet spin state at the source, and are directed to the left and to the right where their spins are measured by Stern–Gerlach analyzers. The analyzer on the left is SG1, and that on the right is SG2. We shall refer to the particle detected in SG1 as particle 1, and the state describing particle 1 in a spin-up state as $|\uparrow\rangle_1$; and similarly for particle 2. However, it is often awkward to include the particle subscript, particularly with bras, so we generally use the positional notation. Instead of $|\uparrow_{\mathbf{n}}\rangle_1 \, |\downarrow_{\mathbf{n}}\rangle_2$ we write simply $|\uparrow_{\mathbf{n}}\downarrow_{\mathbf{n}}\rangle$. The corresponding bra would be $\langle\uparrow_{\mathbf{n}}\downarrow_{\mathbf{n}}|$. The first symbol *always* refers to the first particle (here, that detected on the left) and the second symbol refers to the second particle. Thus, $\langle ab| = \langle a|_1 \langle b|_2$ is the bra corresponding to $|ab\rangle = |a\rangle_1 |b\rangle_2$.

Concerning the detectors in Figure 6.4, they always measure the spin component in the $xz$-plane, i.e. normal to the direction of the particle motion, which is along the $\pm y$-axis. Vector $\mathbf{n}$, defining the direction in which the spin component is measured up or down, is at angle $\theta$ to the $z$-axis and $(90° - \theta)$ to the $x$-axis. Because both measurements are in the $xz$-plane, both $\phi$ angles are zero, though we shall leave them in the equations in the first steps before setting them to zero.

$\theta$ for both detectors is always measured down from the positive $z$-axis towards the positive $x$-axis. It is a special case of the spherical polar coordinate $\theta$, with $\phi = 0$.

### 6.3.2 Bohm's experiment with parallel analyzers

Section 6.2.1 already tells us what to expect if detectors SG1 and SG2 are aligned in the $z$-direction. If particle 1 is found to be spin-up, then particle 2 will be found to be spin-down, and vice versa. The same would be true if SG1 and SG2 are both aligned in the direction of the unit vector $\mathbf{n}$: whatever $\mathbf{n}$ is chosen, if particle 1 is found to be spin-up, then particle 2 will be found to be spin-down, and vice versa.

Even these results, with analyzers SG1 and SG2 oriented at the same angle, are deeply perplexing. Let us say that the orientation of SG1 is chosen randomly to be in either the $x$-direction or the $z$-direction when a pair of spin-$\frac{1}{2}$ particles in a singlet state leave the source to be detected at SG1 and SG2. Suppose the spin measurement at SG2 is made before there was time for any signal at the speed of light to reach SG2 from the measurement at SG1. The orientation of SG2 is also independently chosen from the $x$-direction or $z$-direction. We now consider only the cases where SG2 happens to be oriented along the same direction as SG1. Once the measurement at SG1 has been made, the results are entirely predictable: spin-up in the $x$-direction at SG1 implies spin-down in the $x$-direction at SG2, and vice versa; it is the same if both are oriented along the $z$-direction.

In quantum mechanics, the explanation is straightforward. The two particles are initially in an entangled singlet state, which can be represented in any orthonormal basis. If particle 1 is found to be spin-up in the $x$-direction, we can represent the singlet state as $(|\uparrow_x\downarrow_x\rangle - |\downarrow_x\uparrow_x\rangle)/\sqrt{2}$, and say that it collapses to $|\uparrow_x\downarrow_x\rangle$, a state in which particle 2 is spin-down in the $x$-direction. If particle 1 is found to be spin-up in the $z$-direction, we can represent the same singlet state as $(|\uparrow_z\downarrow_z\rangle - |\downarrow_z\uparrow_z\rangle)/\sqrt{2}$, and say that it collapses to $|\uparrow_z\downarrow_z\rangle$, a state in which a measurement of $S_z$ for particle 2 is certain to give spin-down.

Einstein, Podolsky and Rosen, in their consideration of an analogous experiment, took a very different view. They noted that it is possible to predict either the value of $S_x$ or the value of $S_z$ for particle 2 (depending on the measurements made, and the results obtained, for particle 1). Bearing in mind that the large separation between the particles should preclude any influence on the measurement at SG2 by the measurement at SG1, they claimed that the most reasonable interpretation is to say that particle 2 actually has definite values of both $S_x$ and $S_z$, presumably determined ever since it split up from particle 1. This is the **EPR argument**. Of course, the conclusion is inconsistent with quantum mechanics, but to Einstein this simply meant that quantum mechanics was incomplete; nowadays, we would interpret 'incomplete' as 'being in need of hidden variables'.

Here 'preclude any influence' refers to the fact that the spatial separation of SG1 and SG2 is greater than the speed of light times the time interval between the measurements at SG1 and SG2 in the rest frame of the detectors. In the background is the firm prediction of special relativity that information cannot travel faster than light. Indeed, it has been shown that the non-local correlations described here do not break this fundamental rule.

Again, we are at an impasse. Standard quantum mechanics says one thing, and hidden-variable theories say something else, but there is nothing other than prejudice or taste to decide between the two descriptions. To distinguish between hidden-variable theories and quantum mechanics, we must consider experiments with non-parallel detectors. That is what we shall do next.

### 6.3.3 Quantum correlations for the singlet state

Before analyzing Bohm's hypothetical experiment for non-parallel detectors, let us review some basic results obtained in Chapter 3. Let us suppose that a spin-$\frac{1}{2}$ particle is in the spin state $|\uparrow_z\rangle = |\uparrow\rangle$, and that its spin component is measured in the $\mathbf{n}$-direction, defined by the angles $\theta$ and $\phi$ of spherical coordinates. For simplicity, we take $\phi = 0$ so, if the particle is travelling along the $y$-axis, the spin measurement can be made with a Stern–Gerlach analyzer with its orientation vector in the $xz$-plane, at an angle $\theta$ to the $z$-axis.

What is the probability of measuring spin-up in the $\mathbf{n}$-direction in this state? We remind you of the result. The probability amplitude for this outcome is $\langle \uparrow_{\mathbf{n}} \mid \uparrow \rangle$ where, from Equation 6.8,

$$\langle \uparrow_{\mathbf{n}} \mid = \cos(\theta/2) \langle \uparrow \mid + \sin(\theta/2) \langle \downarrow \mid. \tag{6.12}$$

(Going from ket to bra requires taking the complex conjugates of all coefficients, but they are real here since $\phi = 0$.) It follows that the probability for the particle to be measured as being spin-up in the direction $\mathbf{n}$ defined by angle $\theta$ is

$$P(\uparrow_{\mathbf{n}}) = \left|\langle \uparrow_{\mathbf{n}} \mid \uparrow \rangle\right|^2,$$

where

$$\begin{aligned}\langle \uparrow_{\mathbf{n}} \mid \uparrow \rangle &= \cos(\theta/2) \langle \uparrow \mid \uparrow \rangle + \sin(\theta/2) \langle \downarrow \mid \uparrow \rangle \\ &= \cos(\theta/2),\end{aligned}$$

recalling from Chapter 3 that $\langle \uparrow \mid \uparrow \rangle = 1$ and $\langle \downarrow \mid \uparrow \rangle = 0$, from the orthonormality of the spinors. Hence

This is the $\cos^2(\theta/2)$ rule.

$$P(\uparrow_{\mathbf{n}}) = \cos^2(\theta/2). \tag{6.13}$$

Similarly, the probability of a spin-$\frac{1}{2}$ particle in the spin state $\mid \uparrow_z \rangle = \mid \uparrow \rangle$ being measured to have spin component $-\frac{1}{2}\hbar$ in the $\mathbf{n}$-direction is

$$P(\downarrow_{\mathbf{n}}) = \left|\langle \downarrow_{\mathbf{n}} \mid \uparrow \rangle\right|^2 = \sin^2(\theta/2).$$

**Exercise 6.2** Show that $P(\downarrow_{\mathbf{n}}) = \sin^2(\theta/2)$. ■

With that brief review, we are ready to consider spin measurements on both particles of an entangled singlet state. We have in mind that the entangled state is created at some central location and the two particles fly off in opposite directions as shown in Figure 6.4. Some distance in each direction are Stern–Gerlach analyzers SG1 and SG2 oriented at different angles. Let us say that SG1 on the left is oriented so that spin-up is along the $z$-axis, i.e. at $\theta_1 = \phi_1 = 0$. SG2 on the right is rotated in the $xz$-plane through some angle $\theta$, with its orientation defined by a unit vector $\mathbf{n}$ with spherical coordinate angles $\theta_2 = \theta$ and $\phi_2 = 0$.

We refer to the angle of SG2 as $\theta$ rather than $\theta_2$ to unclutter many equations.

We ask: what is the probability that *both* particles of an entangled pair will be measured to be spin-up in their respective detectors?

To answer this question, we must calculate the probability of detecting the particles in the state represented by $\mid \uparrow \uparrow_{\mathbf{n}} \rangle$, for which the bra is $\langle \uparrow \uparrow_{\mathbf{n}} \mid$. The probability we seek is $\left|\langle \uparrow \uparrow_{\mathbf{n}} | S = 0, M_S = 0 \rangle\right|^2$, where

$$|S = 0, M_S = 0\rangle = \frac{1}{\sqrt{2}}\left(\mid \uparrow\downarrow \rangle - \mid \downarrow\uparrow \rangle\right) \qquad \text{(Eqn 6.1)}$$

represents the singlet state. The corresponding probability amplitude is

$$\begin{aligned}\langle \uparrow \uparrow_{\mathbf{n}} | S = 0, M_S = 0 \rangle &= \frac{1}{\sqrt{2}}\left(\langle \uparrow \uparrow_{\mathbf{n}} \mid \uparrow \downarrow \rangle - \langle \uparrow \uparrow_{\mathbf{n}} \mid \downarrow \uparrow \rangle\right) \\ &= \frac{1}{\sqrt{2}}\left(\langle \uparrow \mid \uparrow \rangle \langle \uparrow_{\mathbf{n}} \mid \downarrow \rangle - \langle \uparrow \mid \downarrow \rangle \langle \uparrow_{\mathbf{n}} \mid \uparrow \rangle\right).\end{aligned} \tag{6.14}$$

Notice that the first (left-hand) entry in the bra, $\langle \uparrow\uparrow_{\mathbf{n}} \mid$ goes with the first (left-hand) entry in each of the kets in Equation 6.1, and the second entry in the bra goes with the second entries in each of the kets. The first and third bra-kets of Equation 6.14 are easy: $\langle \uparrow \mid \uparrow \rangle = 1$ and $\langle \uparrow \mid \downarrow \rangle = 0$. We therefore have

$$\begin{aligned}\langle \uparrow \uparrow_{\mathbf{n}} | S = 0, M_S = 0 \rangle &= \frac{1}{\sqrt{2}} \langle \uparrow_{\mathbf{n}} \mid \downarrow \rangle \\ &= \frac{1}{\sqrt{2}} \big( \cos(\theta/2) \langle \uparrow \mid \downarrow \rangle + \sin(\theta/2) \langle \downarrow \mid \downarrow \rangle \big) \\ &= \frac{1}{\sqrt{2}} \big( \cos(\theta/2) \times 0 + \sin(\theta/2) \times 1 \big).\end{aligned}$$

Hence the probability amplitude that we seek is

$$\langle \uparrow \uparrow_{\mathbf{n}} | S = 0, M_S = 0 \rangle = \frac{1}{\sqrt{2}} \sin(\theta/2). \tag{6.15}$$

It follows that the probability that *both* spin measurements, in SG1 and SG2, will result in a spin-up measurement is

$$\text{probability}(\text{up}, \text{up}) = \tfrac{1}{2} \sin^2(\theta/2). \tag{6.16}$$

The probability of finding both particles to be spin-down is also $\frac{1}{2}\sin^2(\theta/2)$, as is most easily seen by remembering that the singlet state is the same from all angles (Section 6.2.3), so 'both up' and 'both down' are essentially the same to a singlet state.

What now is the probability of finding one of an entangled pair to be spin-up in SG1 and the other spin-down in SG2?

**Exercise 6.3** For this situation, fill in the spaces containing asterisks in the expression for the required probability amplitude: $\langle * * \mid * * \rangle$. ■

Evaluating $\langle \uparrow \downarrow_{\mathbf{n}} | S = 0, M_S = 0 \rangle$, using Equation 6.1, we obtain

$$\begin{aligned}\langle \uparrow \downarrow_{\mathbf{n}} | S = 0, M_S = 0 \rangle &= \langle \uparrow \downarrow_{\mathbf{n}} | \frac{1}{\sqrt{2}} \big( | \uparrow\downarrow \rangle - | \downarrow\uparrow \rangle \big) \\ &= \frac{1}{\sqrt{2}} \big( \langle \uparrow \downarrow_{\mathbf{n}} \mid \uparrow \downarrow \rangle - \langle \uparrow \downarrow_{\mathbf{n}} \mid \downarrow \uparrow \rangle \big) \\ &= \frac{1}{\sqrt{2}} \big( \langle \uparrow \mid \uparrow \rangle \langle \downarrow_{\mathbf{n}} \mid \downarrow \rangle - \langle \uparrow \mid \downarrow \rangle \langle \downarrow_{\mathbf{n}} \mid \uparrow \rangle \big) \\ &= \frac{1}{\sqrt{2}} \langle \downarrow_{\mathbf{n}} \mid \downarrow \rangle.\end{aligned}$$

From Equation 6.9, $\langle \downarrow_{\mathbf{n}} \mid = -\sin(\theta/2) \langle \uparrow \mid + \cos(\theta/2) \langle \downarrow \mid$ and so $\langle \uparrow \downarrow_{\mathbf{n}} | S = 0, M_S = 0 \rangle = \frac{1}{\sqrt{2}} \cos(\theta/2)$.

Hence the probability of finding particle 1 to be spin-up and particle 2 to be spin-down is

$$\text{probability}(\text{up}, \text{down}) = \tfrac{1}{2} \cos^2(\theta/2). \tag{6.17}$$

Again, because of the symmetry of the singlet state, the probability of spin-up in SG1 and spin-down in SG2 is the same as spin-up in SG2 and spin-down in SG1, namely $\frac{1}{2}\cos^2(\theta/2)$.

**Exercise 6.4** Verify that this last result is consistent with the basic property of the singlet state that the particles are certain to be found with opposite spin components along any given direction. ■

### 6.3.4 Quantifying the correlations

There is a specific quantity that characterizes the correlations between measurements in SG1 and SG2 that turns out to be the key for testing for local hidden variables. It is the **correlation function** $C(\theta)$, defined as follows for the arrangement with SG1 aligned along the $z$-axis and SG2 at angle $\theta$:

$$\begin{aligned} C(\theta) = &+ \text{the probability of measuring both particles up} \\ &+ \text{the probability of measuring both particles down} \\ &- \text{the probability of measuring particle 1 up and particle 2 down} \\ &- \text{the probability of measuring particle 2 up and particle 1 down.} \end{aligned}$$

In brief, $C(\theta)$ is 'the probability of getting them the same' minus 'the probability of getting them different'. A positive value of $C(\theta)$ indicates a tendency for the spin measurements to be the same; a negative value indicates a tendency for the spin measurements to be opposite.

The first two terms in the correlation function are each $\frac{1}{2}\sin^2(\theta/2)$, from Equation 6.16, and the second two terms are each $\frac{1}{2}\cos^2(\theta/2)$, from Equation 6.17. Hence, using these results,

$$C(\theta) = \sin^2(\theta/2) - \cos^2(\theta/2) = -\cos\theta. \qquad (6.18)$$

We need one more step — to simplify the calculations, we took SG1 to be aligned along the $z$-axis and SG2 to be at an angle $\theta$ to it. But the singlet states are independent of basis, and we don't 'know' which is the $z$-direction. All that really matters for the measured probability is the angle between SG1 and SG2. So let us say that they are respectively at $\theta_1$ and $\theta_2$ to the $z$-axis (keeping $\phi_1 = \phi_2 = 0$). Then we can finally write

$$C(\theta_1 - \theta_2) = -\cos(\theta_1 - \theta_2). \qquad (6.19)$$

**Essential skill**

Interpreting probabilities

**Worked Example 6.2**

Measurements on 10 000 pairs of spin-$\frac{1}{2}$ particles in singlet spin states are made by a pair of Stern–Gerlach analyzers oriented at 30° and 90° to the vertical. What is the most likely number of pairs where both particles are found to be spin-up? What is the most likely number of pairs where one particle is found to be spin-up and the other spin-down? Why do we ask for 'the most likely number' rather than 'the number'?

**Solution**

In this case $\theta_1 - \theta_2 = 60°$. The probability of both particles being measured to be spin-up is $\frac{1}{2}\sin^2(30°) = 1/8$, so the most likely number of such pairs is $10\,000/8 = 1250$.

There are two ways for one particle to be found to be spin-up and the other spin-down, so the most likely number of such pairs is $2 \times \frac{1}{2}\cos^2(30°) \times 10\,000 = 7500$.

Quantum-mechanical predictions are statistical, and just as the measured value of an observable only closely approaches the expectation value as the number of measurements becomes large, so the actual number of times an outcome occurs approaches the predicted number only as the total number of measurements becomes large. Hence we ask for 'the most likely number'.

**Exercise 6.5** Many singlet pairs of spin-$\frac{1}{2}$ particles are observed with SG1 and SG2 oriented at $0°$ and $90°$ to the vertical, respectively. What are the predicted relative proportions of up-up, up-down, down-up and down-down results? ■

Equation 6.19 is the quantum-mechanical prediction for the correlation function. If many measurements are made with SG1 and SG2 at fixed angles $\theta_1$ and $\theta_2$, we can define the corresponding experimental quantity $D(\theta_1 - \theta_2)$ as follows:

$$\begin{aligned} D(\theta_1 - \theta_2) = &+ \text{the proportion of measurements with both spin-up} \\ &+ \text{the proportion of measurements with both spin-down} \\ &- \text{the proportion of measurements with particle 1 up and particle 2 down} \\ &- \text{the proportion of measurements with particle 2 up and particle 1 down.} \end{aligned}$$

If, in the limit of many measurements, $D(\theta_1 - \theta_2)$ approaches $C(\theta_1 - \theta_2)$ for all $(\theta_1 - \theta_2)$, we would say that the quantum-mechanical prediction is confirmed.

### 6.3.5 Bell's inequalities

Stepping outside the standard formalism of quantum mechanics, John Bell asked a very pertinent question: *if hidden variables did exist, would that impose any restrictions on the correlation function,* $C(\theta_2 - \theta_1)$*?*

In 1964, Bell established an inequality that must be satisfied for *any* hidden variable theory within a broad class known as **local hidden-variable theories**. Roughly speaking, these are hidden-variable theories that do not include any non-local effects. More precisely, the assumptions made by Bell in establishing his inequality were *realism* and *locality*. In this context,

**Realism** implies that observables have values independently of any measurement.

**Locality** implies that events at any location cannot influence what happens at another location before a light signal could travel between the two locations.

The main attraction of hidden variable theories would be that they rescue realism, but most proponents of hidden variables would not want this to be achieved at the expense of sacrificing locality. Taken together, the assumptions made by Bell are commonly referred to as **local-realism**.

In the context of Bohm's hypothetical experiment, Bell showed that, for any local hidden-variable theory (a theory embodying local-realism), logic imposes a constraint on the possible values of the correlation function, $C(\theta_2 - \theta_1)$. Note that this is *not* a quantum-mechanical result. It is the result of an entirely classical analysis, telling us what local hidden-variable theories are capable of explaining. In its original form, the inequality derived by Bell was not well-adapted to comparing theory with experiment. However, there are various similar inequalities, all of which we shall call **Bell's inequalities**. In particular, inspired by Bell's work, Clauser, Horne, Shimony and Holt in 1969 used the same assumption of local-realism to prove a form of Bell's inequality called the CHSH inequality; this is very suitable for comparing theory with experiment.

By *Bohm-type measurements*, we simply refer to measurements like those we have been discussing, involving the set-up shown in Figure 6.4.

**The CHSH inequality.** Consider a series of Bohm-type measurements made with SG1 aligned at two angles $\theta_1$ and $\theta_1'$, and SG2 aligned at two angles $\theta_2$ and $\theta_2'$. That makes four possible kinds of correlation function, which can be combined to form the sum

$$\Sigma = C(\theta_1 - \theta_2) + C(\theta_1 - \theta_2') + C(\theta_1' - \theta_2) - C(\theta_1' - \theta_2'). \qquad (6.20)$$

CHSH proved, on the basis of assumptions equivalent to local-realism, that

$$|\Sigma| \leq 2. \qquad (6.21)$$

A proof of the CHSH inequality can be found on the course website.

This form of Bell's inequality is known as the **CHSH inequality**. Because the arguments are quite lengthy and because no quantum mechanics is involved, we shall not prove the CHSH inequality here, but we shall make use of its existence.

The comparison is between measured $D$ and predicted $C$: *if* the measured values of $D(\theta)$ allow us to conclude that $|\Sigma| > 2$ for particular angles, *then* the assumptions upon which CHSH based their derivation cannot hold. In that case, either realism or locality would have to be rejected. In effect, either hidden variables would not exist, or if they did exist, they would be non-local. So values of $\Sigma$ greater than 2 would rule out local hidden-variable theories.

Now, the key question is: does quantum mechanics violate the CHSH inequality? That is, does quantum mechanics predict that $|\Sigma| > 2$ for some possible choice of angles? You can answer this in the following exercise.

**Exercise 6.6** What would quantum theory predict for $\Sigma$ for the following angles: $\theta_1 = 0°$, $\theta_1' = 90°$, $\theta_2 = 45°$, $\theta_2' = -45°$? ■

So quantum theory predicts that for some combinations of angles, $|\Sigma| > 2$, as exemplified for the angles in the exercise above, for which $|\Sigma| = 2\sqrt{2}$. It follows, according to CHSH, that the results of quantum-mechanical measurements cannot be explained by hidden-variable theories. This result is known as Bell's theorem.

**Bell's theorem**: No physical theory involving local hidden variables can reproduce all the predictions of quantum mechanics.

In 1975, the physicist Henry Stapp was moved to call this 'the most profound discovery in the history of science'. The full implications of Bell's theorem are discussed by physicists and philosophers in hundreds of papers every year and we cannot do more than state the overwhelming consensus that experiments confirming the quantum-mechanical predictions for the spin correlations, and thereby exhibiting breaches of the CHSH inequality, preclude the possibility of local hidden variables. There is a deep non-locality in Nature. An electron really does not have a value of its spin component on an arbitrary axis until it is measured by a Stern–Gerlach or equivalent apparatus to have such a value.

## 6.4 Experiments testing for hidden variables with photons

Despite the great success of quantum mechanics, it is just possible that quantum mechanics is wrong in just those places where its predictions disagree with Bell's inequalities. To rule out this possibility we must carry out real experiments and see whether the results agree with quantum mechanics or with local hidden-variable theories. We refer to such experiments, that necessarily involve entangled states of particles, as Bell's inequality (or EPR) experiments.

Most actual Bell's inequality experiments have been carried out with polarized photons and not with atoms or electrons. The most famous were those of Aspect and colleagues in Paris, conducted between 1978 and 1982. In order to relate such photon experiments to what we have just said about spin-$\frac{1}{2}$ particles, this section begins with an account of the key properties of entangled states of polarized photons, starting with the quantum theory of photon polarization.

### 6.4.1 The quantum mechanics of polarized photons

#### Polarization of light according to classical electromagnetic theory

Light is a transverse electromagnetic wave, meaning that the electric and magnetic fields oscillate at right angles to the direction of propagation. This means that light can be **linearly polarized**, in which case the electric field is restricted to oscillating along some fixed direction (Figure 6.5a). In unpolarized light, the electric field oscillates in random directions perpendicular to the direction of propagation. Unpolarized light, such as light from an old-fashioned incandescent bulb, can be polarized by passing it through a sheet of Polaroid.

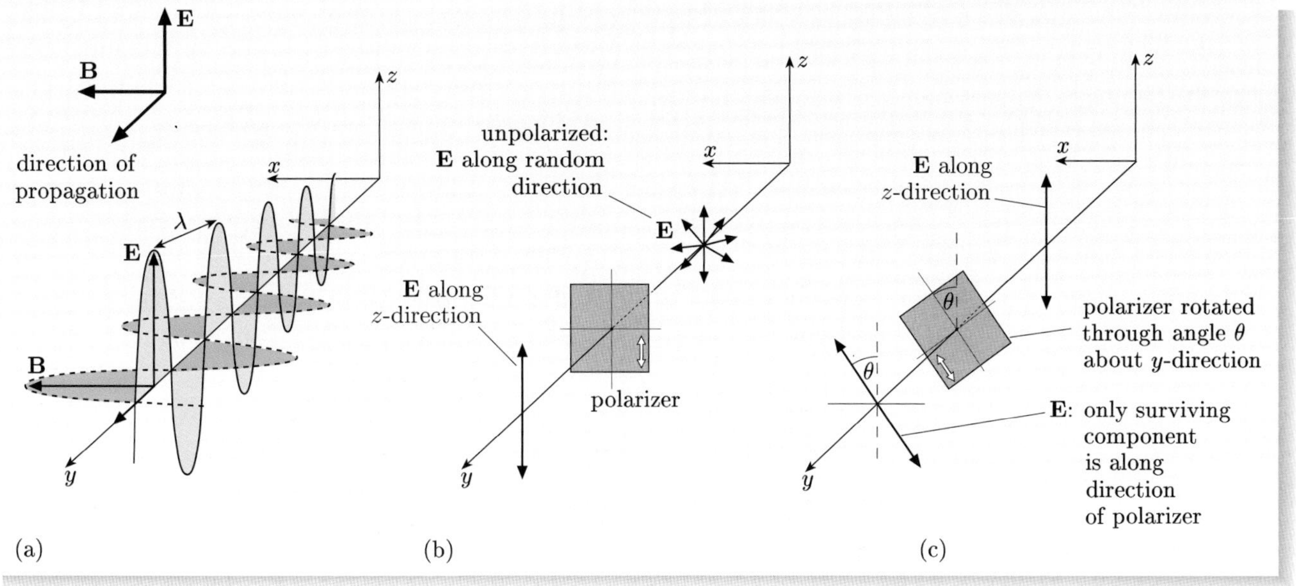


**Figure 6.5** (a) The relationship between the direction of propagation along the $y$-direction, and the oscillating electric and magnetic fields for electromagnetic radiation polarized in the $z$-direction. (b) Unpolarized light propagating in the $y$-direction has the direction of the electric field fluctuating randomly in the $xz$-plane. After passing through a piece of polarizing material such as Polaroid, only the light with the electric field oscillating along the direction of the polarizer axis (shown by the white two-headed arrow) is transmitted. (c) If the light is now passed through a further polarizer rotated through angle $\theta$, only the component having an electric field in this rotated direction is transmitted.

In Figure 6.5b, unpolarized light passes through a piece of Polaroid whose polarizer axis is marked with a white two-headed arrow pointing in the $\pm z$-direction. It is along this direction that the electric field oscillates after passing through the polarizer. If the light is then passed through a second polarizer, as in Figure 6.5(c), made in the same way but rotated about the $y$-direction so that the polarizer axis now makes an angle $\theta$ with the $z$-axis, then the intensity of the light that is transmitted varies as $\cos^2\theta$; this is known as **Malus's law**. If the two polarizers are orthogonal ('crossed'), so that $\theta = \pi/2$, then the transmitted intensity is zero. Note that $\theta = \pi$ and $\theta = 0$ both correspond to complete transmission: there is nothing to distinguish an electric field oscillating 'up-and-down' from one oscillating 'down-and-up' — hence the two-headed arrows on the Polaroids in Figure 6.5. This might seem a trivial point, but it is very different from what we saw for spin-$\frac{1}{2}$ particles, where the equivalent of Malus's law was the $\cos^2(\theta/2)$ transmission by a pair of Stern–Gerlach analyzers, and where spin-up was clearly distinguished from spin-down.

Étienne-Louis Malus, 1775–1812.

#### Polarization of light according to quantum theory

Although a photon is a spin-1 particle, it does not have the expected three possible values of spin component along a specific axis. For reasons to do with their masslessness and relativity, photons have only *two* possible components of spin: $+\hbar$ and $-\hbar$ along the direction of motion of the photon. This means that their quantum-mechanical description is rather like that for electrons, but with a difference.

Classically, we can also say that, since light is a transverse wave, it cannot be polarized in the direction of propagation; there are just two independent directions of polarization perpendicular to the direction of propagation.

Having in mind propagation along the $y$-direction, let us define two basis states of linear polarization: $|\mathrm{V}\rangle$ and $|\mathrm{H}\rangle$ (V for vertical, along the $z$-axis, and H for horizontal, along the $x$-axis). A photon in state $|\mathrm{V}\rangle$ is 100% certain of passing through a Polaroid with its polarizer axis oriented in the $z$-direction, and certain not to pass through one oriented in the $x$-direction. Likewise, a photon in state $|\mathrm{H}\rangle$ passes through a Polaroid oriented in the $x$-direction, but not one oriented in the $z$-direction. *Any* state of polarization can be described by the linear combination

$$|\text{general}\rangle = a|\mathrm{H}\rangle + b|\mathrm{V}\rangle, \tag{6.22}$$

where $a$ and $b$ are complex probability amplitudes, subject only to the normalization condition $|a|^2 + |b|^2 = 1$. The states $|\mathrm{H}\rangle$ and $|\mathrm{V}\rangle$ form a *complete orthonormal basis* for describing the polarization of photons, so that:

- any state of polarization can be expressed in the form of Equation 6.22 (completeness),
- $\langle\mathrm{V}|\mathrm{H}\rangle = \langle\mathrm{H}|\mathrm{V}\rangle = 0$ (orthogonality),
- $\langle\mathrm{V}|\mathrm{V}\rangle = \langle\mathrm{H}|\mathrm{H}\rangle = 1$ (normalization).

A photon in the state given by the superposition

$$|\mathrm{V}_\theta\rangle = \cos\theta\,|\mathrm{V}\rangle + \sin\theta\,|\mathrm{H}\rangle \tag{6.23}$$

has the property that it is assured of passage through a Polaroid with its polarizer axis at an angle $\theta$ to the $z$-axis and $(90° - \theta)$ to the $x$-axis. We say it represents a photon that is vertically polarized at angle $\theta$ (Figure 6.6).

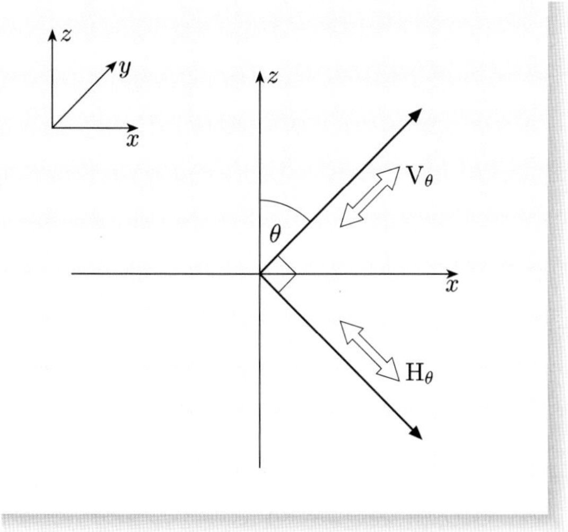


**Figure 6.6** A sheet of Polaroid oriented at an angle of $\theta$ to the $z$-axis (the two-headed arrow labelled $V_\theta$) passes light vertically polarized in a plane at an angle of $\theta$ to the $z$-axis. Note that light that is vertically polarized at an angle of $(\theta + \pi/2)$ is also horizontally polarized relative to the Polaroid at angle $\theta$. This figure presumes light incident along the $y$-direction.

A photon that is vertically polarized at an angle of $\theta + \pi/2$ is horizontally polarized with respect to angle $\theta$, and is represented by

$$\begin{aligned}|\mathrm{H}_\theta\rangle = |\mathrm{V}_{\theta+\pi/2}\rangle &= \cos(\theta + \pi/2)|\mathrm{V}\rangle + \sin(\theta + \pi/2)|\mathrm{H}\rangle \\ &= -\sin\theta|\mathrm{V}\rangle + \cos\theta|\mathrm{H}\rangle. \end{aligned} \tag{6.24}$$

- Is the state $|\mathrm{V}_\theta\rangle$ normalized to unity?
- Yes, since $\langle\mathrm{V}|\mathrm{V}\rangle = \langle\mathrm{H}|\mathrm{H}\rangle = 1$ and $\langle\mathrm{V}|\mathrm{H}\rangle = \langle\mathrm{H}|\mathrm{V}\rangle = 0$, we obtain

$$\begin{aligned}\langle\mathrm{V}_\theta|\mathrm{V}_\theta\rangle &= \big(\cos\theta\,\langle\mathrm{V}| + \sin\theta\,\langle\mathrm{H}|\big)\big(\cos\theta|\mathrm{V}\rangle + \sin\theta|\mathrm{H}\rangle\big) \\ &= \cos^2\theta + \sin^2\theta = 1.\end{aligned}$$

The probability amplitude for a photon in state $|\text{general}\rangle$ of Equation 6.22 to be transmitted through a polarizer oriented in the $x$-direction is

$$\langle\mathrm{H}|\text{general}\rangle = \langle\mathrm{H}|\big(a|\mathrm{H}\rangle + b|\mathrm{V}\rangle\big) = a\langle\mathrm{H}|\mathrm{H}\rangle + b\langle\mathrm{H}|\mathrm{V}\rangle = a,$$

so the transmission probability is

$$\text{transmission probability} = \big|\langle\mathrm{H}|\text{general}\rangle\big|^2 = |a|^2. \tag{6.25}$$

The corresponding probability for transmission through a vertically-oriented Polaroid is $\big|\langle\mathrm{V}|\text{general}\rangle\big|^2 = |b|^2$. In each case, *the transmitted photon is, in accord with Principle 6a of Section 5.6, in the state defined by the Polaroid.* That is, a photon initially in the state $|\text{general}\rangle$ has a probability $|a|^2$ of being transmitted by a horizontally-oriented Polaroid, and if it is transmitted, its state will have collapsed to state $|\mathrm{H}\rangle$; it will be a horizontally-polarized photon. Needless to say, the usual quantum caveats apply: e.g. a photon cannot be said to be transmitted until it has been detected on the far side of the Polaroid.

Now we can derive Malus's law: when a photon that has been prepared in the state $|\mathrm{V}_\theta\rangle$ (Equation 6.23) is subject to a polarization measurement with a polarizer in the $z$-direction, the probability of a photon being transmitted (in the state $|V\rangle$) is

$$\begin{aligned}\text{transmission probability} &= \big|\langle V|V_\theta\rangle\big|^2\\ &= \big|\langle V|\big(\cos\theta|V\rangle + \sin\theta|H\rangle\big)\big|^2\\ &= |\cos\theta\,\langle V|V\rangle + \sin\theta\,\langle V|H\rangle|^2\\ &= \cos^2\theta.\end{aligned}$$

Malus's law for light is reminiscent of the $\cos^2(\theta/2)$-rule for spin-$\frac{1}{2}$ particles but involves $\theta$ rather than $\theta/2$.

This verifies Malus's law for incoming photons polarized at angle $\theta$ incident on a vertical analyzer, but physically the transmission can depend only upon the angle between the plane of polarization and the orientation of the Polaroid, so Malus's law holds in general.

### 6.4.2 Circular polarization of light

The fact that photons obey a $\cos^2\theta$ rule, rather than the $\cos^2(\theta/2)$ rule for spin-$\frac{1}{2}$ particles, has its origin in the fact that photons are massless spin-1 particles. As it turns out, there are two states that do have well-defined values, $\pm\hbar$, of spin angular momentum in the direction of propagation of the photons. To define these we have to consider states with *complex* probability amplitudes $a$ and $b$. Real amplitudes $a = \cos\theta$ and $b = \sin\theta$ allow us to describe any possible 'linear polarization' of a photon. But we know that probability amplitudes are complex in general, so what states might

$$\frac{1}{\sqrt{2}}\big(|H\rangle \pm i|V\rangle\big) \tag{6.26}$$

represent?

The definitions of right- and left-handed circular polarization are not universal: we use the convention adopted in optics, electrical engineers use the opposite convention.

We use the term *linear polarization* to describe the state produced by a simple sheet of Polaroid, but there are indeed other forms of polarization, one of which is *circular polarization*. Classically, **circular polarization** means that the electric field vector **E** is actually rotating about the direction of propagation, the $y$-axis in Figure 6.5. Such polarization is produced by passing plane-polarized light through a transparent plate that introduces an appropriate phase difference between the vertically- and horizontally-polarized components. That phase is exactly what the $\pm i = e^{\pm i\pi/2}$ term provides in the quantum states presented in Equation 6.26. We define states of 'right-handed circular polarization' $|R\rangle$ and 'left-handed circular polarization' $|L\rangle$ as follows:

$$|R\rangle = -\frac{1}{\sqrt{2}}\big(|H\rangle + i|V\rangle\big) \qquad |L\rangle = \frac{1}{\sqrt{2}}\big(|H\rangle - i|V\rangle\big). \tag{6.27}$$

Photons cannot have zero angular momentum in the direction of propagation, for reasons arising from their masslessness and special relativity.

Although photons are spin-1 particles, their spin component has only *two* (instead of three) possible values. The angular momentum carried by a right-hand circularly-polarized photon, $|R\rangle$, is $-\hbar$ *along the direction of propagation*, and the angular momentum carried by a left-hand circularly-polarized photon, $|L\rangle$, is $+\hbar$ along the direction of propagation, here the $y$-axis.

**Exercise 6.7** Verify that $|R\rangle$ and $|L\rangle$ are orthonormal. ■

If a circularly-polarized photon is absorbed or emitted by an atom, the internal angular momentum of the atom changes by $\pm\hbar$ in the direction in which the photon is moving, and this is often very useful in experiments.

### 6.4.3 The Aspect experiments

In the now celebrated 1980s experiments of Alain Aspect and his colleagues, two entangled photons were produced from the decay of a calcium atom in an excited state having zero angular momentum. This state of calcium is forbidden by selection rules from decaying directly to the ground state which also has zero angular momentum, and decays first to an excited state which promptly decays to the ground state. The net angular momentum carried off when the atom jumps in two steps from one state with zero angular momentum to another must be zero. The two photons that are emitted in rapid succession in this process are entangled (Figure 6.7).

More recently, a more efficient way of producing entangled pairs of photons has superseded the method used by Aspect; it is described in the DVD video on quantum information.

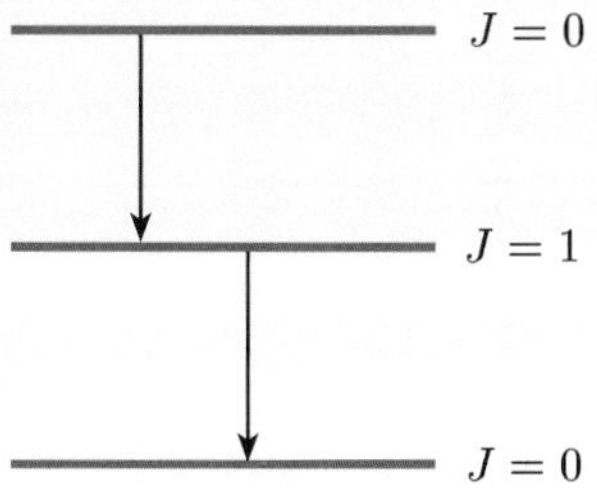


**Figure 6.7** The atom jumps in two steps from the second excited state with angular momentum quantum number $J = 0$, via the first excited state with $J = 1$, to the ground state with $J = 0$. ($J$ is a quantum number for total angular momentum as you will see in Book 3.) An atom cannot jump between two $J = 0$ states by emitting a single photon, since the photon has angular momentum, but it can do so by emitting two photons with opposite angular momenta.

A pair of photons travelling in opposite directions along the direction of the $y$-axis would carry zero angular momentum if one had angular momentum $+\hbar$ in the $y$-direction and the other $-\hbar$ in the $y$-direction. Because they are going in opposite directions, this means they would have the *same* circular polarization.

It turns out that the entangled state of two photons, when written in terms of $|\mathrm{V}\rangle$ and $|\mathrm{H}\rangle$ for each photon, is

$$|\text{photon pair}\rangle = \frac{1}{\sqrt{2}}\big(|\mathrm{VV}\rangle + |\mathrm{HH}\rangle\big). \tag{6.28}$$

This last equation uses the positional notation whereby the first V or H refers to the photon that appears in detector 1 and the second refers to the photon that appears in detector 2.

Equation 6.28 shows that if one photon is found to have vertical polarization along the $z$-direction, then the other will also be found to be vertically polarized. If one rotates the angle along which vertical polarization is measured through some angle $\theta$, defining the new states represented by $|\mathrm{V}_\theta\rangle$ and $|\mathrm{H}_\theta\rangle$, then the above equation can further be written

$$|\text{photon pair}\rangle = \frac{1}{\sqrt{2}}\big(|\mathrm{V}_\theta\mathrm{V}_\theta\rangle + |\mathrm{H}_\theta\mathrm{H}_\theta\rangle\big). \tag{6.29}$$

This is analogous to the fact that a singlet state for spin-$\frac{1}{2}$ particles looks similar in all bases.

**Exercise 6.8** Using Equations 6.23 and 6.24, show that

$$\frac{1}{\sqrt{2}}\big(|\mathrm{V}_\theta\mathrm{V}_\theta\rangle + |\mathrm{H}_\theta\mathrm{H}_\theta\rangle\big) = \frac{1}{\sqrt{2}}\big(|\mathrm{VV}\rangle + |\mathrm{HH}\rangle\big).$$

■

This is now rather like the case of two spin-$\frac{1}{2}$ particles entangled in a singlet state. In this case, if one photon is found to be vertically polarized *in any direction*, the other is certain to be found to be vertically polarized in the same direction. As in the case of spin-$\frac{1}{2}$ particles, the crucial angles for confronting hidden-variable theories are not the angles where these perfect correlations occur. Indeed, the CHSH inequality applies, but with a slight twist. The clue comes from comparing Malus's law in Section 6.4.1 (involving $\cos^2\theta$) with the comparable expression for spin-$\frac{1}{2}$ particles from Chapter 3, and also Equation 6.13 (involving $\cos^2(\theta/2)$). It turns out that the equations involving spin-1 photons are obtained from the corresponding spin-$\frac{1}{2}$ equations by replacing $\theta/2$ by $\theta$. Thus the key quantity is again the correlation function

$$\begin{aligned} C_{\text{photon}}(\theta) = &+ \text{the probability of measuring both vertical} \\ &+ \text{the probability of measuring both horizontal} \\ &- \text{the probability of measuring particle 1 vertical} \\ &\quad \text{and particle 2 horizontal} \\ &- \text{the probability of measuring particle 2 vertical} \\ &\quad \text{and particle 1 horizontal.} \end{aligned}$$

The quantum-mechanical prediction for this correlation function is

$$C_{\text{photon}}(\theta) = \cos(2\theta), \tag{6.30}$$

and this must be compared with the experimental quantity, $D_{\text{photon}}(\theta)$, which is similar to $C_{\text{photon}}(\theta)$ but with probabilities replaced by proportions of measurements.

The CHSH inequality $|\Sigma| \leq 2$ (Equation 6.21) applies to local hidden-variable theories of photons exactly as for spin-$\frac{1}{2}$ particles; $\Sigma$ is again defined by Equation 6.20, but now with $C_{\text{photon}}(\theta)$.

Aspect and his collaborators measured $D_{\text{photon}}(\theta)$ not just for a few angles, but over a wide range of angles, comparing it with the quantum-mechanical $C_{\text{photon}}(\theta)$, getting a perfect fit. From these results they could show that $\Sigma$ reached $2\sqrt{2}$, far beyond the CHSH limit of 2, verifying the profound non-locality of Nature.

You may wish to view the accompanying DVD which contains a film of the Aspect experiments, including interviews with John Bell and Alain Aspect. This archive film quotes yet another form of Bell's inequality: $|3C(\theta) - C(3\theta)| \leq 2$.

In connection with the next exercise, recall that a photon moving along the $y$-axis in state $|\text{V}\rangle$ is polarized in a plane including the $z$-axis, and a photon in state $|\text{H}\rangle$ is polarized in a plane including the $x$-axis. A photon in the state $|\text{V}_\theta\rangle$ of Equation 6.23 is polarized in a plane at angle $\theta$ to the $z$-axis. From Equation 6.23, such a photon with $\theta = 90°$ is in the state $|\text{H}\rangle$. This is natural: a photon 'vertically polarized relative to the $x$-direction' is 'horizontally polarized relative to the $z$-direction'.

**Exercise 6.9** Many pairs of photons are prepared in the entangled state of Equation 6.28. They travel in opposite directions along the $y$-axis, and fall on sheets of Polaroid, one close to the source of photons and one further away (in opposite directions from the source). Discuss, in terms of entanglement and the collapse of the state vector, what is observed behind the 'far' Polaroid in the following cases.

(a) The near Polaroid passes photons vertically polarized in the $z$-direction, and the far Polaroid is oriented to pass photons polarized in the $x$-direction.

(b) The near Polaroid passes photons vertically polarized in the $x$-direction, and the far Polaroid is oriented to pass photons polarized in the $x$-direction.

(c) The near Polaroid passes photons vertically polarized in the $z$-direction, and the far Polaroid is oriented to pass photons polarized in a plane at $45°$ to the $x$-direction. ■

The Aspect experiments did not study the polarization of the photons using sheets of Polaroid, which either pass the photon or not, just as a Stern–Gerlach preparer with one exit blocked either passes a spin-$\frac{1}{2}$ particle or not. Instead, devices known as **polarizing beam splitters** were used, which send a photon in one of two directions depending on whether the photon is vertically or horizontally polarized. This is analogous to a Stern–Gerlach analyzer that deflects spin-up and spin-down atoms in two directions. Polarizing beam splitters will be described in the next chapter.

### 6.4.4 Experiments with sets of three entangled particles

Experiments like those of Aspect, that verify non-locality and provide evidence against local hidden variables, all involve statistical measurements. The polarizations of many pairs of particles are measured, and, from the correlations between the photons that are measured to be horizontally and vertically polarized, the quantities $D(\theta_1 - \theta_2), D(\theta_1 - \theta_2'), D(\theta_1' - \theta_2)$ and $D(\theta_1' - \theta_2')$ are determined. Knowing these, it is possible to test whether there are sets of angles for which the CHSH inequality $|\Sigma| \leq 2$ (Equation 6.21) is disobeyed. As we know, quantum theory says there are such angles. Since only a small fraction of the emitted photons can actually be detected in such experiments, some people have said that (however strange this might seem) the apparatus is somehow selecting pairs of photons which weight the statistics to make the measured $|\Sigma|$ exceed 2.

It is the existence of such alleged loopholes that gives a special value to tests of hidden variables that do not depend on statistics, and for which, in principle, a single measurement would suffice to exclude hidden variables. Such a test was proposed by Greenberger, Horne and Zeilinger in 1989. In its original form, it was based on special entangled states of *three* spin-$\frac{1}{2}$ particles. These **GHZ states**, as they are referred to, take the form, for spin-$\frac{1}{2}$ particles,

$$|\text{GHZ}\rangle = \frac{1}{\sqrt{2}}\left(|\tfrac{1}{2}, \tfrac{1}{2}, \tfrac{1}{2}\rangle - |-\tfrac{1}{2}, -\tfrac{1}{2}, -\tfrac{1}{2}\rangle\right). \tag{6.31}$$

Note that we have now extended positional notation to states of three particles.

This is a superposition of two states: the first has all three particles spin-up with respect to the $z$-axis, i.e. with $m_S = +\frac{1}{2}$, and the second has all three particles spin-down, with $m_S = -\frac{1}{2}$. The particles travel in the $y$-direction and the $x$-axis is then defined as the third axis of a right-handed coordinate system.

**Exercise 6.10** Assume that the $z$-component of the spin of one particle in the three-particle entangled state of Equation 6.31 has been measured and found to be positive. What would the $z$-components of the spins of the other two particles turn out to be if they were measured? What would be the result if the spin component of the first particle turned out to be negative? Explain in terms of the collapse of state vectors. ■

The test conceived by GHZ is not obvious, and involves measuring the spin of the three particles in the $x$-direction rather than the $z$-direction. The test involves three spin-$\frac{1}{2}$ particles in the GHZ state, Equation 6.31. Consider the case that the spin in the $x$-direction is measured for all three particles. GHZ showed that if there were hidden variables, and *no* non-local effects, then there would always be an *odd* number of particles with spin-up in the $x$-direction. In other words, combinations of $S_x$ measurements such as $+\frac{1}{2}\hbar, -\frac{1}{2}\hbar, -\frac{1}{2}\hbar$ and $+\frac{1}{2}\hbar, +\frac{1}{2}\hbar, +\frac{1}{2}\hbar$, in which the product of the spins is *positive*, would necessarily occur. But quantum mechanics implies that an odd number of particles with spin-down in the $x$-direction must always be measured, e.g. $-\frac{1}{2}\hbar, -\frac{1}{2}\hbar, -\frac{1}{2}\hbar$. A single experimental measurement in

You may wish to look at the article by N. D. Mermin in the *American Journal of Physics* (1990) vol. 58, page 731, which gives the derivation of the results summarized here.

which the product of the spins in the $x$-direction is negative would be evidence of non-locality and evidence against local hidden variables.

Two different views can be taken concerning this result.

Einstein was always clear that he did not doubt the practical correctness of quantum mechanics; it was its completeness that he questioned.

1. GHZ have found a contradiction between quantum mechanics and local hidden-variable theories. Since we believe quantum mechanics, and the question of local hidden variables was raised only in connection with the completeness of quantum mechanics, that is all there is to say: there cannot be local hidden variables.

2. On the other hand, it might be possible that quantum mechanics is correct everywhere *except* just those places where specific consequences of hidden variables become evident. Hence it is worth verifying by experiment that quantum mechanics always holds true, even in the cases where it contradicts hidden-variable theories.

It is just the second point of view that inspired Aspect and others to carry out the experiments discussed in Section 6.4.3. More recently, experiments were carried out on GHZ states, and these verify the predictions of quantum mechanics. As with the experiments with entangled pairs, these were also carried out with photons rather than spin-$\frac{1}{2}$ particles; the GHZ state for three photons was

$$\frac{1}{\sqrt{2}}\big(|\mathrm{V},\mathrm{V},\mathrm{V}\rangle + |\mathrm{H},\mathrm{H},\mathrm{H}\rangle\big). \tag{6.32}$$

The three photons are in a superposition of two states: $|\mathrm{V},\mathrm{V},\mathrm{V}\rangle$ in which all three are vertically polarized, and $|\mathrm{H},\mathrm{H},\mathrm{H}\rangle$ in which all three are horizontally polarized.

In the experiment, the polarization of the three photons is measured along an axis rotated by $45°$ to the original axis. We denote by H′ and V′ horizontal and vertical polarization along this new axis. The alternatives for this system are as follows.

**Hidden variables** If the polarizations have values prior to measurement (i.e. there are local hidden variables), then the following combinations of measured polarizations are possible: V′V′V′, H′H′V′, H′V′H′ and V′H′H′; i.e. there is an odd number of vertically-polarized photons.

**Quantum mechanics** There is an odd number of horizontally-polarized photons, i.e. the permitted combinations are: H′H′H′, H′V′V′, V′H′V′ and V′V′H′.

In Figure 6.8 we show you what was found by Pan et al. in 2000.

This was a difficult experiment, and the results seen in Figure 6.8(c) agree with the quantum theory predictions in Figure 6.8(a) to within experimental error. The small numbers of counts in the 'wrong' bins are consistent with predictions that take into account the known experimental difficulties. The experimental uncertainties are not related to underlying quantum probabilities. The detection efficiencies were small, and so the 'fair sampling' hypothesis assumption is still invoked. With this in mind, these results are a clear vindication of quantum theory, and strong evidence that Nature is non-local and that there are no local hidden variables. If observables had values prior to measurement, then the experimental results would have been like part (b) of the figure, not part (a).

You may wish to look at the paper by Jian-Weh Pan et al. in *Nature* (2000) vol. 403, page 515.

## 6.5 The significance of entanglement

This chapter has introduced entanglement, and shown how it makes very fundamental questions about the nature of reality a matter for experimental study. The results of some experiments can only be understood as the results of non-local effects, and in terms of the fact that some quantities do not have values prior to measurement. Einstein had expressed the views of a scientist who thought very hard and clearly about the implications of deeply held common-sense views about the world. The fact that experiments performed years later clearly contradict these views is a measure of just how startling quantum mechanics really is.

But these conceptual results are very far from exhausting the great current interest in the consequence of entanglement. Here is a quote that gives some measure of the interest:

> 'Entanglement is a uniquely quantum-mechanical *resource* that plays a key role in many of the most interesting applications of quantum computation and quantum information; entanglement is iron to the classical world's bronze age. In recent years there has been a tremendous effort trying to better understand the properties of entanglement considered a fundamental resource of Nature, of comparable importance to energy, information, entropy, or any other fundamental resource.'
>
> Nielsen and Chuang, *Quantum computation and quantum information*

Elsewhere, it has been suggested that studying the applications of entanglement will lead to a new understanding of Nature, just as the study of the efficiency of steam engines lead Carnot and others to fundamental laws of thermodynamics.

The next chapter will give an account of some of the contemporary applications of entanglement that have aroused intense interest around the world.

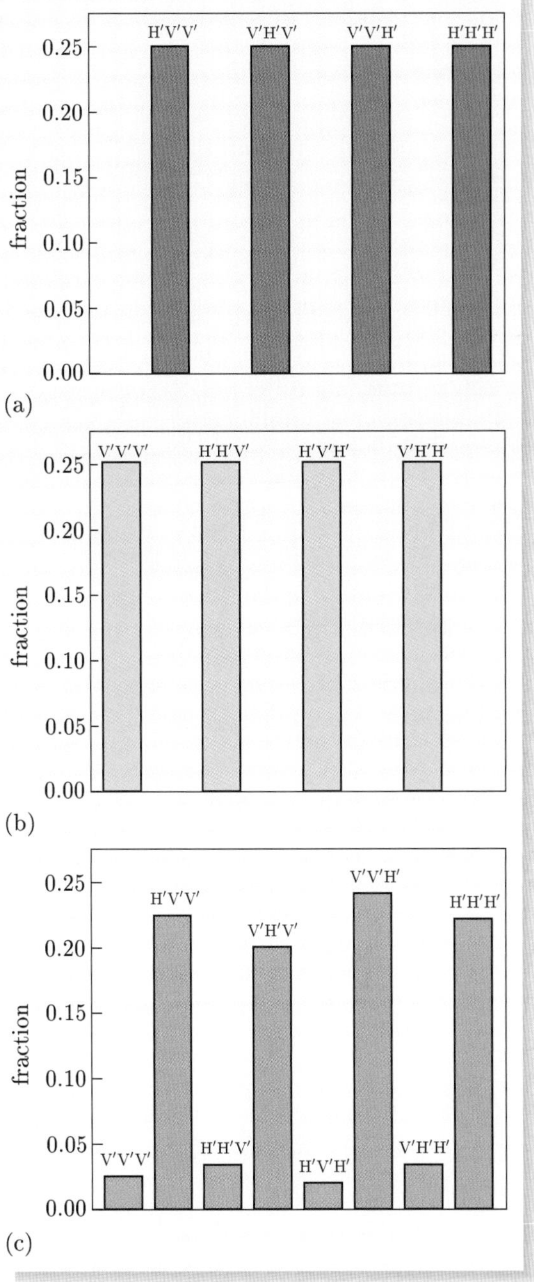


**Figure 6.8** Histograms showing the fraction of the measurements of the polarization of three GHZ photons in each of eight possible combinations: (a) the results predicted by quantum mechanics; (b) the predictions of hidden-variable theories; (c) the experimental results.

## Summary of Chapter 6

**Section 6.1** Do quantum systems have properties before they are measured? This fundamental question, raised in this section, is an ongoing question for the rest of the chapter.

**Section 6.2** A two-particle system is in an entangled state if its state vector cannot be expressed as a product of terms representing each particle, and so neither particle on its own has definite properties, though the pair does. Entangled states exhibit non-locality — Einstein's 'spooky action at a distance' — a deeply non-classical property. An example is provided by the singlet state of a pair of spin-$\frac{1}{2}$ particles. A significant property of singlet states is that they have a similar form in all bases; as a result, for whatever angle the spin component of one particle is measured, the spin component of the second particle, measured at the same angle, will be the opposite. Entanglement is not restricted to the spin states of pairs of particles; it also applies to spatial states and to photons.

**Section 6.3** Entanglement can be studied experimentally. Bohm's hypothetical experiment involves the singlet state of a pair of spin-$\frac{1}{2}$ particles. According to quantum mechanics, such a pair of singlet states exhibits correlations that *cannot* be exhibited by any system governed by local hidden variables (Bell's theorem). In this sense, Nature is non-local. The question is whether Nature obeys the laws of quantum mechanics or satisfies some limits – Bell's inequalities – satisfied by any system with local hidden variables.

**Section 6.4** Experiments to test for hidden variables have been carried out involving polarized light (photons). The quantum description of such polarization is rather like the quantum description of spin-$\frac{1}{2}$ particles, with some differences (mainly $\theta/2 \to \theta$). Two experiments are described: the classic experiments of Aspect and colleagues carried out in the early 1980s, and the more recent experiments involving entangled states of three photons. In each case, the quantum-mechanical predictions are decisively reproduced: Nature is non-local and there are no local hidden variables.

**Section 6.5** Entanglement is of great current interest and may be regarded as a fundamental resource of nature. Practical applications will be discussed in the next chapter.

## Achievements from Chapter 6

*After studying this chapter, you should be able to:*

**6.1** Explain the meanings of the newly defined (emboldened) terms and symbols, and use them appropriately.

**6.2** Briefly outline the issues relating to the possible existence of hidden variables.

**6.3** Explain what it means to say that the singlet state of two spin-$\frac{1}{2}$ particles is entangled.

**6.4** Give two further examples of entangled systems, apart from the singlet state of two spin-$\frac{1}{2}$ particles.

**6.5** Explain what it means to say that the singlet state of two spin-$\frac{1}{2}$ particles takes a similar form in all bases, demonstrate this fact, and explain the consequences for the measurement of the spins of two particles in such a state.

**6.6** Give an account of Bohm's hypothetical experiment based on spin measurements on the singlet state of two spin-$\frac{1}{2}$ particles; in particular, give an account of the role of entanglement.

**6.7** Apply the expression for the ket representing the spin state for a spin-$\frac{1}{2}$ particle that is spin-up in direction $\mathbf{n}$ to derive the correlation function $C(\theta)$.

**6.8** Interpret the CHSH inequality, and explain its significance for Bohm's experiment and the evidence for non-locality.

**6.9** Appreciate the key features of linear and circular polarization of light and the representation of the polarization states of photons.

**6.10** Give an account of the Aspect experiments, and the significance of what was found for our understanding of quantum mechanics.

**6.11** Give an account of the experiments involving the GHZ states of three entangled particles.

# Chapter 7 Quantum information

## Introduction: quantum entanglement put to work

The previous chapter was devoted to the nature of quantum entanglement, to some experiments that reveal the remarkable consequences of entanglement, and to a discussion of how the existence of entanglement influences our interpretation of quantum mechanics. In this chapter we introduce some applications of entanglement. The applications of entanglement that have attracted the attention of physicists around the world, and of large companies too, include quantum cryptography, quantum teleportation and quantum computing. Together these are referred to as quantum information, giving this chapter its title.

Little in this chapter could have been included in a quantum mechanics course written two decades ago. In Chapter 6 we presented a figure that showed the continuing rise in the number of citations of the paper by Einstein, Podolsky and Rosen (EPR) that first brought the remarkable consequences of entanglement to light. This dramatic rise partly reflects interest in the deeper understanding of quantum mechanics; but it also reflects the intense worldwide commitment to research in a number of fields that seek to exploit entanglement for practical purposes. This research is not just carried out in universities; companies too are investing in entanglement research, as you will see in the DVD film that we recommend you view towards the end of this chapter.

In computing, a **protocol** is a standard or convention that enables data transfer to take place.

Section 7.1 reviews some of the key concepts from Chapter 6 concerning the polarization of photons, adding some extensions and notation that will be used throughout the chapter. Section 7.2 introduces quantum cryptography, a technique that is already becoming increasingly important to banks, for the internet, and in fact to all those for whom secure communications are important. The chapter introduces two 'protocols' for quantum cryptography, one of which (BB84) does not, and one which does, involve entanglement. Section 7.3 introduces quantum teleportation. This was first achieved in the final years of the last century, and is still of considerable interest worldwide. We explain why we are still very far from being able to beam people from place to place, but what has been achieved is impressive nevertheless. Much of the interest in quantum cryptography and teleportation arises from the importance of the technologies that are needed for quantum computing. Section 7.4 is a very brief introduction to quantum computing, a topic that has aroused intense research activity throughout the world. The amount of background information on computing that we would have had to impart makes it impossible for us to give more than a brief glimpse of both the promise and the difficulties to be faced.

## 7.1 Photon polarization revisited

In this section we revisit the description of polarized photons that we met in Section 6.4 of Chapter 6, and introduce a matrix representation that simplifies some calculations. A simple method of preparing light in a given state of linear polarization is to pass it through a Polaroid filter. For incoming classical electromagnetic waves, a Polaroid filter transmits *only* the component of the electromagnetic waves with the electric field along the polarizer axis.

The applications to be described in this chapter call for a **polarization analyzer** in the form of a **polarizing beam splitter** that *separates* the incoming electromagnetic field into two components: one with the electric field along, and one with the electric field perpendicular to, a fixed polarizer axis. Having passed through the polarizing beam splitter, light, polarized in the two perpendicular directions, leaves the polarization analyzer in two different directions. A Wollaston prism (Figure 7.1) is one example of a polarizing beam splitter. Polarizing beam splitters can be used either to prepare light with a defined polarization, or to analyze the polarization of incoming light.

The polarizing beam splitter that you will see in the accompanying film 'Quantum information' on the DVD is not a Wollaston prism but one in which the horizontally- and vertically-polarized components emerge in perpendicular directions.

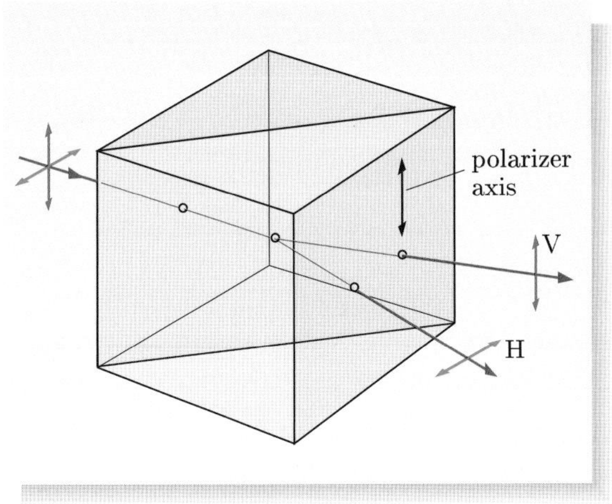


**Figure 7.1** A Wollaston prism separates incoming light into components of orthogonal polarizations which propagate at different angles upon emerging from the prism. One component V (shown in blue) is polarized in the direction along the polarizer axis. The other component H (shown in green) is polarized perpendicular to the polarizer axis. The prism consists of two 'birefringent' calcite crystals, cemented together on their base to form two right-angled triangular prisms with perpendicular 'anisotropy axes'. It separates light into two polarization components just as a Stern–Gerlach apparatus separates spin-$\frac{1}{2}$ particles into spin-up and spin-down components.

For linearly-polarized light entering a polarizing beam splitter, the intensity of the emerging light that is polarized parallel to the polarizer axis follows Malus's law as in Section 6.4.1 of Chapter 6, varying as $\cos^2\theta$, where $\theta$ is the angle between the incoming light polarization direction and the polarizer axis. This is just as it is with a Polaroid filter. But whereas a Polaroid filter absorbs a fraction $\sin^2\theta = 1 - \cos^2\theta$ of the light, none of the total light intensity is lost in an ideal polarizing beam splitter. The intensity of the light emerging polarized perpendicular to the polarizer axis will vary as $\sin^2\theta$. In many ways, a polarizing beam splitter acts very much like a Stern–Gerlach apparatus, but for photons.

We shall be concerned in this chapter with the polarization of individual photons. In order to treat individual photons, we require an orthonormal basis to describe the polarization state, and it will be convenient to use matrix notation. The state of a photon that is vertically polarized in the $z$-direction will be denoted as in Chapter 6 by $|\mathrm{V}\rangle$, while that of a photon polarized orthogonal to the $z$-axis is denoted by $|\mathrm{H}\rangle$. Using matrix notation analogous to the spinor notation for spin-$\frac{1}{2}$ particles, we write

$$|\mathrm{V}\rangle = \begin{bmatrix} 1 \\ 0 \end{bmatrix}, \quad |\mathrm{H}\rangle = \begin{bmatrix} 0 \\ 1 \end{bmatrix}. \tag{7.1}$$

For photons polarized vertically or horizontally relative to a polarizer axis at an angle $\theta$ to the $z$-axis, the corresponding states and matrices are

By convention, $\theta$ is always measured in the $xz$-plane down from the $z$-axis towards the $x$-axis.

$$\begin{aligned} |\mathrm{V}_\theta\rangle &= \cos\theta\,|\mathrm{V}\rangle + \sin\theta\,|\mathrm{H}\rangle = \begin{bmatrix} \cos\theta \\ \sin\theta \end{bmatrix}, \\ |\mathrm{H}_\theta\rangle &= -\sin\theta\,|\mathrm{V}\rangle + \cos\theta\,|\mathrm{H}\rangle = \begin{bmatrix} -\sin\theta \\ \cos\theta \end{bmatrix}. \end{aligned} \tag{7.2}$$

When $\theta = 0°$, we recover $|\mathrm{V}_0\rangle = |\mathrm{V}\rangle$ and $|\mathrm{H}_0\rangle = |\mathrm{H}\rangle$.

**Exercise 7.1** Prove that $|\mathrm{V}_\theta\rangle$ and $|\mathrm{H}_\theta\rangle$ are orthogonal for any value of $\theta$.

**Exercise 7.2** Show that $|\mathrm{V}_\theta\rangle$ and $|\mathrm{H}_\theta\rangle$ are normalized to unity. ■

For a given polarizer axis, set at an angle $\theta$ to the $z$-axis, we define a linear polarization variable $\mathcal{P}(\theta)$ by associating the value of $+1$ with vertical polarization, and the value $-1$ with horizontal polarization. This observable quantity corresponds to a linear Hermitian operator $\widehat{\mathcal{P}}(\theta)$, which turns out to have the matrix representation

We use the symbol $\widehat{\mathcal{P}}$ for the linear polarization matrix to avoid confusion later with the symbol $P$ which represents probability.

$$\widehat{\mathcal{P}}(\theta) = \begin{bmatrix} \cos(2\theta) & \sin(2\theta) \\ \sin(2\theta) & -\cos(2\theta) \end{bmatrix}. \tag{7.3}$$

We call this the **linear polarization matrix**: by definition, it is expected to have eigenvectors $|\mathrm{V}_\theta\rangle$ and $|\mathrm{H}_\theta\rangle$ with eigenvalues $+1$ and $-1$, respectively; the following exercise verifies this.

**Exercise 7.3** Show that the matrix $\widehat{\mathcal{P}}(\theta)$ and the eigenvectors $|\mathrm{V}_\theta\rangle$ and $|\mathrm{H}_\theta\rangle$ satisfy the eigenvalue equations $\widehat{\mathcal{P}}(\theta)\,|\mathrm{V}_\theta\rangle = |\mathrm{V}_\theta\rangle$ and $\widehat{\mathcal{P}}(\theta)\,|\mathrm{H}_\theta\rangle = -|\mathrm{H}_\theta\rangle$.

*Hint*: You'll need to use the following trigonometrical identities:

$$\cos(A \pm B) = \cos A \cos B \mp \sin A \sin B,$$
$$\sin(A \pm B) = \sin A \cos B \pm \cos A \sin B.$$

■

You have probably noticed that the matrix in Equation 7.3 and the eigenvectors in Equations 7.2 are reminiscent of the equations for the description of spin-$\frac{1}{2}$ particles in Chapter 3. In fact, replacing $\theta$ with $2\theta$ and $\hbar/2$ with 1 in the expressions for the general spin matrix and its eigenvectors (with $\phi = 0$), one obtains Equation 7.2 and Equation 7.3. This is no coincidence as these equations describe very similar systems — in both cases we are describing systems with two eigenvectors onto which any given state vector may collapse. It should now be clear why we made the analogy with the Stern–Gerlach apparatus when discussing the polarizing beam splitter. Although it will not greatly affect our arguments, it is also worth noting that there are differences between Stern–Gerlach analyzers and polarizing beam spitters. In contrast to a Stern–Gerlach analyzer, a polarizing beam splitter does not cause photons with different values of angular momentum to travel along different paths. For reasons related to masslessness and relativity, the only angular momentum component that makes sense for a photon is that along its direction of propagation, and this is equal to $-\hbar$ for right-handed circular polarization and $+\hbar$ for left-handed circular polarization. The different paths taken by vertically- and horizontally-polarized light through a polarizing beam splitter are those of *linearly* polarized photons, so are not directly related to different values of angular momentum.

We turn now to consider the measurement of the polarization of a single linearly polarized photon. We assume that this photon is in a general state $|\psi\rangle$, and that its polarization is measured with a polarizer whose axis is at an angle $\theta$ to the $z$-axis. An example of such a situation is shown in Figure 7.2.

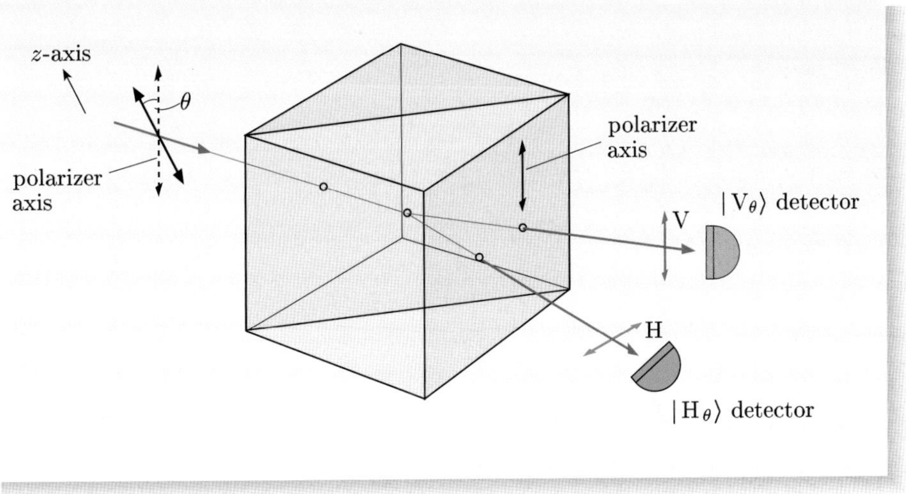


**Figure 7.2** A Wollaston prism can be used as a polarization analyzer by placing a photon detector at each of the out-directions. Each emerging photon is registered by one or other of the detectors. In this example we take the $z$-axis to lie along the polarization direction of the incoming linearly polarized photons (the solid two-headed arrow, not vertical). $\theta$ is then the angle between the incoming photon polarization direction and the polarizer axis. For each incoming photon state $|\psi\rangle$, vertical polarization (relative to the polarizer axis) is detected with probability $|\langle \mathrm{V}_\theta|\psi\rangle|^2$, and horizontal polarization is detected with probability $|\langle \mathrm{H}_\theta|\psi\rangle|^2$.

Since the eigenvectors $|\mathrm{V}_\theta\rangle$ and $|\mathrm{H}_\theta\rangle$ in Equation 7.2 form an orthonormal basis for linear polarization, we can expand $|\psi\rangle$ as

$$|\psi\rangle = \alpha\,|\mathrm{V}_\theta\rangle + \beta\,|\mathrm{H}_\theta\rangle, \qquad (7.4)$$

where $|\alpha|^2 + |\beta|^2 = 1$ to ensure that $|\psi\rangle$ is normalized. Suppose that we have two detectors after the polarizer (Figure 7.2). Each photon will register in only one of the two detectors. A photon detected by the $|\mathrm{V}_\theta\rangle$ (blue) detector will be polarized parallel to the polarizer axis, and a photon detected by the $|\mathrm{H}_\theta\rangle$ (green) detector will be polarized perpendicular to the polarizer axis. We will denote the probability that the $|\mathrm{V}_\theta\rangle$ detector registers by $P_+(\theta)$, and the probability that the $|\mathrm{H}_\theta\rangle$ detector registers by $P_-(\theta)$. We use here the subscripts $\pm$ to denote the eigenvalues $\pm 1$ which correspond to the two eigenvectors of $\widehat{\mathcal{P}}(\theta)$ (see Exercise 7.3). These probabilities can be calculated by taking the modulus squared of the inner product of $|\psi\rangle$ with each of the eigenvectors $|V_\theta\rangle$ and $|H_\theta\rangle$:

$$P_+(\theta) = \left|\langle V_\theta|\psi\rangle\right|^2 = \alpha^2, \tag{7.5a}$$

$$P_-(\theta) = \left|\langle H_\theta|\psi\rangle\right|^2 = \beta^2. \tag{7.5b}$$

Recall that after a measurement, the state of a system (here a photon) is an eigenvector of the appropriate operator, here $\widehat{\mathcal{P}}(\theta)$.

The direction of propagation of an emerging photon determines with absolute certainty which of the two eigenvectors $|V_\theta\rangle$ and $|H_\theta\rangle$ describes the emerging photon's polarization. Consequently, a polarizing beam splitter can also be used to prepare individual photons with a defined polarization state. Again, we mention the analogy with a Stern–Gerlach apparatus preparing spin-$\frac{1}{2}$ particles in a particular state of spin.

**Exercise 7.4** Photons linearly polarized along the $z$-axis are incident upon a polarizing beam splitter oriented at angle $\theta$ to the $z$-axis. Show that the probability of a photon emerging in the state $|V_\theta\rangle$ is equal to $\cos^2\theta$, consistent with Malus's law. ■

When the analyzer axis lies along the $z$-axis ($\theta = 0°$), the eigenvectors are just $|V_0\rangle = |V\rangle$ and $|H_0\rangle = |H\rangle$. We shall refer to this basis (defined by $\theta = 0°$) as the **H/V basis**. For the purposes of our discussion of cryptography in the next section, it is also useful to introduce a second basis, the eigenvectors of $\widehat{\mathcal{P}}(\theta)$ for $\theta = 45°$, corresponding to a polarizing beam splitter oriented at $\theta = 45°$. These eigenvectors are orthonormal (see Exercise 7.1) and are a complete set; we shall refer to them as the **diagonal basis**. Substituting $\theta = 45°$ into Equations 7.2 shows that the eigenvectors in the diagonal basis are

$$|V_{45}\rangle = \frac{1}{\sqrt{2}}\begin{bmatrix}1\\1\end{bmatrix}, \quad |H_{45}\rangle = \frac{1}{\sqrt{2}}\begin{bmatrix}-1\\1\end{bmatrix}. \tag{7.6}$$

These eigenvectors describe light that is linearly polarized at $\pm 45°$ to the $z$-axis.

These two bases have an important relationship that makes them particularly useful for quantum cryptography. Recall that any polarization state of a photon $|\psi\rangle$ can be expressed as a linear superposition in either of these orthonormal bases, as in Equation 7.4. We can therefore expand each of the H/V eigenvectors in terms of the diagonal basis vectors, and vice versa. For example, by writing

$$|V_{45}\rangle = a\,|V\rangle + b\,|H\rangle, \tag{7.7}$$

we can find the values of $a$ and $b$ from $a = \langle V|V_{45}\rangle$ and $b = \langle H|V_{45}\rangle$. This gives the following relationships between the H/V and diagonal bases:

$$|V_{45}\rangle = \frac{1}{\sqrt{2}}\big(|V\rangle + |H\rangle\big), \tag{7.8a}$$

$$|H_{45}\rangle = \frac{1}{\sqrt{2}}\big(-|V\rangle + |H\rangle\big), \tag{7.8b}$$

$$|V\rangle = \frac{1}{\sqrt{2}}\big(|V_{45}\rangle - |H_{45}\rangle\big), \tag{7.8c}$$

$$|H\rangle = \frac{1}{\sqrt{2}}\big(|V_{45}\rangle + |H_{45}\rangle\big). \tag{7.8d}$$

These relationships can also be written in matrix form, for example

$$|V_{45}\rangle = \frac{1}{\sqrt{2}}\begin{bmatrix}1\\1\end{bmatrix} = \frac{1}{\sqrt{2}}\begin{bmatrix}1\\0\end{bmatrix} + \frac{1}{\sqrt{2}}\begin{bmatrix}0\\1\end{bmatrix}. \tag{7.9}$$

From these equations, you can see that the two bases, H/V and diagonal, are not orthogonal to each other and are, in fact, **complementary bases**, meaning that an eigenvector in one basis has equal projections onto the two eigenvectors of the other basis. This implies, for example, that polarization measurements performed on an eigenvector of the diagonal basis, when carried out in the H/V basis, will yield H and V polarized photons with equal probability. This property is crucial in the schemes for quantum cryptography in the next section.

In the following sections, it will also be useful to be able to express the H/V basis eigenvectors in terms of other basis vectors.

**Essential skill**

Connecting measurement bases

**Worked Example 7.1**

Show that the H/V basis may be written in terms of the general eigenvectors of $\widehat{\mathcal{P}}(\theta)$, $|\mathrm{V}_\theta\rangle$ and $|\mathrm{H}_\theta\rangle$, as

$$|\mathrm{V}\rangle = \cos\theta\,|\mathrm{V}_\theta\rangle - \sin\theta\,|\mathrm{H}_\theta\rangle, \tag{7.10a}$$

$$|\mathrm{H}\rangle = \sin\theta\,|\mathrm{V}_\theta\rangle + \cos\theta\,|\mathrm{H}_\theta\rangle. \tag{7.10b}$$

**Solution**

We start by writing $|\mathrm{V}\rangle$ and $|\mathrm{H}\rangle$ in terms of the eigenvectors of $\widehat{\mathcal{P}}(\theta)$ (see Equation 7.4):

$$|\mathrm{V}\rangle = a\,|\mathrm{V}_\theta\rangle + b\,|\mathrm{H}_\theta\rangle, \tag{7.11a}$$

$$|\mathrm{H}\rangle = c\,|\mathrm{V}_\theta\rangle + d\,|\mathrm{H}_\theta\rangle. \tag{7.11b}$$

To find expressions for the coefficients $a$, $b$, $c$ and $d$, we use the orthonormality of $|\mathrm{V}_\theta\rangle$ and $|\mathrm{H}_\theta\rangle$:

$$a = \langle\mathrm{V}_\theta|\mathrm{V}\rangle = \begin{bmatrix}\cos\theta & \sin\theta\end{bmatrix}\begin{bmatrix}1\\0\end{bmatrix} = \cos\theta, \tag{7.12a}$$

$$b = \langle\mathrm{H}_\theta|\mathrm{V}\rangle = \begin{bmatrix}-\sin\theta & \cos\theta\end{bmatrix}\begin{bmatrix}1\\0\end{bmatrix} = -\sin\theta, \tag{7.12b}$$

$$c = \langle\mathrm{V}_\theta|\mathrm{H}\rangle = \begin{bmatrix}\cos\theta & \sin\theta\end{bmatrix}\begin{bmatrix}0\\1\end{bmatrix} = \sin\theta, \tag{7.12c}$$

$$d = \langle\mathrm{H}_\theta|\mathrm{H}\rangle = \begin{bmatrix}-\sin\theta & \cos\theta\end{bmatrix}\begin{bmatrix}0\\1\end{bmatrix} = \cos\theta. \tag{7.12d}$$

Substitution of Equations 7.12 into Equations 7.11 then gives Equations 7.10.

## 7.2 Quantum cryptography

### 7.2.1 Classical and quantum cryptography

Cryptography is the process of concealing the contents of a message from all except the intended recipients, such that a message can be sent between two people without risk that the contents of the message can be read by anyone else who happens to intercept the message en route. Historically, cryptography has

**Figure 7.3** Claude Shannon (1916–2001) founded the subject of information theory, which forms the basis of all modern communications systems, in 1948, but secure (one-time pad) encryption methods had been used as early as 1917, by Gilbert Vernham and Joseph Mauborgne.

been used to ensure secrecy in important communications such as those of spies, military leaders and governments. In today's information age, cryptography is ubiquitous: you probably use cryptography every week for internet banking transactions and internet shopping, and cryptographic techniques are increasingly employed in consumer electronic devices such as digital media players.

Modern methods of transmitting information are based upon encoding the message in binary form, i.e. as a sequence of 1s and 0s, an idea developed by Claude Shannon (Figure 7.3). Each item, i.e. 1 or 0, is a single **bit**. Rendering a message into a standard binary code understood by all computers is not encryption; the resulting binary form of the message is known as **plaintext**. Shannon established that a message could be encrypted by adding to the plaintext a **cryptographic key** to produce a **ciphertext** (or **cryptogram**). The key is a randomly chosen string of 0s and 1s with the same length as the message. How this works is shown in Figure 7.4.

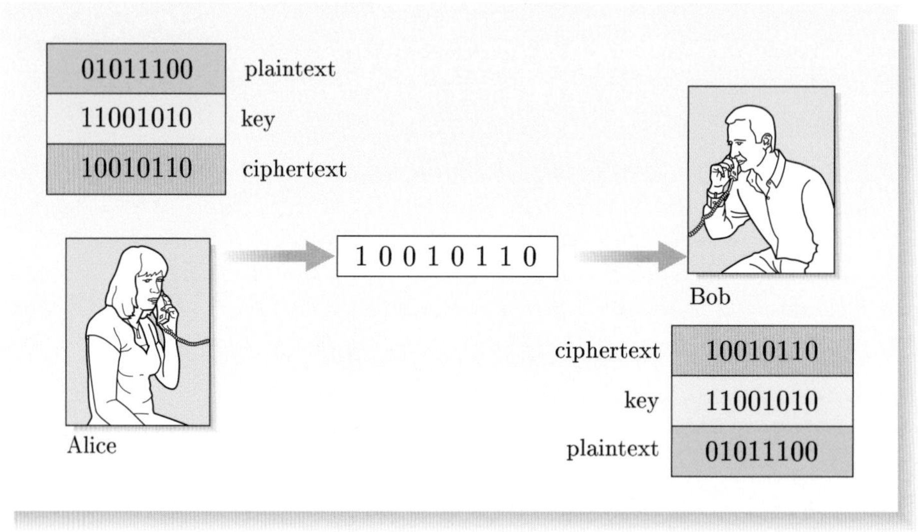


**Figure 7.4** In this simple example of cryptography, the sender adds each bit of the plaintext to the corresponding bit of the key using the rules of binary addition ($0 + 0 = 0$, $0 + 1 = 1$, $1 + 0 = 1$, $1 + 1 = 0$) to obtain the ciphertext. The ciphertext is then transmitted to the receiver who has an exact copy of the key. The receiver is able to unlock the plaintext by once more adding the key to the ciphertext. Any eavesdropper who listens in but doesn't have an exact copy of the key may intercept the ciphertext but will not be able to recover the plaintext, even if she knows the method used for the encryption (simple binary addition in this case).

The randomness of the key destroys any patterns based on the frequency of different letters in the message, making the ciphertext uncrackable.

Once the recipient is in possession of the ciphertext, he can add the key to the ciphertext to recover the message. As long as only the sender and receiver are in possession of the key, anyone else intercepting the ciphertext will not be able to uncover the contents of the message. Shannon was able to show that this type of scheme cannot be cracked provided that the key is random and is as long as the message, and that the key is used only once (i.e. to send one message); such a key is known as a **one-time pad**. In practice, it is rather impractical to use a key as long as the message being sent, so a key length is chosen which ensures that, for any eavesdropper intercepting the message, it would take too long to crack the encryption — typical lengths are 128 or 256 bits. Modern cryptographic techniques also avoid simple binary addition of the cryptographic key and the plaintext, but use some more complicated mathematical operation.

This brings us to the central problem of cryptography: how to arrange for the sender and receiver to have a copy of the cryptographic key without revealing it to any eavesdroppers. This is called the **key distribution problem**. In order to send information securely, both sender and receiver must know the cryptographic key. However, if the communication channel being used to establish the key is monitored by an eavesdropper, the encryption is rendered useless, as the eavesdropper will also have a copy of the key and will be able to unlock the ciphertext when it is sent. Since all information, including cryptographic keys, is encoded in the physical properties of some object or signal, any method relying upon classical physics will be vulnerable to eavesdropping, *since the eavesdropper can measure physical properties without disturbing them*, and so the eavesdropping may go undetected by the sender and receiver. However, we know that measurement of an observable in a quantum-mechanical system necessarily disturbs the state of the system — after measurement, the quantum system will be in one of the eigenvectors of the observable's operator. This fact forms the basis of quantum cryptography. Gilles Brassard, one of the pioneers of quantum cryptography, put it as follows:

> 'Quantum cryptography is the only approach to privacy ever proposed that allows two parties (who do not share a long secret key ahead of time) to communicate with provably perfect secrecy under the nose of an eavesdropper endowed with unlimited computational power and whose technology is limited by nothing but the fundamental laws of nature.'

To date, most methods of **quantum key distribution** (QKD) rely upon encoding the cryptographic key with the polarization of photons. In the following sections we'll explore two different schemes: (i) the *BB84 protocol*, which exploits the fact that any measurement by an eavesdropper will disturb the state of the photons in transmission, and (ii) the *Eckert protocol*, which exploits the non-local correlations of entangled photons. These correlations are destroyed by eavesdropping.

## 7.2.2 QKD with polarized photons — the BB84 protocol

Suppose that two people in different locations, Alice and Bob, wish to establish a cryptographic key in order to communicate securely. Alice and Bob have available to them a **classical communication channel** (such as a telephone line) which is public — eavesdropping on any communications sent via this channel could be undetectable. Alice and Bob also have available a **quantum communication channel** over which they seek to establish a cryptographic key by encoding a sequence of bits in the polarization states of individual photons. Encoding bits in quantum states allows Alice and Bob to determine whether their communications have been intercepted. In the following discussion we'll show how Alice and Bob can establish a common cryptographic key, and ensure it has not been discovered by an eavesdropper. The scheme, often referred to as the BB84 protocol, is depicted in Figure 7.5, and was first introduced by Charles Bennett and Gilles Brassard in 1984.

'Classical' channels will inevitably involve transistors and the like that require quantum mechanics for an understanding of how they work. However, the information is carried by vast numbers of electrons or photons, the behaviour of which can be described by classical theories. Quantum channels typically involve information encoded in single photons.

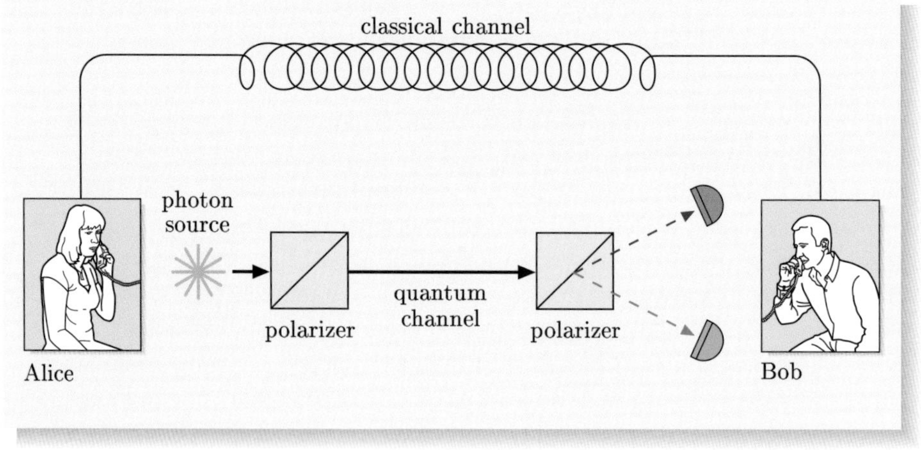


**Figure 7.5** Alice and Bob seek to establish a secure cryptographic key and at the same time ensure that an eavesdropper hasn't discovered the key by listening in on the quantum channel. Alice uses a quantum communication channel to send bits encoded in the polarization of photons to Bob. Alice and Bob can also communicate over a public classical channel (e.g. a telephone line). Any information sent via this classical channel is considered insecure, since it is not possible to ascertain whether or not it has been intercepted by an eavesdropper.

In this scheme, Alice sends the key to Bob by encoding bits of data in the polarization states of photons. We shall assume that Alice and Bob have previously agreed to use a particular correspondence between ones and zeros and the measured polarization states of photons. This correspondence is shown in Table 7.1. These 'quantum bits' are sent over the quantum communication channel, which could be an optical fibre that has been designed to preserve the polarization of the photons during transmission.

**Table 7.1** Correspondence for encoding bits in the polarization of photons. In the H/V basis (red), a vertically polarized photon, $|\mathrm{V}\rangle$, represents 1, etc. The diagonal basis is indicated in purple.

| | | |
|---|---|---|
| H/V | $\lvert\mathrm{V}\rangle$ | $\lvert\mathrm{H}\rangle$ |
| Diagonal | $\lvert\mathrm{V}_{45}\rangle$ | $\lvert\mathrm{H}_{45}\rangle$ |
| Bit | 1 | 0 |

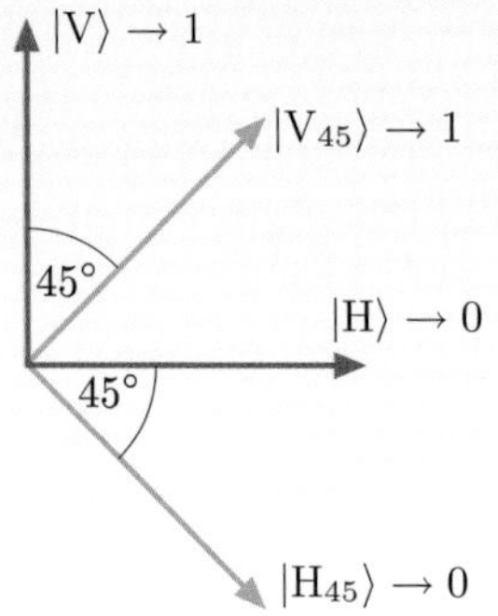


In the following discussion it is important to bear in mind that neither Alice nor Bob knows the cryptographic key prior to going through the process of simultaneously generating and sharing it. In brief, the sequence of actions that Alice and Bob undertake in order to establish and share the key are as follows.

1. For each bit to be transmitted, Alice randomly chooses to use either the H/V basis or the diagonal basis for transmission.
2. In her chosen basis, Alice transmits either a 1 or a 0, chosen randomly, encoded as in Table 7.1.
3. Bob randomly chooses either the H/V basis or the diagonal basis to measure the polarization of the photon sent by Alice in the previous step.
4. Steps 1–3 are repeated until a sufficiently long string of random bits has been transmitted.
5. Bob and Alice let each other know over the (insecure) classical channel which basis they used for each photon. Bob and Alice discard any bits for which they did not employ the same basis.
6. In order to test for eavesdroppers, Alice and Bob then compare a subset of their bit strings. If these bits match, Bob and Alice use the remaining undisclosed bits to make up the cryptographic key.

In order to understand how this process results in a secure key, we need to examine each step carefully. For each photon transmitted, Alice chooses either the H/V or the diagonal basis at random. Alice also chooses at random whether to send a 1 or a 0 bit. Examining Table 7.1, we see that, for example, if Alice has chosen the H/V basis and wishes to send a 1, she must send a photon in the state $|\mathrm{V}\rangle$. As Bob receives the photon he makes a polarization measurement, randomly choosing either the H/V or the diagonal basis to make his measurement. The possible results of his measurements are the subject of the following exercise.

**Exercise 7.5** Fill in the bottom row of the following table showing the possible outcomes of Bob's measurements. Where 0 or 1 cannot be predicted with certainty, write '1 or 0'. The diagonal basis is denoted by a D.

| | | | | | | | | |
|---|---|---|---|---|---|---|---|---|
| Alice's basis | H/V | H/V | H/V | H/V | D | D | D | D |
| Alice's sent bit | 1 | 0 | 1 | 0 | 1 | 0 | 1 | 0 |
| Bob's basis | H/V | H/V | D | D | H/V | H/V | D | D |
| Bob's detected bit | | | | | | | | |

■

Before proceeding, you **must** refer to the solution to Exercise 7.5.

Examining the first and second columns (and the last two columns) in the table, for which Bob measured in the same basis as Alice prepared the photon, we see that Alice and Bob record the same bit. On the other hand, examining columns 3–6, for which Bob measures in a *different* basis to that used by Alice, we see that Bob will measure a 1 or a 0 with equal probability, no matter what Alice sends. This is because the H/V and diagonal bases are *complementary*, as defined in the last section. As a result, Alice and Bob will record different bit values for half (on average) of the occasions when they employ different bases. Bob measures the value of the bit sent by Alice with certainty only if he and Alice happen to use the *same* basis. Once Alice has sent her random string of bits, Alice and Bob communicate publicly, i.e. over the classical channel, concerning which basis they employed for each photon. This information cannot be used by an eavesdropper to reconstruct the string of bits sent by Alice. Alice and Bob then discard all bits for which they did not employ the same basis. The remaining sequence of bits possessed by both Bob and Alice should then be identical copies and so could be used as a cryptographic key.

We now ask: what happens if an eavesdropper, Eve, intercepts photons sent over the quantum channel and makes a polarization measurement in either the H/V or the diagonal basis? If she is to stand a chance of remaining undetected by Bob and Alice, she'll have to forward a photon to Bob that is polarized according to the outcome of her measurement. For example, if Alice and Bob both use the H/V basis, and Alice sends a 0 bit to Bob, which Eve intercepts also in the H/V basis, Eve will measure and send on a 0 in the H/V basis, and her eavesdropping will go undetected. But if Eve measures in the diagonal basis, she may measure 1 or 0 with equal probability, and hence stands a 50% chance of sending a wrongly polarized photon to Bob. As a result, the keys held by Alice and Bob will no longer be identical. If Alice and Bob then compare publicly (over the classical channel) a subset of their respective bit strings, they can detect these errors. If errors are found, they discard the key. Conversely, if no error is found, the key is deemed secure. In this case, Alice and Bob discard the bits they have discussed over the classical channel (since this communication may have been eavesdropped upon), and they can use the remaining (undisclosed) bits of their strings as the cryptographic key.

**Exercise 7.6** A large number of photons are sent by Alice, and the polarization of each photon is measured by Eve, who randomly chooses her measurement basis. In the hope of being undetected, Eve then transmits to Bob a photon in the polarization state that she measures. By constructing a suitable table, determine what percentage of the bits in Alice's and Bob's strings will differ after they've discarded all bits for which they used different bases. ■

### 7.2.3 QKD with entanglement — the Eckert protocol

Secure quantum key distribution can also be carried out by exploiting pairs of entangled photons. As we shall see, the non-local character of entangled states of photons allows Alice and Bob to determine with certainty whether or not anyone has eavesdropped on their key exchange. In the BB84 cryptography scheme, Alice and Bob discarded all measurements in which they used different measurement bases, and then, in order to test whether the resulting key was secure, they compared a subset of the bits of the key. These 'test' bits are subsequently discarded. Here we describe a scheme employing pairs of entangled photons, which uses some of the measurements made with *different* bases to ensure the security of the cryptographic key. For this scheme, it is not necessary to discard bits of the key once it is deemed secure.

The scheme we describe is based on a proposal due to Artur Eckert; we shall call it the **Eckert protocol**.

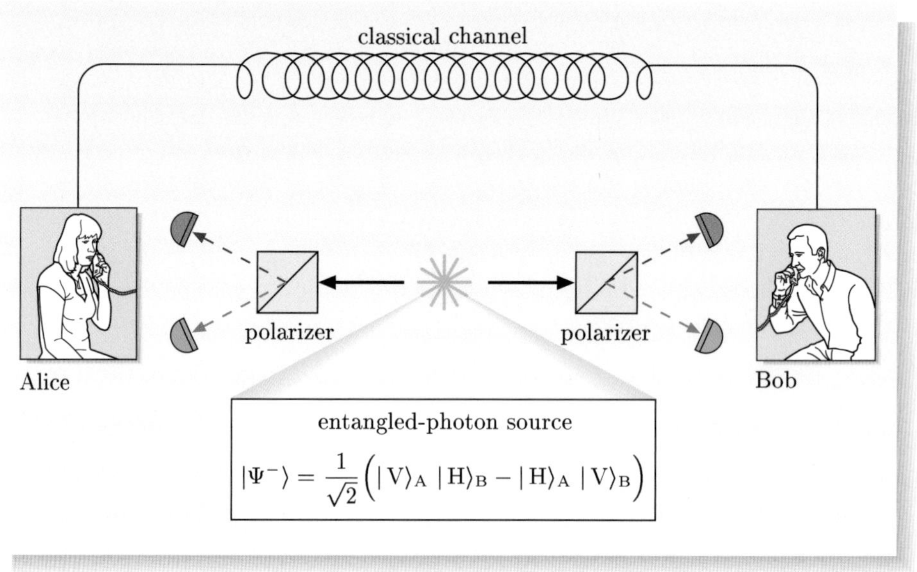


**Figure 7.6** Quantum key distribution with entangled photons. A source of entangled photons exists between Alice and Bob. One photon of each pair is sent to Alice, and the other is sent to Bob. Alice and Bob perform polarization measurements on the photons they receive. They also have a classical channel. Neither Alice nor Bob knows the random cryptographic key prior to the process they go through to generate it.

Suppose that a source producing entangled pairs of photons is located between Alice and Bob, as shown in Figure 7.6. One photon of each pair is sent to Bob, and the other is sent to Alice. The photons might travel in an optical fibre of a quality that preserves the polarization, or even in free space. The method uses the general basis $|V_\theta\rangle$ and $|H_\theta\rangle$, defined in Equations 7.2, for several values of $\theta$. The sequence of events that enables a key to be established is, in outline, as follows.

1. Alice and Bob both make a polarization measurement on their respective photons. Alice chooses randomly from the three bases defined by $\theta = \alpha = (0°, 22.5°, 45°)$, and Bob chooses randomly from the bases defined by $\theta = \beta = (22.5°, 45°, -22.5°)$. The reasons for choosing these angles will become clear later.

Alice:
$\theta = \alpha = (0°, 22.5°, 45°)$

Bob:
$\theta = \beta = (22.5°, 45°, -22.5°)$

2. Alice and Bob reveal over the classical communication channel which basis they used for each measurement.
3. Alice and Bob divide their measurements up into two groups: those for which they employed different bases (group I), and those for which they employed the same basis (group II).
4. Alice and Bob use the group I measurements to determine whether their measurements exhibit quantum non-local correlations. If this is the case, Alice and Bob use the measurements from group II to construct the cryptographic key, and they can be confident that this key is secure.

group I: different bases

group II: same basis

We now examine this process in more detail. Depending on the nature of the source, entangled pairs of photons can be produced in various states. Four particularly important entangled states are known as **Bell states**:

Bell states are also called **maximally-entangled states**.

$$|\Psi^{\pm}\rangle = \frac{1}{\sqrt{2}}\Big(|\mathrm{V}\rangle_\mathrm{A}\,|\mathrm{H}\rangle_\mathrm{B} \pm |\mathrm{H}\rangle_\mathrm{A}\,|\mathrm{V}\rangle_\mathrm{B}\Big), \tag{7.13a}$$

$$|\Phi^{\pm}\rangle = \frac{1}{\sqrt{2}}\Big(|\mathrm{V}\rangle_\mathrm{A}\,|\mathrm{V}\rangle_\mathrm{B} \pm |\mathrm{H}\rangle_\mathrm{A}\,|\mathrm{H}\rangle_\mathrm{B}\Big), \tag{7.13b}$$

where the subscripts A and B label the two photons, and we have in mind that photon A is sent to Alice and photon B is sent to Bob. In Section 6.4.3, we considered the state $|\Phi^{+}\rangle$ in connection with Aspect's experiments. Here, we shall consider a different Bell state:

$$|\Psi^{-}\rangle = \frac{1}{\sqrt{2}}\Big(|\mathrm{V}\rangle_\mathrm{A}\,|\mathrm{H}\rangle_\mathrm{B} - |\mathrm{H}\rangle_\mathrm{A}\,|\mathrm{V}\rangle_\mathrm{B}\Big), \tag{7.14}$$

but this choice is not an essential one for the encryption method we shall describe — any of the four Bell states in Equations 7.13 could be used.

**Exercise 7.7** By expressing the state vector for the entangled photons in Equation 7.14 as a linear combination of $|\mathrm{V}_\theta\rangle$ and $|\mathrm{H}_\theta\rangle$ using the relationships in Equations 7.10, show that Equation 7.14 may be written as

$$|\Psi^{-}\rangle = \frac{1}{\sqrt{2}}\Big(|\mathrm{V}_\theta\rangle_\mathrm{A}\,|\mathrm{H}_\theta\rangle_\mathrm{B} - |\mathrm{H}_\theta\rangle_\mathrm{A}\,|\mathrm{V}_\theta\rangle_\mathrm{B}\Big) \tag{7.15}$$

for any angle $\theta$. ■

This exercise shows that the entangled state $|\Psi^{-}\rangle$ 'looks the same from all angles' in the same way that the state $|\Phi^{+}\rangle$ considered in Chapter 6 looked the same from all angles.

From Equation 7.15 we can see that as long as Alice and Bob choose the same basis for making their measurements (i.e. the same value of $\theta$), their results will be 'anti-correlated', meaning that whenever Alice finds a photon vertically polarized in the $\theta$ direction, the entangled state will collapse onto its first component and, as a result, Bob will find a horizontally-polarized photon when his detector is oriented in the same direction. Similarly, if Alice finds a horizontally-polarized photon, Bob will find a vertically-polarized photon. This is true for any choice of $\theta$ made by Alice and Bob.

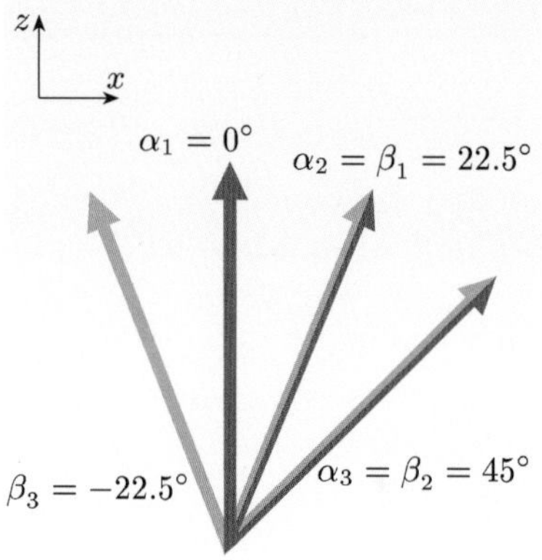


**Figure 7.7** Polarizer axis directions used by Alice ($\alpha$) and Bob ($\beta$).

$P_{\pm\pm}(\alpha, \beta)$ should not be confused with $P_\pm$ defined in Equations 7.5.

Now suppose that entangled pairs of photons (Equation 7.14) are being sent out to Alice and Bob. When each receives a photon, they perform a polarization measurement on it. For these measurements, Alice and Bob select their polarizer axes randomly from three directions: Alice selects her axis direction $\alpha$ randomly from $\alpha_1 = 0°$, $\alpha_2 = 22.5°$ and $\alpha_3 = 45°$, and Bob selects his axis direction $\beta$ from $\beta_1 = 22.5°$, $\beta_2 = 45°$ and $\beta_3 = -22.5°$; see Figure 7.7.

We will describe the correlations between Alice's and Bob's measurements in terms of the probabilities $P_{\pm\pm}(\alpha, \beta)$, describing the probability of measurement outcomes when Alice and Bob set their polarizer axes at angles $\alpha$ and $\beta$, respectively. Here the first subscript refers to Alice's measurement and the second refers to Bob's measurement, and we use a '+' to refer to detection of vertical polarization (value $+1$), and a '$-$' to refer to detection of horizontal polarization (value $-1$). For example, $P_{+-}(\alpha, \beta)$ is the probability that, for a single pair of photons, Alice detects a vertically-polarized photon with her polarizer set at $\theta = \alpha$, and Bob detects a horizontally-polarized photon with his polarizer set at $\theta = \beta$. If the photons remain undisturbed as they travel to Alice and Bob, they will be in the entangled state described by Equation 7.14 when they are detected. That being the case, the probabilities $P_{\pm\pm}(\alpha, \beta)$ can be calculated quantum mechanically, as shown in the following exercise.

**Exercise 7.8** Use Equations 7.12 and 7.14 to find an expression for $P_{++}(\alpha, \beta)$ in terms of the angles $\alpha$ and $\beta$. ■

It can be shown, using arguments similar to those in the exercise above, that the probabilities for the four possible outcomes of a measurement by Alice and Bob on one pair of photons are given by

$$P_{++}(\alpha, \beta) = P_{--}(\alpha, \beta) = \tfrac{1}{2}\sin^2(\alpha - \beta), \tag{7.16a}$$

$$P_{+-}(\alpha, \beta) = P_{-+}(\alpha, \beta) = \tfrac{1}{2}\cos^2(\alpha - \beta). \tag{7.16b}$$

From these equations you will see that when Alice and Bob employ the same basis (i.e. when their polarizer axes are parallel and $\alpha = \beta$), their results are perfectly *anti-correlated*, meaning that $P_{++} = P_{--} = 0$ and $P_{+-} + P_{-+} = 1$.

This provides Alice and Bob with a means for establishing their cryptographic key: Alice and Bob can tell each other over the classical channel which polarizer axis direction they used for each polarization measurement. By taking the results from all measurements where they employed the *same* basis (group II), Alice and Bob will have strings of bits which are perfectly anti-correlated: Alice's key will be the same as Bob's key but with all the 1s replaced with 0s, and vice versa. If one of Alice or Bob, by previous agreement, interchanges 1s and 0s, Alice and Bob will have established a common key.

But can Alice and Bob be sure that their key hasn't been compromised by Eve listening in? They could proceed in the same way as with the BB84 protocol described previously, and compare a subset of their key bits to check for errors induced by Eve's listening in and collapsing the entangled state. However, the entanglement of the photons offers Alice and Bob an alternative means for establishing the security of their key, and it turns out that the quantity that enables them to do this is the *correlation function*

For a rotationally-invariant state we could write $C(\alpha_i, \beta_j) = C(\alpha_i - \beta_j)$. We refrain from doing this here because we will eventually need to consider a non-rotationally-invariant state.

$$C(\alpha_i, \beta_j) = P_{++}(\alpha_i, \beta_j) + P_{--}(\alpha_i, \beta_j) - P_{+-}(\alpha_i, \beta_j) - P_{-+}(\alpha_i, \beta_j). \tag{7.17}$$

This is precisely the quantity introduced in Section 6.3.4 in connection with tests for hidden variables. Substituting Equation 7.16 into Equation 7.17, we find

$$C(\alpha_i, \beta_j) = \sin^2(\alpha_i - \beta_j) - \cos^2(\alpha_i - \beta_j) = -\cos[2(\alpha_i - \beta_j)]. \quad (7.18)$$

This has the opposite sign to the correlation function for entangled photons found in Chapter 6 (Equation 6.30). This is because a different entangled state ($|\Phi^+\rangle$) was considered in the earlier chapter.

so $C(\alpha_i, \beta_j)$ can take values between $-1$ and $+1$. A value of $+1$ indicates that Alice's and Bob's measurements are entirely correlated, meaning that their measurements have the same outcome. A value of $-1$ indicates that their measurements are entirely anti-correlated, having opposite outcomes. A value of 0 indicates that there is no correlation between the results of Alice's and Bob's measurements.

- Give values of $\alpha_i - \beta_j$ for which $C(\alpha_i, \beta_j) = +1$ and $C(\alpha_i, \beta_j) = -1$, and interpret your answers.

- $C(\alpha_i, \beta_j) = +1$ when $\alpha_i - \beta_j = \pi/2$; this corresponds to the fact that orthogonal analyzers will both register vertical or both register horizontal polarized photons, i.e. $P_{++} = P_{--} = \frac{1}{2}$, $P_{+-} = P_{-+} = 0$.

  $C(\alpha_i, \beta_j) = -1$ when $\alpha_i - \beta_j = 0$; this corresponds to the fact that parallel analyzers will register horizontal/vertical or vertical/horizontal polarized photons, i.e. $P_{+-} = P_{-+} = \frac{1}{2}$, $P_{++} = P_{--} = 0$.

In order to establish whether or not the photons arriving at Alice and Bob's detectors are described by the state in Equation 7.14, Alice and Bob communicate over the classical channel the outcomes of some of the measurements where they employed *different* bases (group I). This allows them to calculate, using the measured probabilities, a value of the expression

Comparing with Equation 6.20, we have $\alpha_1 = \theta_1, \beta_1 = \theta_2$, $\alpha_3 = \theta'_1$ and $\beta_3 = \theta'_2$.

$$\Sigma = C(\alpha_1, \beta_1) + C(\alpha_1, \beta_3) + C(\alpha_3, \beta_1) - C(\alpha_3, \beta_3), \quad (7.19)$$

which you will recognize as the expression in the CHSH inequality introduced in Section 6.3. You will recall that the presence of local hidden variables would require $|\Sigma|$ less than or equal to 2. This limit can only be exceeded if there are quantum-mechanical correlations.

**Exercise 7.9** Show, using Equation 7.18, that, for the Bell states described by Equation 7.14, $\Sigma$ takes the value $-2\sqrt{2}$ for the settings $\alpha_1, \alpha_3, \beta_1, \beta_3$ chosen by Alice and Bob ($\alpha_1 = 0°$, $\alpha_3 = 45°$, $\beta_1 = 22.5°$, $\beta_3 = -22.5°$). ■

If the photons behave as a quantum-mechanically entangled system exhibiting non-local correlations, as discussed in Chapter 6, then for the set of angles in the exercise above we expect to find $|\Sigma| = 2\sqrt{2}$. But, what happens to the value of $\Sigma$ if Eve intercepts the photons? Suppose that Eve intercepts one or both of each pair of entangled photons and makes a polarization measurement. She could create and send on a new pair of entangled photons, but this would be pointless because the values obtained by Alice and Bob for the new entangled pair need not be the same as the values obtained by Eve for the intercepted pair, so Eve would learn nothing about Alice and Bob's key. Instead, Eve might try to send on a pair of photons that are polarized according to her measurements, as she did when eavesdropping on the BB84 scheme. But, of course, her act of measurement will have collapsed the state vector and destroyed the entanglement between the photons! This means the quantum non-local correlations between the photons are no longer present.

Measurement destroys entanglement.

For example, suppose that Eve measures the intercepted photons in the H/V basis. Following her measurement, the state vector will collapse onto either

$|V\rangle_A |H\rangle_B$ or $|H\rangle_A |V\rangle_B$. Eve will then need to prepare photons in the same state as she measured them (i.e. $|V\rangle_A |H\rangle_B$ or $|H\rangle_A |V\rangle_B$) and send them to Alice and Bob. However, when Alice and Bob make measurements on these photons, there will be no correlation between their measurement results: if Eve sends the state $|V\rangle_A |H\rangle_B$ to Alice and Bob, the probability that a measurement by Alice at angle $\alpha$ will yield a vertically-polarized photon will be $\cos^2\alpha$, *but it will not depend in any way upon what Bob measures for his photon*. The quantum non-local correlations are gone. To see what this does to the correlation function, we must calculate $P_{\pm\pm}(\alpha,\beta)$ for the states $|V\rangle_A |H\rangle_B$ and $|H\rangle_A |V\rangle_B$; let us do it for $|V\rangle_A |H\rangle_B$, which is the same as $|VH\rangle$, in positional notation. Here are two of the cases, with Alice measuring in the basis at angle $\theta = \alpha$ and Bob at angle $\theta = \beta$:

$$P_{++}(\alpha,\beta) = \left|\langle V_\alpha V_\beta|VH\rangle\right|^2 = \left|\langle V_\alpha|V\rangle_A \langle V_\beta|H\rangle_B\right|^2 = \cos^2\alpha\sin^2\beta,$$
$$P_{--}(\alpha,\beta) = \left|\langle H_\alpha H_\beta|VH\rangle\right|^2 = \left|\langle H_\alpha|V\rangle_A \langle H_\beta|H\rangle_B\right|^2 = \sin^2\alpha\cos^2\beta.$$

**Exercise 7.10** Find expressions for $P_{+-}(\alpha,\beta)$ and $P_{-+}(\alpha,\beta)$ for the state $|V\rangle_A |H\rangle_B$. ■

With these expressions for $P_{\pm\pm}(\alpha,\beta)$, the correlation function $C(\alpha_i,\beta_j)$ in Equation 7.17 will no longer have the form given in Equation 7.18 that applied to the entangled state $|\Psi^-\rangle$. We now have

Note that in this case, $C(\alpha_i,\beta_j)$ is *not* a function of $\alpha_i - \beta_j$; this is because the state sent by Eve does not look the same from different angles.

$$\begin{aligned} C(\alpha_i,\beta_j) &= \cos^2\alpha_i\sin^2\beta_j + \sin^2\alpha_i\cos^2\beta_j \\ &\quad - \cos^2\alpha_i\cos^2\beta_j - \sin^2\alpha_i\sin^2\beta_j \\ &= -(\cos^2\alpha_i - \sin^2\alpha_i)(\cos^2\beta_j - \sin^2\beta_j) \\ &= -\cos(2\alpha_i)\cos(2\beta_j). \end{aligned} \tag{7.20}$$

Substituting for the angles noted above (for Alice, $\alpha_1 = 0°$ and $\alpha_3 = 45°$, and for Bob, $\beta_1 = 22.5°$ and $\beta_3 = -22.5°$) we find

$$C(\alpha_1,\beta_1) = -\frac{1}{\sqrt{2}},$$
$$C(\alpha_1,\beta_3) = -\frac{1}{\sqrt{2}},$$
$$C(\alpha_3,\beta_1) = 0,$$
$$C(\alpha_3,\beta_3) = 0.$$

- Verify the expression for $C(\alpha_1,\beta_1)$.
- $C(\alpha_1,\beta_1) = -\cos(0)\cos(45°) = -1/\sqrt{2}$.

Putting together the values for $C(\alpha_i,\beta_j)$, we find $\Sigma = -\sqrt{2}$. This has a magnitude that is much less than the CHSH limit, whereas if Eve had not eavesdropped, the value of $-2\sqrt{2}$ would have exceeded the CHSH limit of $|\Sigma| \leq 2$. There is therefore clear evidence of eavesdropping.

In summary, the non-local behaviour of entangled particles (in this case photons) can only be maintained if, during their journey, they remain undisturbed. By checking the correlations between measurements, Alice and Bob are able to determine if non-locality has been maintained. If it has, then Alice and Bob can be assured that Eve has learnt nothing about the key.

### 7.2.4 Quantum cryptography in the real world

In 2000, a dramatic experimental demonstration of quantum key distribution was reported by Anton Zeilinger and co-workers in Austria. These scientists successfully implemented the BB84 protocol *and* used a source of entangled photons to implement a cryptographic scheme similar to that described in Section 7.2.3. An image of the Venus of Willendorf was encrypted, transmitted over 360 metres, and successfully decrypted upon receipt. These systems have now been shown to work over many kilometres, and commercial systems for quantum cryptography are now available from several companies which are able to exchange 100 cryptographic keys per second. It seems certain that these systems will be the standard for secure data transmission in future years.

The Venus of Willendorf is about 23 000 years old; she now resides in the Naturhistorisches Museum, Vienna.

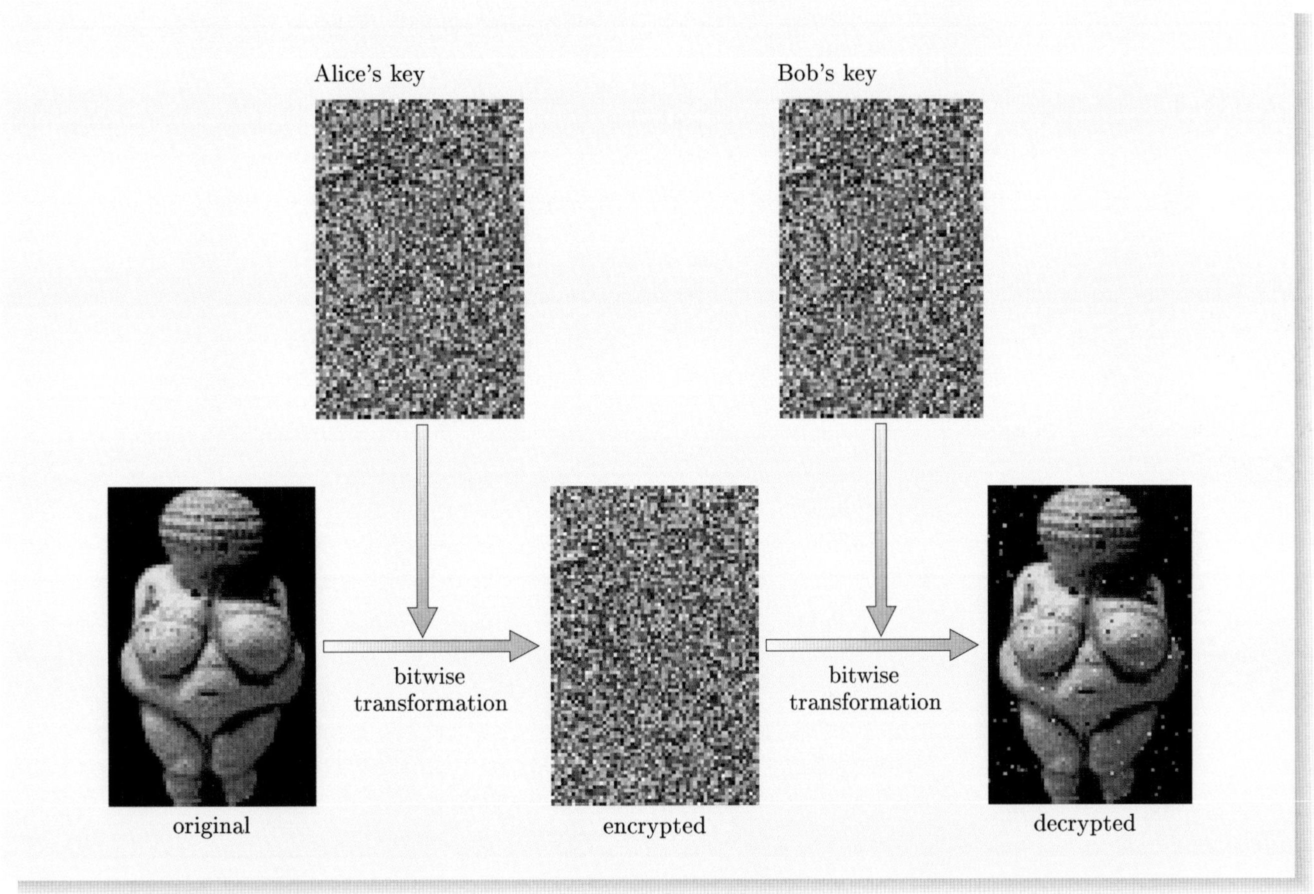


**Figure 7.8** In 2000, researchers in Austria successfully exchanged a 49 984 bit cryptographic key using entangled photons. This key was used to encrypt an image of Venus of Willendorf which was then transmitted over a distance of 360 m and successfully decrypted with good fidelity.

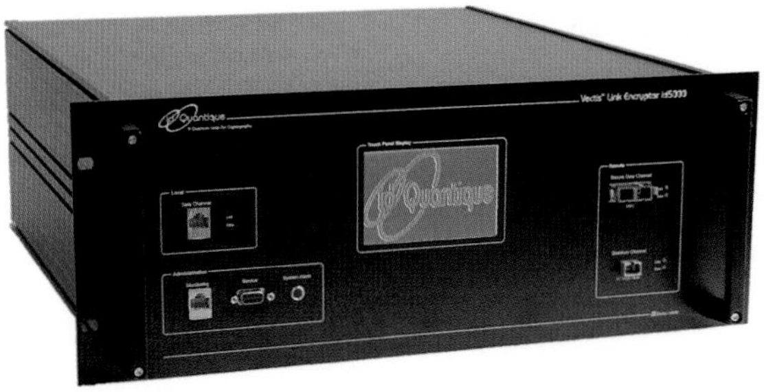

**Figure 7.9** A system for quantum encryption of computer data for secure transmission across a network. This system is capable of transmitting encrypted data over distances of up to 100 km, with new cryptographic keys generated at up to 100 times per second. The system shown in this picture is commercially available and is produced by the company id Quantique.

## 7.3 Quantum teleportation

In science fiction, teleportation describes a process where an object (e.g. a person) disappears in one location and an identical replica object appears at some remote location. One way of achieving this might be to take measurements of all the object's characteristics, transmit these to the remote location, and then construct a copy of the object there. Classically, we would have to measure the positions and velocities of all the particles in the object, something that is ruled out by the uncertainty principle. Quantum-mechanically, it is practically impossible to measure the state of an object without changing that state. There is also a fundamental theorem that prevents us from producing a copy of an object to place beside the original; this is the 'no-cloning theorem' which we now introduce.

### 7.3.1 The no-cloning theorem

Having read about all the problems that Eve faces when trying to eavesdrop on Alice and Bob's key exchanges in the previous sections, you may be wondering why Eve doesn't make a number of identical copies of the photons she intercepts before making her measurements. If she were able to do this, she could send one copy on to Alice or Bob, and make a number of measurements on the remaining copies, allowing her to determine with certainty the state of the intercepted photon. This would then allow her to determine the cryptographic key and remain undetected! So it seems that we should ask the question: 'Is it possible to make an exact copy (a clone) of an arbitrary unknown quantum state?'

Let us consider trying to clone an unknown state of a photon, which we call photon A. We can write a general state of photon A in the H/V basis as

$$|\psi\rangle_{\mathrm{A}} = \alpha\,|\mathrm{V}\rangle_{\mathrm{A}} + \beta\,|\mathrm{H}\rangle_{\mathrm{A}}. \tag{7.21}$$

We could choose any other basis rather than the H/V basis, and the arguments would be unchanged. In order to make a copy of photon A, we need to take another photon (an 'ancillary' photon), which we shall label B, initially in some state $|\phi\rangle_{\mathrm{B}}$, and place it in exactly the same state as photon A. Before our cloning process, the joint state vector for both photons is the product state $|\psi\rangle_{\mathrm{A}}\,|\phi\rangle_{\mathrm{B}}$. Our cloning machine must act on this state to form $|\psi\rangle_A |\psi\rangle_B$, and it must be able to do this for *any* state $|\psi\rangle_A$, i.e. for any choice of $\alpha$ and $\beta$ in Equation 7.21. We should not do anything too violent to the initial state $|\psi\rangle_A |\phi\rangle_B$; in particular, we must avoid taking a measurement that causes the state of photon A to collapse irreversibly. This means that we must consider the normal time-development of states in quantum mechanics, which is governed by Schrödinger's equation. Since Schrödinger's equation is linear, we can represent the effect of the quantum cloning machine by a linear operator $\widehat{\mathrm{U}}$ which needs to act according to the rule

$$\widehat{\mathrm{U}}\,|\psi\rangle_A |\phi\rangle_B = |\psi\rangle_A |\psi\rangle_B. \tag{7.22}$$

Expanding the right-hand side of Equation 7.22 using Equation 7.21 gives

$$\begin{aligned} |\psi\rangle_A |\psi\rangle_B &= \Big(\alpha\,|\mathrm{V}\rangle_A + \beta\,|\mathrm{H}\rangle_A\Big)\Big(\alpha\,|\mathrm{V}\rangle_B + \beta\,|\mathrm{H}\rangle_B\Big) \\ &= \alpha^2\,|\mathrm{V}\rangle_A |\mathrm{V}\rangle_B + \beta^2\,|\mathrm{H}\rangle_A |\mathrm{H}\rangle_B \\ &\quad + \alpha\beta\,|\mathrm{V}\rangle_A |\mathrm{H}\rangle_B + \alpha\beta\,|\mathrm{H}\rangle_A |\mathrm{V}\rangle_B. \end{aligned} \tag{7.23}$$

For our cloning machine to work, Equation 7.22 must hold true for *all* $\psi$. In particular, it must be true if either $\alpha = 0$ and $\beta = 1$ or if $\beta = 0$ and $\alpha = 1$, conditions which lead respectively to

$$\widehat{\mathrm{U}}\,|\mathrm{H}\rangle_A |\phi\rangle_B = |\mathrm{H}\rangle_A |\mathrm{H}\rangle_B, \qquad \widehat{\mathrm{U}}\,|\mathrm{V}\rangle_A |\phi\rangle_B = |\mathrm{V}\rangle_A |\mathrm{V}\rangle_B. \tag{7.24}$$

We now expand the left-hand side of Equation 7.22:

$$\begin{aligned} \widehat{\mathrm{U}}\,|\psi\rangle_A |\phi\rangle_B &= \widehat{\mathrm{U}}\Big(\alpha\,|\mathrm{V}\rangle_A + \beta\,|\mathrm{H}\rangle_A\Big)\,|\phi\rangle_B \\ &= \alpha\Big(\widehat{\mathrm{U}}\,|\mathrm{V}\rangle_A |\phi\rangle_B\Big) + \beta\Big(\widehat{\mathrm{U}}\,|\mathrm{H}\rangle_A |\phi\rangle_B\Big) \\ &= \alpha\,|\mathrm{V}\rangle_A |\mathrm{V}\rangle_B + \beta\,|\mathrm{H}\rangle_A |\mathrm{H}\rangle_B. \end{aligned} \tag{7.25}$$

In this expansion we have used the fact that operator $\widehat{\mathrm{U}}$ is linear to write the second line, and used Equations 7.24 to write the last equality. But wait a minute! The right-hand sides of Equations 7.23 and 7.25 should be equal if the cloning machine is able to clone any state, but they clearly are not. We are forced to the conclusion that it is not possible to clone an arbitrary photon state. In fact, these arguments can be generalized for all quantum-mechanical systems, which gives us

**The no-cloning theorem**

The linearity of operators in quantum mechanics forbids the cloning of quantum states.

### 7.3.2 Specifying a quantum bit

Before looking at a specific scheme that achieves quantum teleportation, we make some remarks that shed light on the scale of the problem. It is helpful to compare the way information is stored in classical and quantum physics. The smallest amount of information in classical (non-quantum) physics is the *bit*, typically represented by a switch being in one of two states: *on* or *off*, representing 1 or 0. Anyone who has recently bought a computer knows that memories are measured in gigabytes ($10^9$ bytes), where one byte is 8 bits. At first sight, the quantum unit of information is similar. The unit of quantum information is called a quantum bit, or **qubit**. In a qubit, the information is contained in the state vector of a system with two orthogonal eigenvectors. An example is provided by the state in Equation 7.21:

$$|\psi\rangle = \alpha\,|\mathrm{V}\rangle + \beta\,|\mathrm{H}\rangle. \tag{7.26}$$

In this case, the information is contained in the polarization states of a photon; since $|\mathrm{V}\rangle$ and $|\mathrm{H}\rangle$ form a complete set for the description of the polarization of a photon, Equation 7.26 is general enough to describe the polarization of any photon. The equivalent to 'on' for a classical bit might be the state with $\alpha = 1$ and $\beta = 0$: a vertically-polarized photon. In that case, classical 'off' would be the equivalent to the state with $\alpha = 0$ and $\beta = 1$: a horizontally-polarized photon.

However, $\alpha$ and $\beta$ need not be equal to 1 or 0, and this makes a quantum bit very different from a classical bit. The classical bit represents a 0 or a 1, the least possible amount of information, whereas the qubit requires, in general, an *infinite* amount of information to specify it. That is one reason why it cannot be cloned, and is also a reason why very special techniques are required to teleport even a single qubit. Teleporting a person, who would be represented by a truly vast number of qubits, is not on the horizon.

To see why a single qubit represents so much information, look again at Equation 7.26. The complex probability amplitudes $\alpha$ and $\beta$ can be expressed using four real numbers. However, since the state vector must be normalized, $|\alpha|^2 + |\beta|^2 = 1$, this condition reduces the number of independent real numbers by one down to three. Moreover, the state vector is independent of an overall phase factor $\mathrm{e}^{\mathrm{i}\phi}$, reducing the number of independent numbers down to two. It can be shown that *any* normalized state of the form in Equation 7.26 can be represented in the form

$$|\psi\rangle = \mathrm{e}^{-\mathrm{i}\overline{\phi}/2}\cos(\overline{\theta}/2)\,|\mathrm{V}\rangle + \mathrm{e}^{\mathrm{i}\overline{\phi}/2}\sin(\overline{\theta}/2)\,|\mathrm{H}\rangle. \tag{7.27}$$

As $\overline{\theta}$ runs from 0 to $\pi$, and $\overline{\phi}$ runs from 0 to $2\pi$, all possible normalized and distinct states are represented. The angles $\overline{\theta}$ and $\overline{\phi}$ are the polar and azimuthal angles representing the points on a sphere, as shown in Figure 7.10.

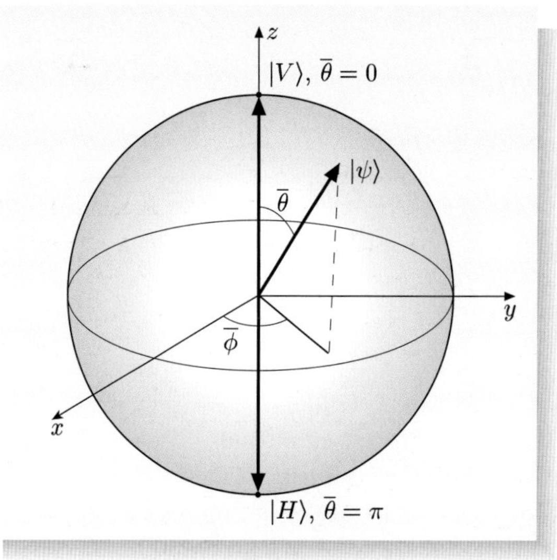


**Figure 7.10** The state of a qubit is defined by two angles, $\overline{\theta}$ and $\overline{\phi}$, representing points on a sphere. For photon polarization states, this sphere is called the **Poincaré sphere**.

As you can verify from Equation 7.27 and as is indicated on the figure, the point with $\overline{\theta} = 0$ (the 'North pole') represents the state $|V\rangle$, and the point with $\overline{\theta} = \pi$ (the 'South pole') represents the state $|H\rangle$. At either of these points, the value of $\overline{\phi}$ is undefined.

The angles $\overline{\theta}$ and $\overline{\phi}$ appearing in the parametrized form, Equation 7.27, have the bar on top for a good reason: $\overline{\theta}$ and $\overline{\phi}$ are not at all related to the angle at which the photon is polarized. According to Equation 7.27, $\overline{\theta} = \pi$ represents not a photon vertically polarized at an angle $\pi$ to the $z$-axis, but a horizontally-polarized photon. The following exercise brings this home.

**Exercise 7.11** What values of $\overline{\theta}$ and $\overline{\phi}$ represent the states $|V_\theta\rangle$ and $|H_\theta\rangle$ for $\theta = \pi/4$? ■

The parametrized form of Equation 7.27 shows that the possible states of polarization of a single photon can be put into one-to-one correspondence with the points on the surface of a sphere, and *there are an infinite number of these points.* Remember that $\overline{\theta}$ and $\overline{\phi}$ could have any values in their allowed ranges. To specify any value of $\overline{\theta}$ or $\overline{\phi}$ requires, in principle, an infinite number of decimal places. Therefore teleporting a single qubit requires an infinite amount of information to be transferred. One simply cannot visualize writing the specification of an arbitrary state on paper, and carrying the paper — even for a single arbitrary qubit.

### 7.3.3 A general scheme for quantum teleportation

At first glance then, it might appear that teleportation is impossible. However, as we'll see below, recreating the exact quantum state of a system at a remote location is possible with the proviso that in the act of teleporting the quantum state no information about that quantum state is gained by the sender. Note that we are talking about teleporting *information* and not actual particles; the information may, however, be used to recreate the state of a particle. It is NOT cloning since the state of the original particle is destroyed by the act of teleportation.

Suppose that Alice is asked to transmit an *unknown* quantum state $|\psi\rangle$ of a particle to Bob at a distant location, without sending the original particle, so that Bob can make an exact replica of $|\psi\rangle$. For the purposes of illustration, we'll consider the case where $|\psi\rangle$ represents the polarization state of a photon which we will label with a subscript 1. In general, the state of photon 1 can be represented as

$$|\psi\rangle_1 = \alpha\,|V\rangle_1 + \beta\,|H\rangle_1, \tag{7.28}$$

with $|\alpha|^2 + |\beta|^2 = 1$ for normalization since $|H\rangle$ and $|V\rangle$ are orthonormal. Clearly, if Alice attempts to learn about the state $|\psi\rangle_1$, her measurement will collapse $|\psi\rangle_1$ onto her measurement basis, destroying the original state in the process, and leaving almost no information about it. In order to teleport the state $|\psi\rangle_1$ to Bob, *an extra entangled pair of photons is required.* We assume that a source of entangled photons is available which produces photons 2 and 3 in one of the Bell states mentioned earlier, the one represented by the state vector

$$|\Psi^-\rangle_{23} = \frac{1}{\sqrt{2}}\Big(|V\rangle_2\,|H\rangle_3 - |H\rangle_2\,|V\rangle_3\Big). \tag{7.29}$$

The source of photons 2 and 3 is arranged so that photon 2 is sent to Alice, and photon 3 is sent to Bob. This establishes the possibility of quantum non-local correlations between Alice and Bob (due to the entanglement between photons 2 and 3), but the entangled photon pair at this point does not contain any information about $|\psi\rangle_1$. A schematic view of the scheme is shown in Figure 7.11, some features of which we explain shortly.

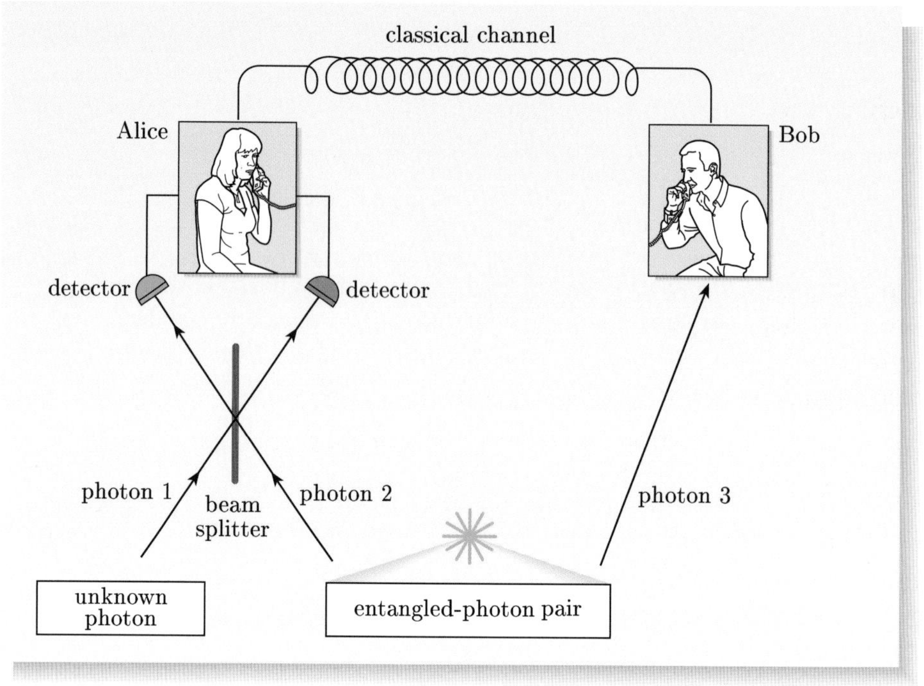


**Figure 7.11** The photon whose state is to be teleported and one of a pair of entangled photons enter Alice's beam splitter. The second of the entangled photons goes directly to Bob, who receives instructions from Alice, via the classical route, as to how to process it.

Any measurement that Bob might make on photon 3 will not reveal any information about $|\psi\rangle_1$. However, if Alice is somehow able to couple together photons 1 and 2, in a way that will be described shortly, then a measurement on photons 1 and 2 can indeed facilitate the transfer of information about photon 1 to photon 3.

To see how this works, we first note that the state vector of all three photons is the product state $|\psi\rangle_1\,|\Psi^-\rangle_{23}$, which may be expanded using Equations 7.28 and 7.29:

$$\begin{aligned}|\Psi\rangle_{123} &= |\psi\rangle_1\,|\Psi^-\rangle_{23}\\ &= \frac{\alpha}{\sqrt{2}}\Big(|\mathrm{V}\rangle_1\,|\mathrm{V}\rangle_2\,|\mathrm{H}\rangle_3 - |\mathrm{V}\rangle_1\,|\mathrm{H}\rangle_2\,|\mathrm{V}\rangle_3\Big)\\ &\quad + \frac{\beta}{\sqrt{2}}\Big(|\mathrm{H}\rangle_1\,|\mathrm{V}\rangle_2\,|\mathrm{H}\rangle_3 - |\mathrm{H}\rangle_1\,|\mathrm{H}\rangle_2\,|\mathrm{V}\rangle_3\Big). \qquad (7.30)\end{aligned}$$

Although it is photons 2 and 3 that are originally prepared in a particular Bell state (Equation 7.29), we shall need to consider the full set of four Bell states mentioned earlier, this time labelled for photons 1 and 2, as follows:

$$|\Psi^{\pm}\rangle_{12} = \frac{1}{\sqrt{2}}\Big(|\mathrm{V}\rangle_1\,|\mathrm{H}\rangle_2 \pm |\mathrm{H}\rangle_1\,|\mathrm{V}\rangle_2\Big), \qquad (7.31a)$$

$$|\Phi^{\pm}\rangle_{12} = \frac{1}{\sqrt{2}}\Big(|\mathrm{V}\rangle_1\,|\mathrm{V}\rangle_2 \pm |\mathrm{H}\rangle_1\,|\mathrm{H}\rangle_2\Big). \qquad (7.31b)$$

We can then express the state vector for the three photons in Equation 7.30 in terms of the Bell states for photons 1 and 2 as

$$|\Psi\rangle_{123} = \frac{1}{2}\Big[|\Psi^-\rangle_{12}\left(-\alpha\,|\mathrm{V}\rangle_3 - \beta\,|\mathrm{H}\rangle_3\right) + |\Psi^+\rangle_{12}\left(-\alpha\,|\mathrm{V}\rangle_3 + \beta\,|\mathrm{H}\rangle_3\right)$$
$$+ |\Phi^-\rangle_{12}\left(\beta\,|\mathrm{V}\rangle_3 + \alpha\,|\mathrm{H}\rangle_3\right) + |\Phi^+\rangle_{12}\left(-\beta\,|\mathrm{V}\rangle_3 + \alpha\,|\mathrm{H}\rangle_3\right)\Big]. \quad (7.32)$$

This is a straightforward but lengthy task, which you need not perform.

To verify Equation 7.32, you can insert the expressions 7.31 into it, and show that it can then be rearranged to give Equation 7.30.

Equation 7.32 can be viewed as a linear combination of the four Bell states for photons 1 and 2, with coefficients that happen to represent states of particle 3. If Alice could make a combined measurement on photons 1 and 2 that collapsed the state vector for those two photons onto one of the four Bell states, a so-called **Bell state measurement**, then photon 3 would collapse to the state represented by the corresponding factor in round brackets in Equation 7.32. For example, if Alice were to make a measurement that collapsed $|\Psi\rangle_{123}$ onto $|\Psi^-\rangle_{12}$, then photon 3 would instantaneously be in the normalized state $-\alpha\,|\mathrm{V}\rangle_3 - \beta\,|\mathrm{H}\rangle_3$.

In summary: if Alice makes a 'Bell state measurement' on photons 1 and 2 in the 'Bell state basis' (the four vectors lists in Equations 7.31), then $|\Psi\rangle_{123}$ will collapse onto one of the four terms in Equation 7.32, each occurring with probability $1/4$. Examining each of the four terms in Equation 7.32, we see that the state of photon 3, call it $|\phi\rangle_3$, following a Bell state measurement by Alice on photons 1 and 2, is related to the original state $|\psi\rangle_1$ of photon 1, as summarized in column two of Table 7.2.

**Table 7.2** If Alice's Bell state measurement places her two photons in the state given in column one, then Bob's photon will collapse onto the corresponding state in column two.

| Measurement | $\|\phi\rangle_3$ |
|---|---|
| $\|\Psi^-\rangle_{12}$ | $-\alpha\,\|\mathrm{V}\rangle_3 - \beta\,\|\mathrm{H}\rangle_3$ |
| $\|\Psi^+\rangle_{12}$ | $-\alpha\,\|\mathrm{V}\rangle_3 + \beta\,\|\mathrm{H}\rangle_3$ |
| $\|\Phi^-\rangle_{12}$ | $\beta\,\|\mathrm{V}\rangle_3 + \alpha\,\|\mathrm{H}\rangle_3$ |
| $\|\Phi^+\rangle_{12}$ | $-\beta\,\|\mathrm{V}\rangle_3 + \alpha\,\|\mathrm{H}\rangle_3$ |

Line one of the table says that if Alice's measurement yields $|\Psi^-\rangle_{12}$, then Bob's photon is indeed in exactly the state that photon 1 had been in, apart from the overall minus sign. But such an overall sign is not significant, from Principle 1b of Section 5.6. However, if Alice's pair collapses onto $|\Psi^+\rangle_{12}$, then the resulting state for particle 3, $-\alpha\,|\mathrm{V}\rangle_3 + \beta\,|\mathrm{H}\rangle_3$, is *not* just a minus sign times the original state of photon 1; relative phases matter even though overall phases do not. Somehow, all the information present in $\alpha$ and $\beta$, with all their (in principle) infinite strings of decimal places, is present in a slightly garbled form. It is even more garbled if Alice finds Bell states $|\Phi^-\rangle_{12}$ or $|\Phi^+\rangle_{12}$ as a result of her Bell state measurement.

**Exercise 7.12** Write down the states of photon 3 as received by Bob in the cases that Alice finds $|\Phi^-\rangle_{12}$ or $|\Phi^+\rangle_{12}$. ■

We now see the point of the classical communication link from Alice to Bob. Alice sends a message, requiring just two classical bits, telling Bob which one of the four Bell states she found. Bob then operates on his photon with the appropriate choice of one out of four well-defined physical transformations. The transformation is chosen to transform the photon that he received into a photon in the exact quantum state of the original photon 1 received by Alice.

The operations required by Bob can be represented as matrix transformations. First note that $|\psi\rangle_3$ can be represented by the matrix of its probability amplitudes, as in Equations 7.1 and 7.2. The four states $|\phi\rangle_3$ in Table 7.2 are, in order, represented by the matrices

$$\begin{bmatrix}-\alpha\\-\beta\end{bmatrix}, \quad \begin{bmatrix}-\alpha\\\beta\end{bmatrix}, \quad \begin{bmatrix}\beta\\\alpha\end{bmatrix}, \quad \begin{bmatrix}-\beta\\\alpha\end{bmatrix}. \quad (7.33)$$

Matrices that maintain the normalization of any vector during multiplication, and have an inverse, are called *unitary matrices*, and they describe *unitary transformations*.

Now, Table 7.3 presents the $2 \times 2$ square matrices that transform the state of the photon (photon 3) received by Bob into the state of the original unknown photon (photon 1). The transformation in the first row is simply $-1$ times the unit matrix. The transformations all maintain the normalization of any state vector on which they operate.

**Table 7.3** Transforming $|\phi\rangle_3$ into $|\psi\rangle_3$.

| $\lvert\phi\rangle_3$ | Matrix form | Transformation matrix |
|---|---|---|
| $-\alpha\,\lvert V\rangle_3 - \beta\,\lvert H\rangle_3$ | $\begin{bmatrix} -\alpha \\ -\beta \end{bmatrix}$ | $\begin{bmatrix} -1 & 0 \\ 0 & -1 \end{bmatrix}$ |
| $-\alpha\,\lvert V\rangle_3 + \beta\,\lvert H\rangle_3$ | $\begin{bmatrix} -\alpha \\ \beta \end{bmatrix}$ | $\begin{bmatrix} -1 & 0 \\ 0 & 1 \end{bmatrix}$ |
| $\beta\,\lvert V\rangle_3 + \alpha\,\lvert H\rangle_3$ | $\begin{bmatrix} \beta \\ \alpha \end{bmatrix}$ | $\begin{bmatrix} 0 & 1 \\ 1 & 0 \end{bmatrix}$ |
| $-\beta\,\lvert V\rangle_3 + \alpha\,\lvert H\rangle_3$ | $\begin{bmatrix} -\beta \\ \alpha \end{bmatrix}$ | $\begin{bmatrix} 0 & 1 \\ -1 & 0 \end{bmatrix}$ |

**Exercise 7.13** Show that the transformation described by the fourth transformation matrix, $\begin{bmatrix} 0 & 1 \\ -1 & 0 \end{bmatrix}$, preserves the normalization of any state vector. You should consider the action of this matrix on the general polarization state $\gamma\,|V\rangle + \delta\,|H\rangle$, where $|\gamma|^2 + |\delta|^2 = 1$.

**Exercise 7.14** Verify that the third transformation matrix does indeed transform $|\phi\rangle_3$, as represented in the third row, into $|\psi\rangle_3$. ■

Once Alice has sent her two pieces of classical information to Bob specifying which of the four Bell states for photons 1 and 2 resulted from her measurement, then Bob can use suitable equipment that applies the required transformation to photon 3, converting it into an exact replica of photon 1, and teleportation of the state of photon 1 to photon 3 is achieved! But what about Alice — does she have any information regarding the initial state $|\psi\rangle_1$ of photon 1? Her Bell state measurement has left photons 1 and 2 in one of the four Bell states given in Equations 7.31, and these equations contain no information about $|\psi\rangle_1$. Thus, in the process of teleporting the state of photon 1, Alice has learnt nothing about this state; the original state $|\psi\rangle_1$ has been destroyed. In short, the infinite amount of information required to define the quantum state has been teleported to Bob, without Alice ever knowing that information.

### 7.3.4 The first teleportation experiment

The first successful teleportation experiment was reported by D. Bouwmeester *et al.* (1997) *Nature*, vol. 390, page 575.

In Figure 7.11, photons 1 and 2 are shown incident upon a beam splitter belonging to Alice. This beam splitter plays a key role in the Bell state measurement in the first published teleportation measurement due to Bouwmeester *et al.* in Zeilinger's group in Austria. Although successful, it was not complete, in the following sense: only one of the four Bell state measurements could be made. The equipment shown schematically in Figure 7.11 is able to give a signal when the combined state of photons 1 and 2 collapses onto $|\Psi^-\rangle_{12}$, which will happen 25% of the time. When this happens, Alice sends a signal by the classical channel to Bob, who can then, and only then, declare that the state of photon 1 has been teleported to him (remember that an overall factor of $-1$ does not change the nature of the state). Although the teleportation scheme of Zeilinger's team only worked 25% of the time, it was nevertheless a great achievement.

But how is Alice's Bell state measurement carried out? The next subsection gives the details. It is an important part of the story, but may be skimmed if you are short of time.

### 7.3.5 Carrying out the Bell state measurement

You have previously met beam splitters, in the form of half-silvered mirrors, in Chapter 1 of Book 1, and also in Chapter 5 of this book.

Alice's Bell state measurement is based on the peculiar properties of interference between two photons falling simultaneously on a (non-polarizing) 50:50 beam splitter (Figure 7.12). Such a beam splitter is an optical device that splits an incoming beam of light in two by reflecting one half of the beam and transmitting the other half.

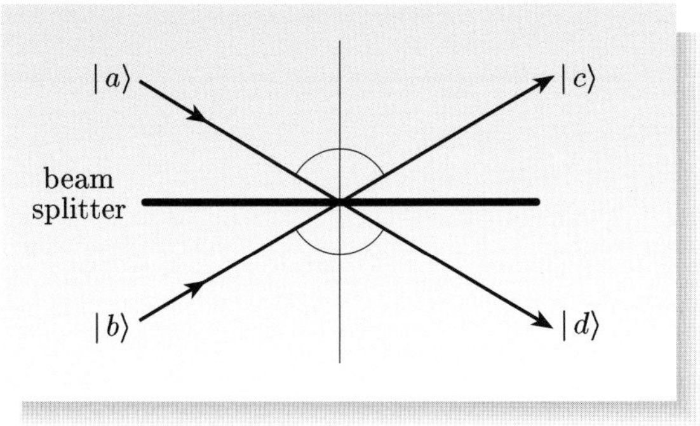


**Figure 7.12** A beam splitter splits a beam of light in two by reflecting one half of the incoming beam and transmitting the other half. At the single photon level, each photon has an equal probability of being detected in the reflected and transmitted directions. A beam splitter has two input directions, or input 'spatial modes', which we denote by $|a\rangle$ and $|b\rangle$, and two output spatial modes, which we denote by $|c\rangle$ and $|d\rangle$. For example, a photon in the input spatial mode $|a\rangle$ may be detected as being reflected into the output spatial mode $|c\rangle$ or transmitted into the output spatial mode $|d\rangle$.

Photons 1 and 2 are initially distinguishable by virtue of the fact that they are coming from different places — Alice can tell which is which by virtue of their propagation direction in space. If Alice is to make a measurement which projects onto one of the four Bell states of photons 1 and 2 (Equations 7.31), she must arrange for the photons to be indistinguishable. In order to make photons 1 and 2 indistinguishable, Alice must discard all photons that are not of exactly the same frequency, with a frequency filter. She must also find a way to make their spatial wave functions overlap. This can be achieved using a 50:50 beam splitter.

So far, the only property of photons that we have specified is their polarization, which we represent with kets such as $|\text{H}\rangle$ and $|\text{V}\rangle$. We must now also consider the spatial part of the photon state, and to do this we augment the ket specifying the photon polarization with a ket specifying its path through space. The total state vector for the photon $|\Psi\rangle$ is the product of a ket $|\chi\rangle$ specifying the spatial state and a polarization ket $|\psi\rangle$: $|\Psi\rangle = |\psi\rangle\,|\chi\rangle$. A beam splitter has two possible input directions, or input spatial modes, which we will denote by $|a\rangle$ and $|b\rangle$; see Figure 7.12. So, for example, the state of a horizontally-polarized photon propagating in the direction corresponding to the $|a\rangle$ spatial mode is $|\text{H}\rangle|a\rangle$.

A photon arriving at the beam splitter, in either input mode, has equal probabilities of being reflected or transmitted; see Figure 7.12. This figure also shows the two output modes, $|c\rangle$ and $|d\rangle$. It turns out that the action of the beam splitter on the input modes can be written as

$$|a\rangle \Longrightarrow \frac{\mathrm{i}}{\sqrt{2}}\,|c\rangle + \frac{1}{\sqrt{2}}\,|d\rangle, \tag{7.34}$$

$$|b\rangle \Longrightarrow \frac{1}{\sqrt{2}}\,|c\rangle + \frac{\mathrm{i}}{\sqrt{2}}\,|d\rangle. \tag{7.35}$$

These equations say that a photon initially prepared in the input spatial mode $|a\rangle$ will emerge from the beam splitter in a superposition of output spatial modes $|c\rangle$ and $|d\rangle$, as will a photon initially in mode $|b\rangle$. A photon incident in either input mode can thus be detected with equal probability in either of the output modes $|c\rangle$ and $|d\rangle$. The factor i present in one term of both right-hand sides arises because there is a phase change when light is reflected.

- If a photon represented by the state vector $|\Psi\rangle = \frac{1}{\sqrt{2}}\big(|\mathrm{V}\rangle - |\mathrm{H}\rangle\big)\,|b\rangle$ is incident upon a beam splitter, write down the state vector after the beam splitter.

- We use the rule in Equation 7.35 to write the state vector after the beam splitter as

$$\tfrac{1}{2}\big(|\mathrm{V}\rangle - |\mathrm{H}\rangle\big)\big(|c\rangle + \mathrm{i}\,|d\rangle\big).$$

**Exercise 7.15** If a horizontally-polarized photon is incident upon a beam splitter in spatial mode $|a\rangle$, write down the total state vector following the beam splitter. ■

Now suppose that Alice, following the scheme shown in Figure 7.11, arranges for photon 1 to be in input mode $|a\rangle$ and photon 2 to be in input mode $|b\rangle$. Each photon has the same 50:50 probability of being transmitted or reflected, and so four different possibilities arise (see Figure 7.13): (i) both photons are transmitted; (ii) photon 1 is reflected and photon 2 is transmitted; (iii) photon 1 is transmitted and photon 2 is reflected; (iv) both photons are reflected. Each of these cases occurs with equal probability. If Alice detects a photon in either output mode, she cannot tell whether it is photon 1 or photon 2 — the photons have been rendered indistinguishable by the action of the beam splitter and the frequency filter that eliminates photons that do not have the same frequency.

In order to understand the effect of Alice's measurement on photons 1 and 2, we need to examine what happens to the state $|\Psi\rangle_{123}$ in Equation 7.30. However, to keep the book-keeping simple, we'll examine what happens to the general state of photons 1 and 2 given by the following product of two terms, one term being a linear combination of kets for photon 1, and the other a linear combination of kets for photon 2:

$$|\Psi_{\mathrm{in}}\rangle = \Big(\alpha\,|\mathrm{V}\rangle_1 + \beta\,|\mathrm{H}\rangle_1\Big)\,|a\rangle_1 \times \Big(\gamma\,|\mathrm{V}\rangle_2 + \delta\,|\mathrm{H}\rangle_2\Big)\,|b\rangle_2. \tag{7.36}$$

In this equation, we have written the polarization part of the wave state vector for each photon as a superposition in the H/V basis, allowing any polarization state of the photons to be represented with suitable amplitudes $\alpha$, $\beta$, $\gamma$ and $\delta$. From Equations 7.34 and 7.35, this state evolves into the following state after the beam splitter:

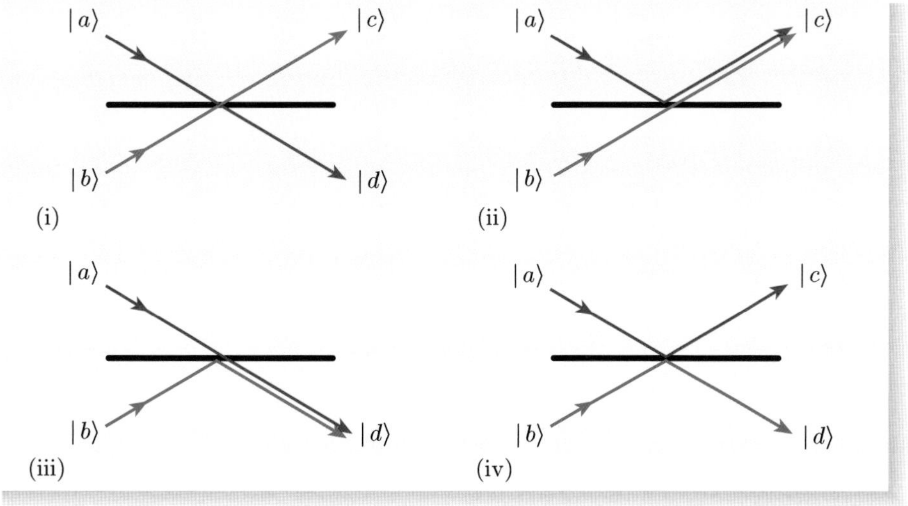


**Figure 7.13** The four possible output mode combinations for one photon in each of the input modes $|a\rangle$ and $|b\rangle$: (i) both photons are transmitted and one photon is detected in each of the output modes $|c\rangle$ and $|d\rangle$; (ii) and (iii) one photon is reflected and one photon is transmitted such that both photons are detected in the same output mode; (iv) both photons are reflected such that the photons are detected in different output modes.

$$|\Psi\rangle_{12} = \frac{1}{\sqrt{2}}\Big(\alpha\,|\mathrm{V}\rangle_1 + \beta\,|\mathrm{H}\rangle_1\Big)\Big(\mathrm{i}\,|c\rangle_1 + |d\rangle_1\Big) \times \frac{1}{\sqrt{2}}\Big(\gamma\,|\mathrm{V}\rangle_2 + \delta\,|\mathrm{H}\rangle_2\Big)\Big(|c\rangle_2 + \mathrm{i}\,|d\rangle_2\Big). \tag{7.37}$$

Because the photons (bosons) are indistinguishable after passing through the beam splitter, the total two-photon state vector after the beam splitter, including both the spatial and polarization parts, must be symmetric with respect to exchange of the labels 1 and 2. This requires that we symmetrize the final state vector as

$$|\Psi_{\mathrm{out}}\rangle = \frac{1}{\sqrt{2}}\Big(|\Psi\rangle_{12} + |\Psi\rangle_{21}\Big), \tag{7.38}$$

where $|\Psi\rangle_{21}$ is formed from $|\Psi\rangle_{12}$ by interchanging the 1 and 2 subscripts throughout:

$$|\Psi\rangle_{21} = \frac{1}{\sqrt{2}}\Big(\alpha\,|\mathrm{V}\rangle_2 + \beta\,|\mathrm{H}\rangle_2\Big)\Big(\mathrm{i}\,|c\rangle_2 + |d\rangle_2\Big) \times \frac{1}{\sqrt{2}}\Big(\gamma\,|\mathrm{V}\rangle_1 + \delta\,|\mathrm{H}\rangle_1\Big)\Big(|c\rangle_1 + \mathrm{i}\,|d\rangle_1\Big). \tag{7.39}$$

- Verify explicitly that $|\Psi_{\mathrm{out}}\rangle$ is symmetric under the interchange of photons 1 and 2.

- By construction, interchanging subscripts 1 and 2 throughout all terms in $|\Psi_{\mathrm{out}}\rangle$ simply interchanges $|\Psi\rangle_{21}$ and $|\Psi\rangle_{12}$, leaving $|\Psi_{\mathrm{out}}\rangle$ unchanged.

After substituting Equations 7.37 and 7.39 into Equation 7.38 and some tedious algebra, we obtain the following expression for the final state vector of the two photons:

$$
\begin{aligned}
|\Psi_{\text{out}}\rangle = {} & \mathrm{i}\frac{(\alpha\gamma+\beta\delta)}{\sqrt{2}}\frac{1}{\sqrt{2}}\Big(|c\rangle_1|c\rangle_2+|d\rangle_1|d\rangle_2\Big)\frac{1}{\sqrt{2}}\Big(|\mathrm{V}\rangle_1|\mathrm{V}\rangle_2+|\mathrm{H}\rangle_1|\mathrm{H}\rangle_2\Big)\\
& +\mathrm{i}\frac{(\alpha\gamma-\beta\delta)}{\sqrt{2}}\frac{1}{\sqrt{2}}\Big(|c\rangle_1|c\rangle_2+|d\rangle_1|d\rangle_2\Big)\frac{1}{\sqrt{2}}\Big(|\mathrm{V}\rangle_1|\mathrm{V}\rangle_2-|\mathrm{H}\rangle_1|\mathrm{H}\rangle_2\Big)\\
& +\mathrm{i}\frac{(\alpha\delta+\beta\gamma)}{\sqrt{2}}\frac{1}{\sqrt{2}}\Big(|c\rangle_1|c\rangle_2+|d\rangle_1|d\rangle_2\Big)\frac{1}{\sqrt{2}}\Big(|\mathrm{V}\rangle_1|\mathrm{H}\rangle_2+|\mathrm{H}\rangle_1|\mathrm{V}\rangle_2\Big)\\
& +\frac{(\alpha\delta-\beta\gamma)}{\sqrt{2}}\frac{1}{\sqrt{2}}\Big(|d\rangle_1|c\rangle_2-|c\rangle_1|d\rangle_2\Big)\frac{1}{\sqrt{2}}\Big(|\mathrm{V}\rangle_1|\mathrm{H}\rangle_2-|\mathrm{H}\rangle_1|\mathrm{V}\rangle_2\Big).
\end{aligned}
\tag{7.40}
$$

This rather complicated equation reveals that the state vector after the beam splitter is a superposition of the four Bell states in Equations 7.31. Each of the four terms has (i) a factor specifying the spatial state, and (ii) a factor involving $|\mathrm{H}\rangle$ and $|\mathrm{V}\rangle$ terms specifying the joint polarization states — it represents one of the four Bell states. For the first three terms in the equation, the spatial factor is

$$\frac{1}{\sqrt{2}}\Big(|c\rangle_1|c\rangle_2+|d\rangle_1|d\rangle_2\Big), \tag{7.41}$$

which corresponds to the photons being detected on the *same* side of the beam splitter — either both in the $|c\rangle$ mode, or both in the $|d\rangle$ mode.

- Explain why this last statement is true.

- If one photon is detected in a counter corresponding to emergence from the beam splitter in spatial mode $|c\rangle$, for example, then the state function 7.41 will collapse onto the first term, $|c\rangle_1|c\rangle_2$. If one photon is measured to be in the $|d\rangle$ state, then the state vector will collapse onto the second term, $|d\rangle_1|d\rangle_2$. Hence detection of coincident photons on the same side of the beam splitter indicates that $|\Psi_{\text{out}}\rangle$ has collapsed onto a state represented by one of the first three terms in Equation 7.40.

On the other hand, the spatial part of the fourth term is

$$\frac{1}{\sqrt{2}}\Big(|d\rangle_1|c\rangle_2-|c\rangle_1|d\rangle_2\Big), \tag{7.42}$$

which tells us that the photons are detected coming from the beam splitter in *different* spatial modes — if photon 1 is detected in mode $|c\rangle$, then photon 2 will be detected in mode $|d\rangle$, and vice versa. In both cases, the output spatial modes of the two photons have become entangled. Equation 7.40 therefore tells us that the photons collapse onto the Bell state $|\Psi^-\rangle_{12}$ if and only if they are detected in different output modes after the beam splitter, in which case the state vector Equation 7.40 has collapsed onto the fourth term. This will happen 25% of the time.

**Exercise 7.16** Photon detectors are placed on each side of a beam splitter in paths corresponding to spatial states $|c\rangle$ and $|d\rangle$. What can you conclude when two photons are detected in coincidence (a) in the same detector, and (b) in different detectors? ■

We can now give an overview of how the beam splitter indicated in Figure 7.11 allowed Zeilinger and co-workers to achieve teleportation in 1997. To teleport the state of photon 1, Alice directs photons 1 and 2 to the input modes of a 50:50 beam splitter and places photon detectors in the output ports of the beam splitter. Whenever Alice simultaneously registers a photon arrival in both detectors, the state vector in Equation 7.40 must have collapsed onto the fourth term, and so the state vector in Equation 7.32 has collapsed onto the first term, involving the Bell state $|\Psi^-\rangle_{12}$. She knows with certainty that photon 3 is in precisely the same state in which photon 1 was initially prepared (up to a constant factor of $-1$), although she knows nothing about this state. All that remains is for Alice to communicate to Bob (via a classical communication channel) that the photon state has been teleported to his photon. It is important to realize that information has not propagated instantaneously between Alice and Bob, as the classical signal will necessarily travel slower than the speed of light. The teleportation of the polarization state of photons was achieved in 1997 by Anton Zeilinger and co-workers using exactly the scheme outlined here.

Special relativity tells us that no *information* can travel faster than light; it always turns out, as here, that the quantum non-local effects do not transgress this rule.

### 7.3.6 Unrestricted quantum teleportation

We have explained the restricted Bell state measurement that enabled Zeilinger and his colleagues to achieve teleportation with a 25% strike rate. The problem with that arrangement is that whereas one particular Bell state results in photons appearing simultaneously on each side of the beam splitter, the other three Bell states all correspond to the same thing: two photons appearing simultaneously on one side or the other side. Such an apparatus cannot discriminate between the three Bell states that are not $|\Psi^-\rangle_{12}$. It turns out that complete Bell state measurements are possible, but with significantly more elaborate apparatus that is well beyond the scope of this chapter to describe. More recent experiments have achieved measurements that distinguish all the Bell states, thus enabling less restricted teleportation. We certainly expect interesting developments over the life of this course.

**Exercise 7.17** Make an outline of points that would be incorporated in an essay on 'Quantum teleportation'. ■

## 7.4 Quantum computing

Recent theoretical advances concerning quantum entanglement, as well as technical advances such as new sources of entangled photons, have stimulated an enormous worldwide enthusiasm for research in **quantum information**. This burgeoning field includes quantum cryptography and teleportation, and also quantum computing. Indeed, it is quantum computing that has generated the largest volume of research activity. There is not enough space in this chapter to give a technical introduction to this field, partly because we would need to establish the technical jargon (registers, gates, etc.) of computing itself. However, the subject is too important to ignore completely.

It is hard today to imagine a world without the internet, mobile phones, bank cash machines, CDs and DVDs, and desktop computers. Until now, all of these technologies have relied on the idea of storing, processing and transmitting data as strings of 1s and 0s (classical bits), and information technology has stored classical bits by controlling the macroscopic properties of materials. In a computer chip, the bit values of 1 and 0 have been associated with electrical switches, involving transistors, being on or off, but they may be represented in other ways. For example, the two data states of a bit can be represented by two different orientations of a magnetic domain on a computer disk. All such methods of representing data behave according to classical physics, involving the concerted behaviour of a great many of the electrons and atoms that comprise the device. As a result, a classical bit is always in one state or the other; each bit can be either 1 or 0, but not both.

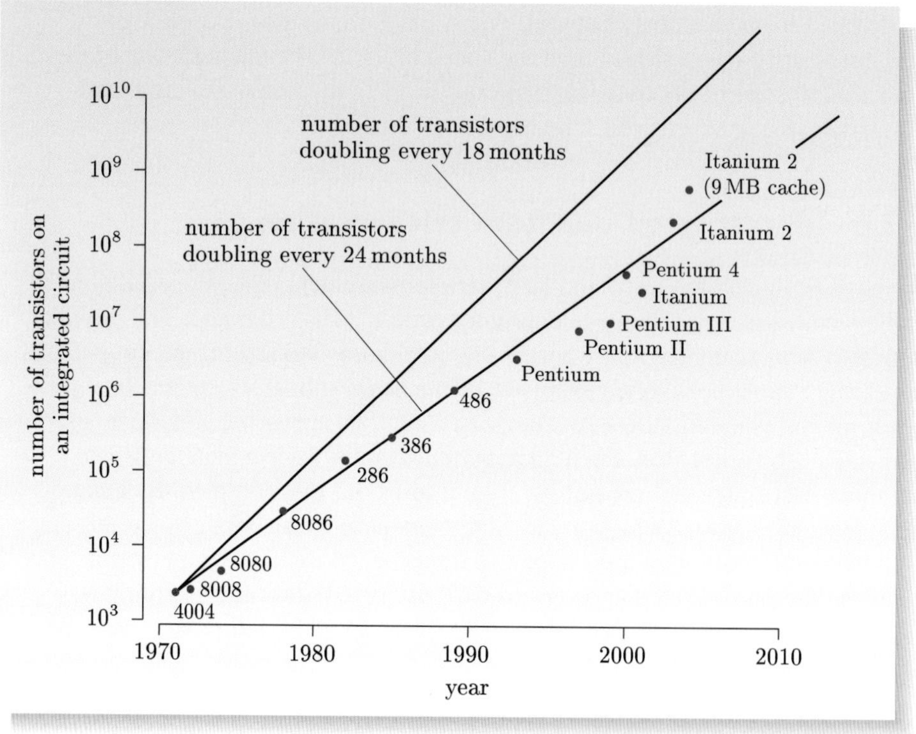


**Figure 7.14** Growth of the number of transistors for Intel computer processors (dots) and Moore's law predictions for the number of transistors doubling every 18 months, and every 24 months.

In 1965, Gordon Moore, a co-founder of Intel, predicted that the number of transistors on a silicon computer chip would double roughly every 18 months. As Figure 7.14 shows, this prediction has held roughly correct to the present day; as a result, computational speed has increased by a factor of 1000 every 15 years. The increase in transistor density on computer chips entails a decrease in transistor size. By 2006, the features etched into a silicon wafer to form transistors had shrunk to a size of 65 nm, and by 2020 will probably be below 10 nm. At this point, the size of the transistors will approach atomic dimensions and the number of electrons per circuit element will be just one or two. The operation of the logic elements on a chip will then no longer be determined by classical physics, as quantum effects will dominate. This presents a limitation to conventional information technology but also brings new possibilities.

The central idea behind 'quantum information' is that bits are encoded in quantum states of individual particles rather than in macroscopic properties. For example, a horizontally-polarized photon could represent a 0, and a vertically-polarized photon could represent a 1. As we saw earlier, however, the state of a photon can be an arbitrary normalized linear superposition of states corresponding to vertical polarization and horizontal polarization, and this means that quantum bits (or qubits) are much richer in information than classical bits. Moreover, reading the value of a classical bit does not affect the value of the bit, whereas measuring the value of a qubit will cause the state of the qubit irreversibly to collapse onto either a 1 or a 0 state, with a probability depending upon the particular measurement as well as on the state of the qubit before measurement.

A quantum computer does not, of course, store information in just one qubit; there are many qubits in an entangled state. It turns out that $n$ qubits represent a linear superposition of $2^n$ quantum states, a vast number when $n$ gets into the hundreds. Because of the quantum correlation between the entangled qubits, an operation on one of them would simultaneously affect the state of all of them. This opens the way to massively parallel processing that may allow quantum computers to succeed in tackling particular classes of problem that are effectively beyond the power of classical computers to solve in a reasonable time.

This would be a suitable time to view the filmed sequence 'Quantum information' on the DVD. Two leading researchers in the field of quantum information discuss quantum cryptography, quantum teleportation and quantum computing, and demonstrate some laboratory equipment involved in experiments in these areas.

As an example, we mention an algorithm devised by Shor that is specifically adapted to quantum computers. This algorithm is for finding the prime factors of very large numbers, something effectively beyond the capability of classical computers. To date, a quantum computer has actually shown only that the prime factors of 15 are 3 and 5, but the principle has been proven. One of the main difficulties in constructing a more practical quantum computer is the fact that the entangled linear superpositions of quantum states needed by the computer are generally very sensitive to external disturbances. Learning how to cope with such difficulties is at the forefront of current research.

## Summary of Chapter 7

**Section 7.1** The polarization of photons is a major vehicle for the transport of quantum information. Polarizing beam analyzers can be used to measure the linear polarization of a photon relative to a given polarizer axis, with the possible outcomes being vertical polarization (value $+1$) and horizontal polarization (value $-1$). The corresponding quantum-mechanical operator $\widehat{\mathcal{P}}(\theta)$ has eigenvectors $|\mathrm{V}_\theta\rangle$ and $|\mathrm{H}_\theta\rangle$, with eigenvalues $+1$ and $-1$. These eigenvectors form a basis for any state of linear polarization of a photon.

**Section 7.2** Quantum key distribution, QKD, enables the secure transmission of information. The essential idea is that quantum measurements, unlike classical measurements, inevitably disturb the measured system. Quantum protocols for quantum cryptography have been devised to exploit this fact. Any eavesdropper would inevitably collapse the state of quantum particles bearing the transmitted information. The BB84 protocol does not involve entanglement, but another protocol, based on a proposal due to Artur Eckert, uses entanglement in an essential way. Both methods have been shown to work and are being developed for commercial applications.

**Section 7.3** Quantum teleportation is the exact transfer of the unknown quantum state of a particle (usually a photon) to a distant particle. At first sight, three features of quantum mechanics appear to make this difficult. Firstly, it is impossible to measure an arbitrary state of a system exactly, without disturbing it. Secondly, the no-cloning theorem tells us that the linearity of operators in quantum mechanics forbids the cloning of states. Thirdly, quantum bits (or qubits) contain an infinite amount of information. Nevertheless, another feature of quantum mechanics — entanglement — can be exploited to make teleportation work.

One scheme for teleporting the state of a single photon (labelled 1) involves creating a separate entangled pair of photons (labelled 2 and 3) and using a beam splitter to combine photons 1 and 2. By making a Bell state measurement, the distant photon 3 can be collapsed onto a state that is closely related to the original state of photon 1. Classical communication can inform the recipient of photon 3 what needs to be done to it to make its state the same as the initial state of photon 1. The first successful teleportation experiment succeeded in teleporting the state of 25% of the photons. This limitation was due to the fact that only one of the four 'Bell state measurements' is straightforward.

**Section 7.4** A quantum computer stores information in entangled linear superpositions of quantum states. Although sensitive to external disturbances, quantum computers may allow massively parallel processing, allowing special classes of problem (including the factoring of large numbers) to be solved in cases that are beyond the powers of ordinary computers.

## Achievements from Chapter 7

*After studying this chapter you should be able to:*

**7.1** Explain the meanings of the newly defined (emboldened) terms and symbols, and use them appropriately.

**7.2** Calculate the probability of the outcomes of measurement of photon polarization, given a photon polarization state vector.

**7.3** Explain the BB84 protocol for establishing secure cryptographic keys, and answer questions concerning its implementation.

**7.4** Give an account of the Eckert protocol whereby entangled photons can be employed for establishing secure cryptographic keys.

**7.5** Explain why it is not possible to clone the state of a quantum-mechanical system.

**7.6** Explain the general nature of quantum teleportation, including a description of what is and what is not transported, and a statement of its significance, calling upon the no-cloning theorem, and the information contained in a qubit.

**7.7** Outline (with a suitable diagram) the steps involved in teleporting the state of a photon.

**7.8** Explain the role of entanglement and Bell state measurements in quantum teleportation, and explain the limitations of the first successful teleportation experiments in terms of Bell state measurements.

**7.9** Give a very brief overview of the prospects for quantum computing.

# Chapter 8 Mathematical toolkit

## Introduction

This *Mathematical toolkit* provides additional support for some mathematical topics that you will meet elsewhere in this book. It deals with the concepts of vectors and matrices, and shows you how to carry out some basic manipulations that involve them.

## 8.1 Vectors in ordinary space

You will have met vectors in the context of physical quantities such as force, acceleration and velocity. Vectors like this, in ordinary three-dimensional space, may be referred to as **ordinary vectors**. This is to distinguish them from the more general abstract vectors we need to discuss later on. Here, we briefly review the properties of ordinary vectors.

First, we need to define a scalar. A **scalar** quantity is fully described by a single number, together with an appropriate unit of measurement. For example, mass, charge and temperature are scalar quantities. Some scalars, such as mass, turn out to be non-negative but others, such as charge, can be positive, zero or negative. The **magnitude** of a scalar quantity is the size of the quantity ignoring any possible negative sign. If $x$ is a scalar, we denote its magnitude by $|x|$ so, with $x = -5\,\text{m}$, we have $|x| = 5\,\text{m}$. Magnitudes can never be negative.

### 8.1.1 Geometric interpretation of vectors

An (ordinary) **vector** is a quantity that is characterized by both a *magnitude* and a *direction* in (ordinary) space. For example, the velocity of a particle is a vector because it has a magnitude (the particle's speed) and a direction (the particle's direction of motion). In print, vectors are usually denoted by bold type, e.g. $\mathbf{v}$. In handwritten work, they are generally denoted by underlining with straight or curly lines (e.g. $\underline{a}$ or $\underset{\sim}{a}$). The **magnitude** of a vector $\mathbf{a}$ can be written as $|\mathbf{a}|$. More commonly, though, it is written simply as $a$, where the absence of bold print (or underlining) serves to show that $a$ is not a vector.

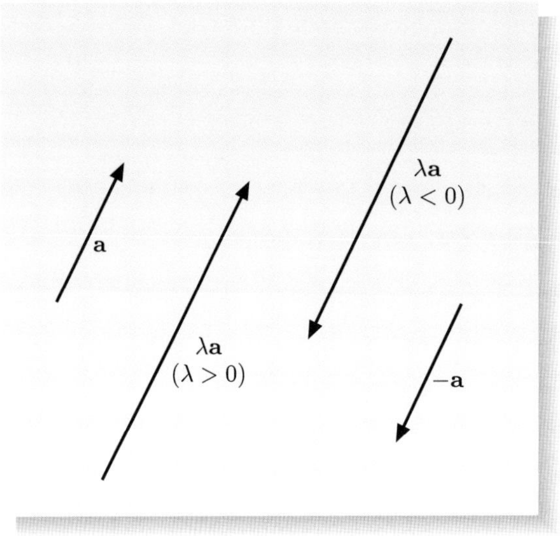

**Figure 8.1** Multiplying a vector by a scalar.

#### Multiplying a vector by a scalar

We often need to multiply a vector by a scalar. Figure 8.1 shows how this is interpreted. Given any vector $\mathbf{a}$ and any scalar $\lambda$, the product $\lambda\mathbf{a}$ is a new vector with magnitude $|\lambda|a$, pointing either parallel or antiparallel to $\mathbf{a}$. If $\lambda$ is positive, $\lambda\mathbf{a}$ points in the same direction as $\mathbf{a}$; if $\lambda$ is negative, $\lambda\mathbf{a}$ points in the opposite direction.

The vector $(1/a)\,\mathbf{a}$ is a vector of unit magnitude pointing in the same direction as $\mathbf{a}$. Such a vector is called a **unit vector**. Any unit vector is dimensionless and has magnitude 1 — not 1 metre, 1 newton, or 1 anything else.

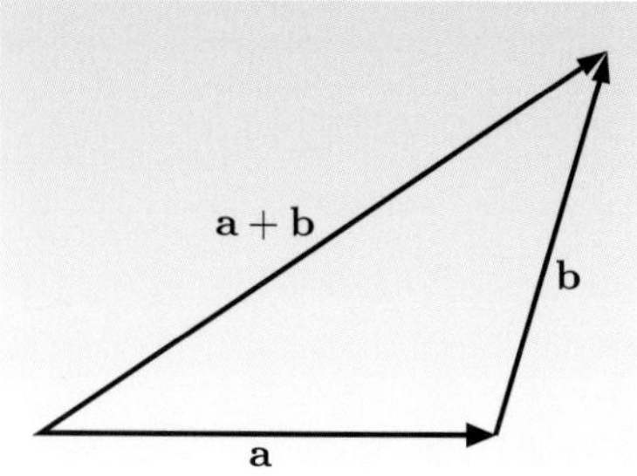


**Figure 8.2** The triangle rule of vector addition.

### Adding two vectors

We can also add vectors together to produce a new vector. The geometric rule for adding two vectors is shown in Figure 8.2. Arrows representing the vectors are drawn with the head of the first arrow, $\mathbf{a}$, coincident with the tail of the second arrow, $\mathbf{b}$. The arrow joining the tail of $\mathbf{a}$ to the head of $\mathbf{b}$ then represents the vector sum $\mathbf{a} + \mathbf{b}$. This is called the **triangle rule** of vector addition. Any number of vectors can be added together by repeated applications of this rule. In geometric terms, it is clear that

$$|\mathbf{a} + \mathbf{b}| \leq |\mathbf{a}| + |\mathbf{b}|,$$

and this is called the **triangle inequality**.

**Exercise 8.1** The positions of points 1 and 2 are represented by the position vectors $\mathbf{r}_1$ and $\mathbf{r}_2$. What interpretation can be given to (a) $\mathbf{r}_2 - \mathbf{r}_1$; (b) $|\mathbf{r}_2 - \mathbf{r}_1|$ and (c) $(\mathbf{r}_2 + \mathbf{r}_1)/2$? ■

## 8.1.2 Components of vectors

Strictly speaking, vectors are independent of any coordinate system, but in practice it is difficult to describe or manipulate them without using a fixed coordinate system. We generally use a **Cartesian coordinate system** — a set of three mutually perpendicular axes meeting at an origin. Three vectors of unit length (called **basis vectors**) point along the directions of the three axes. The usual way of labelling a Cartesian coordinate system is shown in Figure 8.3a: the three axes are called the $x$-axis, $y$-axis and the $z$-axis, and the corresponding basis vectors are labelled $\mathbf{e}_x$, $\mathbf{e}_y$ and $\mathbf{e}_z$.

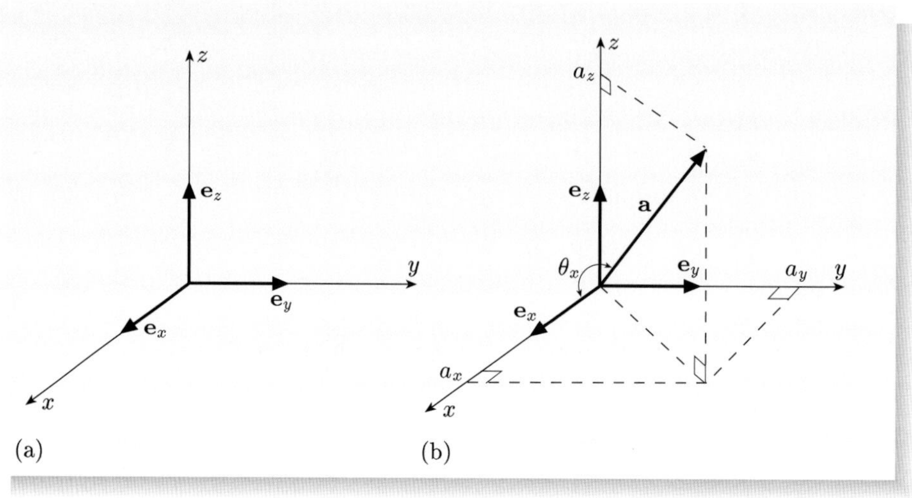


**Figure 8.3** (a) A Cartesian coordinate system with three mutually perpendicular axes and three basis vectors $\mathbf{e}_x$, $\mathbf{e}_y$ and $\mathbf{e}_z$; (b) in the given coordinate system, a vector $\mathbf{a}$ has components $a_x$, $a_y$ and $a_z$.

The set of three basis vectors is said to provide a **basis** for ordinary three-dimensional space. This means that any vector $\mathbf{a}$ can be expressed as a linear combination of the three basis vectors:

$$\mathbf{a} = a_x\mathbf{e}_x + a_y\mathbf{e}_y + a_z\mathbf{e}_z, \tag{8.1}$$

where the coefficients in the sum are the (scalar) **components** of the vector. If all three components are equal to zero, the vector is called the **zero vector**, $\mathbf{0}$.

The components are defined by dropping perpendiculars onto the axes, as in Figure 8.3b. If the vector **a** has magnitude $a$ and points in a direction that makes an angle $\theta_x$ with the positive $x$-direction, the $x$-component of **a** is given by

$$a_x = a\cos\theta_x \quad \text{where } 0 \le \theta_x \le \pi, \tag{8.2}$$

with similar definitions for $a_y$ and $a_z$.

Vector operations are simply expressed in terms of components. To multiply a vector by a scalar, $\lambda$, we multiply each of its components by $\lambda$:

$$\lambda\,\mathbf{a} = (\lambda a_x)\,\mathbf{e}_x + (\lambda a_y)\,\mathbf{e}_y + (\lambda a_z)\,\mathbf{e}_z.$$

To add or subtract two vectors, we add or subtract their components:

$$\mathbf{a} + \mathbf{b} = (a_x + b_x)\mathbf{e}_x + (a_y + b_y)\mathbf{e}_y + (a_z + b_z)\mathbf{e}_z,$$

$$\mathbf{a} - \mathbf{b} = (a_x - b_x)\mathbf{e}_x + (a_y - b_y)\mathbf{e}_y + (a_z - b_z)\mathbf{e}_z,$$

and, more generally, any linear combination of vectors involves a similar linear combination of components:

$$\lambda\mathbf{a} + \mu\mathbf{b} = (\lambda a_x + \mu b_x)\mathbf{e}_x + (\lambda a_y + \mu b_y)\mathbf{e}_y + (\lambda a_z + \mu b_z)\mathbf{e}_z.$$

**Exercise 8.2** Given that $\mathbf{a} = \mathbf{e}_x + 3\mathbf{e}_y$ and $\mathbf{b} = 5\mathbf{e}_x - 7\mathbf{e}_y$, find $3\mathbf{a} + 2\mathbf{b}$. ■

## 8.1.3 Scalar products of vectors

The **scalar product** (or *dot product*) of two vectors **a** and **b**, is defined by

$$\mathbf{a}\cdot\mathbf{b} = a_x b_x + a_y b_y + a_z b_z, \tag{8.3}$$

where $a_x, a_y$ and $a_z$, and $b_x, b_y$ and $b_z$, are the components of the vectors in a given Cartesian coordinate system. It can be shown that the right-hand side of Equation 8.3 is independent of the orientation of the coordinate system. Let us temporarily choose a coordinate system whose $x$-axis is aligned with the vector **a** so that $a_y = a_z = 0$. In this special coordinate system, Equations 8.2 and 8.3 give

$$\mathbf{a}\cdot\mathbf{b} = a_x b_x = (a\cos 0) \times (b\cos\theta) = ab\cos\theta, \tag{8.4}$$

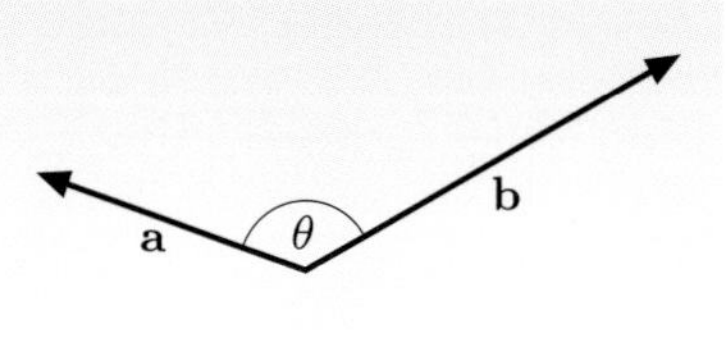


Figure 8.4 The angle $\theta$ between the directions of **a** and **b** is taken to be in the range $0 \le \theta \le \pi$.

where $a$ and $b$ are the magnitudes of **a** and **b** and $\theta$ is the angle between their directions, which is taken to lie in the range $0 \le \theta \le \pi$ (Figure 8.4). Now, the extreme right-hand side of Equation 8.4 involves only quantities $a$, $b$ and $\theta$ that do not depend of the choice of coordinate system, so the formula

$$\mathbf{a}\cdot\mathbf{b} = ab\cos\theta \tag{8.5}$$

provides an alternative definition of the scalar product, valid in any coordinate system.

In the special case where $\mathbf{b} = \mathbf{a}$, we have $\theta = 0$, so $\mathbf{a}\cdot\mathbf{a} = a^2$. It follows that the *magnitude* of any vector **a** is given by

$$a = \sqrt{\mathbf{a}\cdot\mathbf{a}} = \sqrt{a_x^2 + a_y^2 + a_z^2}, \tag{8.6}$$

This formula can be thought of as a three-dimensional version of Pythagoras' theorem.

In particular, we can say that $\mathbf{n} = n_x\mathbf{e}_x + n_y\mathbf{e}_y + n_z\mathbf{e}_z$ is a *unit vector* if

$$\mathbf{n}\cdot\mathbf{n} = n_x^2 + n_y^2 + n_z^2 = 1. \tag{8.7}$$

Vectors satisfying this condition are said to be **normalized**.

If two vectors are perpendicular, the angle $\theta$ between their directions is $\pi/2$ radians, and $\mathbf{a}\cdot\mathbf{b} = ab\cos(\pi/2) = 0$. So two vectors pointing in perpendicular directions obey

$$\mathbf{a}\cdot\mathbf{b} = a_x b_x + a_y b_y + a_z b_z = 0. \tag{8.8}$$

Vectors satisfying this condition are said to be **orthogonal**. By definition, the zero vector is orthogonal to any other vector. The three basis vectors $\mathbf{e}_x$, $\mathbf{e}_y$ and $\mathbf{e}_z$ are said to be **orthonormal** because each is normalized and each pair of these vectors is orthogonal.

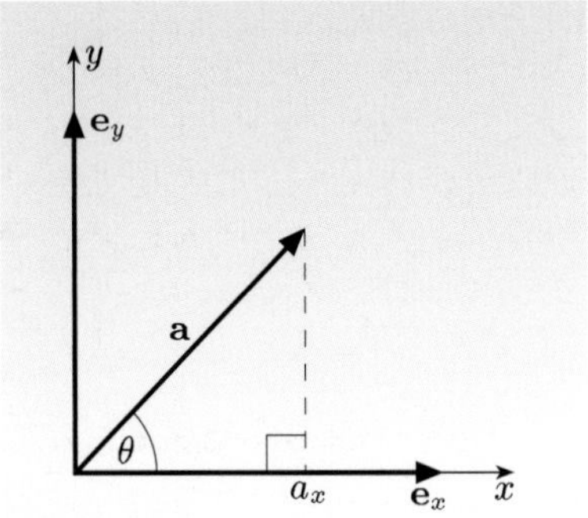


**Figure 8.5** The $x$-component of a vector $\mathbf{a}$ is given by $a_x = a\cos\theta = \mathbf{e}_x\cdot\mathbf{a}$. In geometric terms, this is found by projecting $\mathbf{a}$ onto the $x$-axis.

Because the basis vectors are orthonormal, taking the scalar product of a basis vector $\mathbf{e}_x$ with any vector $\mathbf{a}$ gives

$$\begin{aligned}\mathbf{e}_x\cdot\mathbf{a} &= \mathbf{e}_x\big(a_x\mathbf{e}_x + a_y\mathbf{e}_y + a_z\mathbf{e}_z\big)\\ &= a_x\mathbf{e}_x\cdot\mathbf{e}_x + a_y\mathbf{e}_x\cdot\mathbf{e}_y + a_z\mathbf{e}_x\cdot\mathbf{e}_z = a_x.\end{aligned} \tag{8.9}$$

More generally, any component of the vector can be found by taking its scalar product with a basis vector. In geometric terms, this is interpreted as a projection onto the corresponding coordinate axis (Figure 8.5).

The scalar product has all the properties you would expect of a product. For example, if $\mathbf{a} = \mathbf{b}$, and $\mathbf{c}$ is any vector, you can take the scalar product on both sides to form a valid scalar equation $\mathbf{c}\cdot\mathbf{a} = \mathbf{c}\cdot\mathbf{b}$. Moreover,

$$\mathbf{a}\cdot\mathbf{b} = \mathbf{b}\cdot\mathbf{a}, \tag{8.10}$$

$$\mathbf{a}\cdot(\mathbf{b}+\mathbf{c}) = \mathbf{a}\cdot\mathbf{b} + \mathbf{a}\cdot\mathbf{c}, \tag{8.11}$$

$$\mathbf{a}\cdot(\lambda\mathbf{b}) = \lambda(\mathbf{a}\cdot\mathbf{b}), \tag{8.12}$$

and

$$\mathbf{a}\cdot\mathbf{a} \geq 0. \tag{8.13}$$

Because $\cos^2\theta \leq 1$, Equations 8.5 and 8.6 also lead to the inequality

$$|\mathbf{a}\cdot\mathbf{b}|^2 \leq (\mathbf{a}\cdot\mathbf{a})\,(\mathbf{b}\cdot\mathbf{b}),$$

a result known as the **Cauchy–Schwarz inequality**.

**Exercise 8.3** Show that the vectors $\mathbf{a} = 0.6\,\mathbf{e}_x + 0.8\,\mathbf{e}_y$ and $\mathbf{b} = -0.8\,\mathbf{e}_x + 0.6\,\mathbf{e}_y$ are normalized and orthogonal to one another. Is the Cauchy–Schwarz inequality satisfied in this case?

**Exercise 8.4** Two vectors satisfy $\mathbf{a}\cdot\mathbf{b} = -ab$. What are their relative directions? ■

### 8.1.4 Vector products

The scalar product takes two vectors, $\mathbf{a}$ and $\mathbf{b}$, and produces a scalar, $\mathbf{a}\cdot\mathbf{b}$. However, we can also multiply two vectors to produce another vector, written as $\mathbf{a}\times\mathbf{b}$ and called the vector product (or *cross product*) of $\mathbf{a}$ and $\mathbf{b}$. Vector products are not as important in this course as scalar products, but they have an important role in Chapter 2 in the definition of angular momentum.

The **vector product** of $\mathbf{a}$ and $\mathbf{b}$ is a vector quantity defined by

$$\mathbf{a} \times \mathbf{b} = (a_y b_z - a_z b_y)\mathbf{e}_x + (a_z b_x - a_x b_z)\mathbf{e}_y + (a_x b_y - a_y b_x)\mathbf{e}_z, \quad (8.14)$$

where the components of the vectors are taken in a (right-handed) Cartesian coordinate system.

There is the strong pattern in Equation 8.14. The $x$-component of the vector product is the difference of two terms. The first term is the $y$-component of the first vector times the $z$-component of the second vector; the second term takes these components in the opposite order. The $y$- and $z$-components of the vector product follow a similar pattern, based on the cyclic permutation $x \to y \to z \to x$. This pattern can also be represented by a *determinant*:

$$\mathbf{a} \times \mathbf{b} = \begin{vmatrix} \mathbf{e}_x & \mathbf{e}_y & \mathbf{e}_z \\ a_x & a_y & a_z \\ b_x & b_y & b_z \end{vmatrix}, \quad (8.15)$$

Determinants are discussed further in Section 8.3.5.

which can be expanded to give

$$\mathbf{a} \times \mathbf{b} = \begin{vmatrix} a_y & a_z \\ b_y & b_z \end{vmatrix} \mathbf{e}_x - \begin{vmatrix} a_x & a_z \\ b_x & b_z \end{vmatrix} \mathbf{e}_y + \begin{vmatrix} a_x & a_y \\ b_x & b_y \end{vmatrix} \mathbf{e}_z,$$

and Equation 8.15 is recovered when we expand the $2 \times 2$ determinants.

**Exercise 8.5** Find the vector product $\mathbf{a} \times \mathbf{b}$, for $\mathbf{a} = 3\mathbf{e}_x + 4\mathbf{e}_y$ and $\mathbf{b} = -4\mathbf{e}_x + 3\mathbf{e}_y$. ■

An equivalent definition of the vector product $\mathbf{a} \times \mathbf{b}$ is that it is a vector of magnitude

$$|\mathbf{a} \times \mathbf{b}| = ab \sin\theta, \quad (8.16)$$

where $a$ and $b$ are the magnitudes of $\mathbf{a}$ and $\mathbf{b}$ and $\theta$ is the smaller of the angles between their directions, which lies in the range $0 \le \theta \le \pi$. The direction of $\mathbf{a} \times \mathbf{b}$ is given by the **right-hand rule** shown in Figure 8.6: point the fingers of your right hand in the direction of the first vector in the product, $\mathbf{a}$, and bend them (rotating your wrist if necessary) in the direction of the second vector, $\mathbf{b}$. The vector product $\mathbf{a} \times \mathbf{b}$ is then perpendicular to both $\mathbf{a}$ and $\mathbf{b}$, in the sense indicated by your outstretched right thumb.

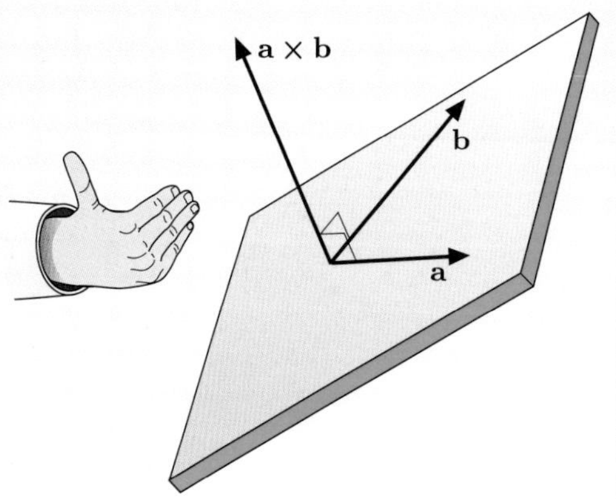

**Figure 8.6** Using the right-hand rule to find the direction of a vector product.

The vector product has many of the properties you would expect of a product. For example,

$$\mathbf{a} \times (\mathbf{b} + \mathbf{c}) = \mathbf{a} \times \mathbf{b} + \mathbf{a} \times \mathbf{c}$$

and

$$\mathbf{a} \times (\lambda\mathbf{b}) = (\lambda\mathbf{a}) \times \mathbf{b} = \lambda(\mathbf{a} \times \mathbf{b}).$$

However, it is important to note that the order of the vectors in a vector product is significant. As Equation 8.14 shows,

$$\mathbf{a} \times \mathbf{b} = -\mathbf{b} \times \mathbf{a}.$$

The vector product of a vector with itself is equal to the zero vector:

$$\mathbf{a} \times \mathbf{a} = \mathbf{0}.$$

and, more generally, the vector product $\mathbf{a} \times \mathbf{b} = \mathbf{0}$ if $\mathbf{a}$ and $\mathbf{b}$ are collinear (i.e. are parallel or antiparallel).

**Exercise 8.6** A vector $\mathbf{a}$ is directed horizontally to the South and vector $\mathbf{b}$ is directed horizontally to the West; what is the direction of $\mathbf{a} \times \mathbf{b}$? ■

## 8.2 Abstract vector spaces

In this book, our main interest in vectors lies in generalizations beyond ordinary three-dimensional space. In Chapter 1 you will see that wave functions can be represented as vectors with complex components in a space with infinitely-many dimensions. Some echoes of this have filtered down into the language of wave mechanics: for example, we talk of two functions as being normalized and orthogonal to one another. Moreover, in Chapter 3 you will see that the spin of an electron can be represented by a complex vector in a two-dimensional space.

### 8.2.1 First steps towards generalization

It is important to use appropriate notation. First, we shall abandon the labels $x$, $y$ and $z$ used to identify axes and components in ordinary space. In a space of many dimensions, it is much more sensible to use the labels 1, 2, 3, ..., which can be continued indefinitely.

We shall also denote abstract vectors in a different way. This is to avoid confusion with ordinary vectors, and to use a notation that will be helpful in quantum mechanics. Instead of using bold print to indicate a vector, as in $\mathbf{a}$, we shall place a non-bold symbol in an angular bracket, as in $|a\rangle$. Using this notation, the natural extension of Equation 8.1 is

$$|a\rangle = a_1|e_1\rangle + a_2|e_2\rangle + \ldots = \sum_i a_i|e_i\rangle, \qquad (8.17)$$

where $|a\rangle$ is a vector with components $a_1, a_2 \ldots$, expressed as a linear combination of orthonormal basis vectors $|e_1\rangle, |e_2\rangle, \ldots$. Equation 8.17 makes two important generalizations:

1. There can be any number of orthonormal basis vectors $|e_i\rangle$ — perhaps an infinite number of them, in which case the right-hand side of Equation 8.17 is an infinite sum.
2. The components $a_i$ can be complex (rather than real) numbers.

Apart from these generalizations, the algebraic properties of vectors remain much the same as before. For example, vectors can added together or multiplied by scalars, just as you would expect. We have

$$|a\rangle + |b\rangle = \sum_i (a_i + b_i)|e_i\rangle \qquad (8.18)$$

and

$$\lambda|a\rangle = \sum_i (\lambda a_i)|e_i\rangle. \tag{8.19}$$

We shall also introduce a new notation for scalar products. Rather than writing $\mathbf{a} \cdot \mathbf{b}$, we shall write $\langle a|b\rangle$. We shall also make a slight generalization in the definition of a scalar product. For ordinary vectors, we defined

$$\mathbf{a} \cdot \mathbf{b} = a_1 b_1 + a_2 b_2 + a_3 b_3. \qquad \text{(Eqn 8.3)}$$

Now we are dealing with vectors that can have an arbitrary number of *complex* components, and it is appropriate to define the scalar product of $|a\rangle$ and $|b\rangle$ as follows:

$$\langle a|b\rangle = a_1^* b_1 + a_2^* b_2 + \ldots = \sum_i a_i^* b_i, \tag{8.20}$$

where the components of the first vector, $|a\rangle$, are complex conjugated. This makes no difference to vectors with real components, but it matters in general. It means that the ordering of vectors in the scalar product is significant:

$$\langle b|a\rangle = \langle a|b\rangle^* \tag{8.21}$$

The reason for using the definition given in Equation 8.20 is that it ensures that the scalar product of $|a\rangle$ with itself is

$$\langle a|a\rangle = \sum_i a_i^* a_i = \sum_i |a_i|^2, \tag{8.22}$$

which is the sum of real non-negative terms. It therefore follows that

$$\langle a|a\rangle \geq 0, \tag{8.23}$$

which is the analogue of Equation 8.13. This allows us to interpret $\sqrt{\langle a|a\rangle}$ as the real, non-negative *magnitude* of the vector $|a\rangle$.

A vector $|a\rangle$ with $\langle a|a\rangle = 1$ is said to be *normalized*, and two vectors $|a\rangle$ and $|b\rangle$ with $\langle a|b\rangle = 0$ are said to be *orthogonal*. The basis vectors $|e_i\rangle$ are both normalized and orthogonal (we say that they are orthonormal), so

$$\langle e_i|e_j\rangle = \delta_{ij}, \tag{8.24}$$

where $\delta_{ij}$ is the usual Kronecker delta symbol.

The advantage of expressing a given vector in terms of a linear sum of orthonormal basis vectors is that the coefficients in the sum (the components of the vector) are easily found by taking scalar products. For example, taking the scalar product of both sides of Equation 8.17 with $|e_j\rangle$ gives

$$\langle e_j|a\rangle = \sum_i a_i \langle e_j|e_i\rangle = \sum_i a_i \delta_{ji} = a_j,$$

so the component $a_j$ is given by the scalar product $\langle e_j|a\rangle$. This generalizes Equation 8.9 to any vector space.

You might wonder what all this has to do with 'the real world'. No-one has ever seen 100 vectors pointing in 100 orthogonal directions, and we have not begun to explain what this might mean. Fortunately, there is a more rigorous way of proceeding; this will be sketched in the next two subsections.

### 8.2.2 Vector spaces

Doctor Johnson, in the preface to his Dictionary, pointed out that: 'to explain, requires the use of terms less abstruse than that which is to be explained, and such terms cannot always be found ... for the easiest word, whatever it may be, cannot be translated into one easier'.

This creates a difficulty for mathematics, which needs precise definitions. To get around this difficulty, mathematicians focus on the *rules governing ways objects combine with one another.* Using the properties of ordinary vectors as a guide, mathematicians have drawn up a list of rules that distil the essence of 'behaving like a vector'. Then, anything that obeys these rules is taken — by definition — to be a vector. This way of defining a vector is unambiguous and leads to fruitful generalizations.

Here is the definitive list of vector properties, using the $|a\rangle$ notation introduced above; $\alpha$ and $\beta$ are arbitrary scalars.

**Box 1 Defining properties of vectors**

1. Any two vectors can be added, and the result is a vector; this operation obeys the rules:
$$|a\rangle + |b\rangle = |b\rangle + |a\rangle$$
$$\big(|a\rangle + |b\rangle\big) + |c\rangle = |a\rangle + \big(|b\rangle + |c\rangle\big)$$
2. There is a zero vector, denoted by $|0\rangle$, such that
$$|a\rangle + |0\rangle = |a\rangle \quad \text{for any vector } |a\rangle$$
3. Any vector can be multiplied by a scalar, and the result is a vector; this operation obeys the rules:
$$\alpha\big(\beta|a\rangle\big) = (\alpha\beta)\,|a\rangle$$
$$(\alpha + \beta)\,|a\rangle = \alpha|a\rangle + \beta|a\rangle$$
$$\alpha\big(|a\rangle + |b\rangle\big) = \alpha|a\rangle + \alpha|b\rangle$$
4. Multiplication of any vector $|a\rangle$ by 0 and 1 give
$$0\,|a\rangle = |0\rangle$$
$$1\,|a\rangle = |a\rangle.$$

You need not commit the above rules to memory, but you should be aware that a clear-cut set of rules exists. The main point is that any objects obeying these rules are classified as being (abstract) **vectors**, and any set of vectors generated by applying these rules exhaustively is called a **vector space**. So, a position vector is a *vector*, and the set of all the vectors that describe positions in three-dimensional space is a *vector space*.

However, there are many different vector spaces. One example is provided the set of all cubic polynomials in $x$, i.e. expressions of the form

$$a(x) = a_0 + a_1 x + a_2 x^2 + a_3 x^3, \tag{8.25}$$

where $a_0, \ldots, a_3$ are complex constants (possibly zero) and $x$ is a real variable. If we multiply $a(x)$ by a scalar $\lambda$, we obtain another cubic polynomial:

$$\lambda a(x) = (\lambda a_0) + (\lambda a_1)x + (\lambda a_2)x^2 + (\lambda a_3)x^3.$$

Moreover, if $b(x) = b_0 + b_1 x + b_2 x^2 + b_3 x^3$, then

$$a(x) + b(x) = (a_0 + b_0) + (a_1 + b_1)x + (a_2 + b_2)x^2 + (a_3 + b_3)x^3,$$

so adding any two cubic polynomial produces another cubic polynomial.

In fact, if you go through all the properties in Box 1, you will find that cubic polynomials possess all the defining properties of vectors. Consequently, although it may come as a bit of a surprise, cubic polynomials can be regarded as vectors in an abstract vector space. Because four scalars ($a_0$, $a_1$, $a_2$ and $a_3$) are needed to specify an arbitrary cubic polynomial, the corresponding vector space is four-dimensional. This result can be readily generalized; polynomials of order 99 belong to a vector space of dimension 100.

### 8.2.3 Inner product spaces

Our definition of a vector, and of a vector space, did not include any notion of multiplying vectors together. Nevertheless, when we use vector spaces in physical applications, including quantum mechanics, we usually need to combine vectors to form scalars, so we need to define a *scalar product.* (The vector product of two vectors is much less useful and we shall not need to consider it further.)

In an abstract vector space, the term *scalar product* is usually replaced by the term *inner product.* Equation 8.20 gives a rule for calculating the inner product of two vectors in any vector space, but stating the rule in this way is rather circular because the components are assumed to be defined in an orthonormal basis, and the concept of orthonormality itself relies on inner products (see Equation 8.24).

We therefore adopt the same mathematical tactic as before, collecting a list of required properties. In the following list, $|a\rangle$, $|b\rangle$ and $|c\rangle$ are vectors and $\lambda$ is a scalar.

**Box 2 Defining properties of an inner product**

An inner product of two vectors is a scalar quantity that satisfies the following properties:

1. $\langle b|a\rangle = \langle a|b\rangle^*$,
2. $\langle a|\big(|b\rangle + |c\rangle\big) = \langle a|b\rangle + \langle a|c\rangle$,
3. $\langle a|\big(\lambda|b\rangle\big) = \lambda\langle a|b\rangle$, where $\lambda$ is a scalar,
4. $\langle a|a\rangle \geq 0$, with the equals sign applying only if $|a\rangle = |0\rangle$.

These are just the properties listed in Equations 8.10 to 8.13, but written in our new notation, and with Property 1 now generalized to handle vectors with complex components. Any way of combining vectors that satisfies these properties is an **inner product** and the corresponding vector space is then called an **inner product space**.

In the case of the vector space of cubic polynomials considered previously, one way of defining an inner product is as follows:

$$\langle a|b\rangle = \int_{-1}^{1} a^*(x)\, b(x)\, \mathrm{d}x \tag{8.26}$$

With this choice, the following functions turn out to be orthonormal:

Apart from its extra factor $\sqrt{n+\frac{1}{2}}$, the function $e_n(x)$ is known to mathematicians as a *Legendre polynomial* of order $n$.

$$\begin{aligned} e_0(x) &= \frac{1}{\sqrt{2}}, \\ e_1(x) &= \sqrt{\frac{3}{2}} \times x, \\ e_2(x) &= \sqrt{\frac{5}{2}} \times \frac{1}{2}(3x^2 - 1), \\ e_3(x) &= \sqrt{\frac{7}{2}} \times \frac{1}{2}(5x^3 - 3x), \end{aligned} \tag{8.27}$$

where $x$ is real. That is,

$$\langle e_i|e_j\rangle = \int_{-1}^{1} e_i^*(x)\, e_j(x)\, \mathrm{d}x = \delta_{ij}. \tag{8.28}$$

Since any cubic polynomial can be written as a linear combination of $e_0(x)$, $e_1(x)$, $e_2(x)$ and $e_3(x)$, these four polynomials provide an **orthonormal basis** for the vector space of cubic polynomials.

In quantum mechanics, a particularly important vector space (called *function space*) is provided by the set of all normalizable functions, that is, functions $f(x)$ for which

$$\int_{-\infty}^{\infty} |f(x)|^2\, \mathrm{d}x \text{ is finite.}$$

A suitable inner product for the space of normalized functions is given by

$$\langle f|g\rangle = \int_{-\infty}^{\infty} f^*(x) g(x)\, \mathrm{d}x. \tag{8.29}$$

While it is quite a lengthy task to verify that function space is a vector space (having all the properties in Box 1), it is relatively easy to confirm that Equation 8.29 has all the properties in Box 2, and so provides a valid inner product. An example of an orthonormal basis in this inner product space is given by the set of energy eigenfunctions of a harmonic oscillator, which are orthonormal with respect to the inner product of Equation 8.29, and are complete in the sense that any reasonable function $f(x)$ can be written as a linear combination of them.

**Exercise 8.7** Show that Equation 8.29 satisfies Property 1 in Box 2.

**Exercise 8.8** Show that the functions $e_1(t)$ and $e_2(t)$ in Equation 8.27 are orthogonal with respect to the inner product of Equation 8.26. ■

# 8.3 Matrices and determinants

## 8.3.1 Matrix notation

A **matrix** A is a set of objects (called **matrix elements**) arranged in a rectangular pattern of rows and columns:

$$\mathrm{A} = \begin{bmatrix} A_{11} & A_{12} & \dots & A_{1n} \\ A_{21} & A_{22} & \dots & A_{2n} \\ \vdots & \vdots & & \vdots \\ A_{m1} & A_{m2} & \dots & A_{mn} \end{bmatrix}$$

In the above example, the matrix has $m$ rows and $n$ columns, and is said to be an $m \times n$ (pronounced 'm by n') matrix. Each matrix element $A_{ij}$ carries two indices, the first labelling the row, and the second labelling the column of the matrix element under consideration. A useful mnemonic for this is 'Arc', standing for $\mathrm{A}_{\text{row column}}$. In this course, matrix elements are generally scalars – real or complex numbers with appropriate units of measurement.

Three different shapes of matrix will be important for our purposes: a **square matrix** has the same number of rows and columns, a **row matrix** has a single row, and a **column matrix** has a single column. We will generally consider matrices in two-dimensional situations, and so need to consider matrices of the form:

$$\begin{bmatrix} A_{11} & A_{12} \\ A_{21} & A_{22} \end{bmatrix} \qquad \begin{bmatrix} A_{11} & A_{12} \end{bmatrix} \qquad \begin{bmatrix} A_{11} \\ A_{21} \end{bmatrix}$$

$2 \times 2$ square matrix $\quad$ $1 \times 2$ row matrix $\quad$ $2 \times 1$ column matrix

Two matrices are said to be *equal* to one another if they have the same shape and size and all their corresponding elements are equal.

## 8.3.2 Operations on matrices

Matrices can be combined with scalars and with other matrices in a variety of ways.

### Multiplication by a scalar

To multiply any matrix A by a scalar $\lambda$, we simply multiply each element of the matrix by $\lambda$. So,

$$(\lambda \mathrm{A})_{ij} = \lambda A_{ij}.$$

For example,

$$2\begin{bmatrix} 3 & -1 \\ 2 & -4 \end{bmatrix} = \begin{bmatrix} 6 & -2 \\ 4 & -8 \end{bmatrix}.$$

### Addition of matrices

Two matrices A and B of the same size and shape can be added together to give a new matrix

$$\mathrm{C} = \mathrm{A} + \mathrm{B},$$

where each matrix element of C is found by adding the corresponding elements of A and B:

$$C_{ij} = A_{ij} + B_{ij}.$$

For example,

$$\begin{bmatrix} 3 \\ 2 \end{bmatrix} + \begin{bmatrix} 2 \\ 1 \end{bmatrix} = \begin{bmatrix} 5 \\ 3 \end{bmatrix} \quad \text{and} \quad \begin{bmatrix} 3 & -1 \\ 2 & -4 \end{bmatrix} + \begin{bmatrix} 2 & 1 \\ 1 & 7 \end{bmatrix} = \begin{bmatrix} 5 & 0 \\ 3 & 3 \end{bmatrix}.$$

It is not possible to add two matrices of different shapes or sizes.

### Matrix multiplication

A very important operation between two matrices A and B is that of multiplying them together (matrix multiplication).

$$\mathrm{C} = \mathrm{AB}.$$

This operation only makes sense if the number of *columns* in the first matrix is equal to the number of *rows* in the second matrix. For example, we can define the matrix products

$$\begin{bmatrix} 1 & 2 \\ 3 & 4 \end{bmatrix}\begin{bmatrix} 3 \\ 5 \end{bmatrix} \quad \text{or} \quad \begin{bmatrix} 1 & 2 \\ 3 & 4 \end{bmatrix}\begin{bmatrix} 3 & 4 & 7 \\ 5 & 3 & 1 \end{bmatrix},$$

but we cannot interpret

$$\begin{bmatrix} 1 & 2 \\ 3 & 4 \end{bmatrix}\begin{bmatrix} 3 & 5 \end{bmatrix} \quad \text{or} \quad \begin{bmatrix} 3 \\ 5 \end{bmatrix}\begin{bmatrix} 1 & 2 \\ 3 & 4 \end{bmatrix}.$$

Let us suppose that A is an $m \times n$ matrix and B is an $n \times p$ matrix, then the matrix elements of the product matrix C = AB are defined by

$$C_{ij} = \sum_{k=1}^{n} A_{ik}B_{kj}. \qquad (8.30)$$

Remember, $C_{ij}$ is the element in the $i$th row and $j$th column of C. To find this matrix element, we go along the $i$th row of A and down the $j$th column of B, multiplying corresponding elements and adding the results. This pattern may be visualized as follows:

$$\begin{bmatrix} * & \\ & \end{bmatrix} = \begin{bmatrix} \rightarrow & \rightarrow \\ & \end{bmatrix}\begin{bmatrix} \downarrow & \\ \downarrow & \end{bmatrix}$$

$$\begin{bmatrix} & * \\ & \end{bmatrix} = \begin{bmatrix} \rightarrow & \rightarrow \\ & \end{bmatrix}\begin{bmatrix} & \downarrow \\ & \downarrow \end{bmatrix}$$

$$\begin{bmatrix} & \\ * & \end{bmatrix} = \begin{bmatrix} & \\ \rightarrow & \rightarrow \end{bmatrix} \begin{bmatrix} \downarrow & \\ \downarrow & \end{bmatrix}$$

$$\begin{bmatrix} & \\ & * \end{bmatrix} = \begin{bmatrix} & \\ \rightarrow & \rightarrow \end{bmatrix} \begin{bmatrix} & \downarrow \\ & \downarrow \end{bmatrix},$$

where the $*$ indicates a matrix element in the new matrix, C, and the arrows show how matrix elements in the old matrices are processed to obtain this. The index $k$ in Equation 8.30 tells us how to match up elements in A and B to multiply together. As $k$ increases we simultaneously go along a row of A and down a column of B. However, the choice of the letter $k$ for this purpose is arbitrary — we could equally well have chosen $l$, or anything other than $i$ and $j$ which are reserved for the particular matrix element of C under consideration. Indices like $k$, that are internal to expressions and do not affect the meaning of a whole equation, are called **dummy indices**.

Matrix multiplication does not satisfy all the rules of ordinary multiplication. For example, if A and B are non-square matrices we may be able to form the matrix product AB, but be unable to define BA. For two square matrices of the same size, we can define both AB and BA, but the result we get may depend on the order of multiplication. For example, if

$$\mathrm{A} = \begin{bmatrix} a & 0 \\ 0 & -a \end{bmatrix} \quad \text{and} \quad \mathrm{B} = \begin{bmatrix} 0 & b \\ b & 0 \end{bmatrix},$$

we have

$$\mathrm{AB} = \begin{bmatrix} a & 0 \\ 0 & -a \end{bmatrix} \begin{bmatrix} 0 & b \\ b & 0 \end{bmatrix} = \begin{bmatrix} 0 & ab \\ -ab & 0 \end{bmatrix}$$

$$\mathrm{BA} = \begin{bmatrix} 0 & b \\ b & 0 \end{bmatrix} \begin{bmatrix} a & 0 \\ 0 & -a \end{bmatrix} = \begin{bmatrix} 0 & -ab \\ ab & 0 \end{bmatrix},$$

so $\mathrm{AB} \neq \mathrm{BA}$ in this case; we say that the matrices A and B are **non-commuting** or that they do not **commute** with one another.

You should not suppose that all matrices fail to commute. For example, the matrix

$$\mathrm{I} = \begin{bmatrix} 1 & 0 \\ 0 & 1 \end{bmatrix}$$

is called the $2 \times 2$ **unit matrix**. Multiplying by this matrix leaves any other $2 \times 2$ matrix A unchanged, no matter which order we use for the multiplication:

$$\mathrm{I\,A} = \begin{bmatrix} 1 & 0 \\ 0 & 1 \end{bmatrix} \begin{bmatrix} a & b \\ c & d \end{bmatrix} = \begin{bmatrix} a & b \\ c & d \end{bmatrix}$$

$$\mathrm{A\,I} = \begin{bmatrix} a & b \\ c & d \end{bmatrix} \begin{bmatrix} 1 & 0 \\ 0 & 1 \end{bmatrix} = \begin{bmatrix} a & b \\ c & d \end{bmatrix}.$$

It is interesting to note the role played by matrix multiplication at the birth of quantum mechanics. In the early summer of 1925, Heisenberg spent several weeks on the island of Heligoland trying to reduce the effects of hay fever. In this secluded environment, he made the first tentative steps towards quantum mechanics, drawing up square tables of numbers and devising rules for combining them. On his return to the mainland, Heisenberg showed his very promising results to Born who pointed out that mathematicians would call the square tables *matrices*, and call Heisenberg's rule for combining them *matrix multiplication*. Heisenberg had never heard of matrices! At first, the non-commutativity of matrices alarmed Heisenberg; he wondered whether it was reasonable to describe physical quantities by non-commuting objects, but it soon became clear that this was a characteristic feature of the new quantum physics. Before long, the properties of matrices were being studied by physicists all over the world.

### 8.3.3 Vectors as column matrices

In an $n$-dimensional vector space, any vector $|a\rangle$ can be expressed as

$$|a\rangle = \sum_{i=1}^{n} a_i|e_i\rangle,$$

where the coefficients $a_i$ are the components of $|a\rangle$ in the orthonormal basis $|e_i\rangle$. Provided we agree on the choice of basis, the set of components $a_i$ is a compact way of specifying the vector. The coefficients can be arranged as a column matrix, allowing us to say that:

$$\text{The vector } |a\rangle \text{ is represented by the column matrix } \begin{bmatrix} a_1 \\ a_2 \\ \vdots \\ a_n \end{bmatrix}.$$

*Bases* is the plural of *basis*.

We have said 'is represented by' because the vector $|a\rangle$ has the same meaning in all bases, while a specific column matrix represents the vector only in a specific basis. Nevertheless, with the choice of basis fixed, no harm is done in linking these two concepts with an equals sign, and that is what we shall do here. For any vector $|a\rangle$ in a two-dimensional space, we write

$$|a\rangle = \begin{bmatrix} a_1 \\ a_2 \end{bmatrix}.$$

In particular, the basis vectors, with components $(a_1 = 1, a_2 = 0)$ and $(a_1 = 0, a_2 = 1)$, are given by

$$|e_1\rangle = \begin{bmatrix} 1 \\ 0 \end{bmatrix} \quad \text{and} \quad |e_2\rangle = \begin{bmatrix} 0 \\ 1 \end{bmatrix}.$$

In this representation, everything is consistent because column matrices obey rules appropriate for vectors. For example, the equation

$$|a\rangle = a_1|e_1\rangle + a_2|e_2\rangle$$

becomes the identity

$$\begin{bmatrix} a_1 \\ a_2 \end{bmatrix} = a_1 \begin{bmatrix} 1 \\ 0 \end{bmatrix} + a_2 \begin{bmatrix} 0 \\ 1 \end{bmatrix} = \begin{bmatrix} a_1 \\ 0 \end{bmatrix} + \begin{bmatrix} 0 \\ a_2 \end{bmatrix} = \begin{bmatrix} a_1 \\ a_2 \end{bmatrix}.$$

The inner product of two vectors $|a\rangle$ and $|b\rangle$ can also be represented as the product of two matrices. However, we cannot simply multiply the two column matrices representing $|a\rangle$ and $|b\rangle$. This is because matrix multiplication is not defined for two column matrices. Instead, we convert the first column matrix $|a\rangle$ into a row matrix and take the complex conjugate of all its elements. This process of converting the columns of a matrix into rows and taking the complex conjugates of the elements is called **Hermitian conjugation** – it is like complex conjugation with the additional twist that columns are converted into rows. We use the symbol $\langle a|$ to indicate the row matrix that is the Hermitian conjugate of the column matrix $|a\rangle$. So,

Other books indicate row and column matrices by $\mathbf{a}$ and $\mathbf{a}^\dagger$, but our notation is very frequently used in quantum mechanics.

$$\text{if } |a\rangle = \begin{bmatrix} a_1 \\ a_2 \end{bmatrix} \quad \text{then} \quad \langle a| = \begin{bmatrix} a_1^* & a_2^* \end{bmatrix}.$$

Recalling that the inner product of two vectors $|a\rangle = a_1|e_1\rangle + a_2|e_2\rangle$ and $|b\rangle = b_1|e_1\rangle + b_2|e_2\rangle$ is defined to be

$$\langle a|b\rangle = a_1^* b_1 + a_2^* b_2,$$

we now see that the equivalent matrix representation is

$$\langle a|b\rangle = \begin{bmatrix} a_1^* & a_2^* \end{bmatrix} \begin{bmatrix} b_1 \\ b_2 \end{bmatrix}$$

where we use matrix multiplication to combine the row and column matrices.

**Exercise 8.9** Given that $|a\rangle = \begin{bmatrix} 1 \\ \mathrm{i} \end{bmatrix}$ and $|b\rangle = \begin{bmatrix} \mathrm{i} \\ 1 \end{bmatrix}$, find the inner product $\langle a|b\rangle$. ■

## 8.3.4 Operators as square matrices

Let us consider the effect of applying an operation to a vector. Think, for example, of rotating a vector, or stretching it, or applying some combination of rotation and stretching. Suppose that the initial vector is $|v\rangle$, and that the result of acting on it with the linear operator $\widehat{\mathrm{A}}$ is a new vector

$$|v'\rangle = \widehat{\mathrm{A}}|v\rangle. \tag{8.31}$$

This operation is illustrated in Figure 8.7. We can write the initial vector as

$$|v\rangle = \sum_j v_j|e_j\rangle, \tag{8.32}$$

where the $|e_j\rangle$ are orthonormal basis vectors and the $v_j$ are the components of $|v\rangle$ in this basis. Substituting this expression into Equation 8.31 gives

$$|v'\rangle = \widehat{\mathrm{A}}|v\rangle = \widehat{\mathrm{A}}\Big(\sum_j v_j|e_j\rangle\Big) = \sum_j v_j\Big(\widehat{\mathrm{A}}|e_j\rangle\Big), \tag{8.33}$$

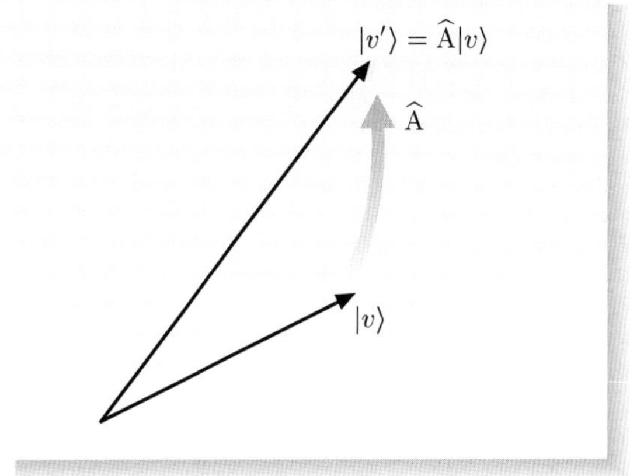


**Figure 8.7** Visualizing the effect of an operator $\widehat{\mathrm{A}}$ on a vector $|v\rangle$.

where the last step follows because the operator is linear.

Now $|v'\rangle$ is a vector in the same vector space as $|v\rangle$, so it can be expanded in the same basis to give

$$|v'\rangle = \sum_j v_j'|e_j\rangle. \tag{8.34}$$

We ask: what is the relationship between the components $v_i'$ and $v_i$ of the transformed and initial vectors?

To answer this question, we use the familiar trick of taking the inner product of both sides of Equation 8.34 with one of the basis vectors, $|e_i\rangle$. Using the orthonormality of the basis vectors ($\langle e_i|e_j\rangle = \delta_{ij}$), we obtain

$$\langle e_i|v'\rangle = \sum_j v_j'\langle e_i|e_j\rangle = \sum_j v_j'\delta_{ij} = v_i'.$$

Combining this result with Equation 8.33, we see that

$$v_i' = \langle e_i|v'\rangle = \sum_j v_j\,\langle e_i|\widehat{\mathrm{A}}|e_j\rangle. \tag{8.35}$$

The quantity $\langle e_i|\widehat{\mathrm{A}}|e_j\rangle$ is a scalar that depends on the operator $\widehat{\mathrm{A}}$ and the choice of two basis vectors, $|e_i\rangle$ and $|e_j\rangle$. For reasons that will soon become apparent, it is convenient to denote this quantity by $A_{ij}$, so we have

$$A_{ij} = \langle e_i|\widehat{\mathrm{A}}|e_j\rangle. \tag{8.36}$$

Using this notation in Equation 8.35, we then obtain

$$v_i' = \sum_j A_{ij}v_j. \tag{8.37}$$

Finally, we can use the rule for matrix multiplication to express this result as:

$$\begin{bmatrix} v_1' \\ v_2' \\ \vdots \\ v_n' \end{bmatrix} = \begin{bmatrix} A_{11} & A_{12} & \dots & A_{1n} \\ A_{21} & A_{22} & \dots & A_{2n} \\ \vdots & \vdots & & \vdots \\ A_{n1} & A_{n2} & \dots & A_{nn} \end{bmatrix} \begin{bmatrix} v_1 \\ v_2 \\ \vdots \\ v_n \end{bmatrix} \tag{8.38}$$

The matrix A may also be written as $\widehat{\mathrm{A}}$ in cases where we wish to emphasize its role as an operator acting on column matrices.

where A is the square matrix whose matrix elements are given by Equation 8.36. This matrix represents the operator $\widehat{\mathrm{A}}$, in much the same way that the column matrices in Equation 8.38 represent the initial and final vectors $|v\rangle$ and $|v'\rangle$. For this reason, the numbers $A_{ij}$ are often called the **matrix elements** of the operator $\widehat{\mathrm{A}}$. Note that the square matrix and the column matrices have definite descriptions in any given basis, but the numbers that appear in these matrices may vary from basis to basis.

As an example of these ideas, consider the operator $\widehat{\mathrm{R}}(\theta)$ that rotates real two-dimensional vectors through an anticlockwise angle $\theta$. Figure 8.8 shows the effect of this operation on a pair of orthonormal basis vectors.

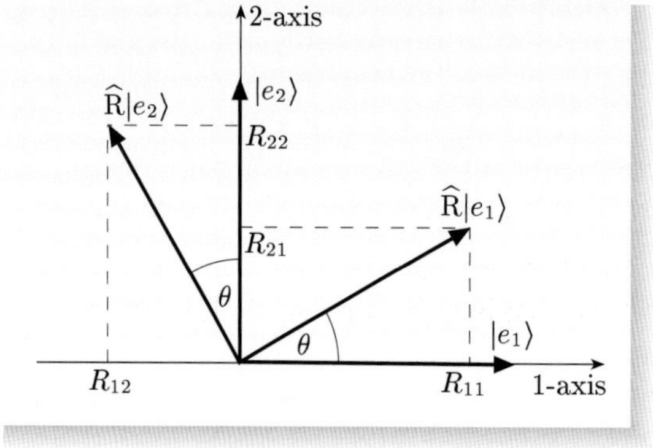


**Figure 8.8** The operator $\widehat{\mathrm{R}}(\theta)$ rotates vectors through an anticlockwise angle $\theta$. A matrix element such as $R_{21} = \langle e_2|\,\widehat{\mathrm{R}}\,|e_1\rangle$ is given by the projection of the rotated vector $\widehat{\mathrm{R}}|e_1\rangle$ onto the 2-axis. In the case shown, $R_{12}$ has a negative value.

Using elementary geometry, we can see that

$$R_{11} = \cos\theta, \quad R_{21} = \sin\theta, \quad R_{12} = -\sin\theta, \quad \text{and} \quad R_{22} = \cos\theta.$$

Hence the anticlockwise rotation matrix is

$$\mathrm{R}(\theta) = \begin{bmatrix} \cos\theta & -\sin\theta \\ \sin\theta & \cos\theta \end{bmatrix}.$$

**Exercise 8.10** Use matrix methods to find the effect of a 90° anticlockwise rotation on

$$|a\rangle = \begin{bmatrix} 1 \\ 1 \end{bmatrix}.$$

**Exercise 8.11** By considering the effect of two successive anticlockwise rotations through $\theta$, obtain general formulae for $\cos(2\theta)$ and $\sin(2\theta)$ in terms of $\cos\theta$ and $\sin\theta$. ■

### Hermitian matrices

In the physics chapters of this book, you will see that most of the operators that are important in quantum physics have the special property of being **Hermitian**. In the context of vector spaces, this means that

$$\langle u|\widehat{\mathrm{A}}|v\rangle \equiv \langle u|\widehat{\mathrm{A}}v\rangle = \langle \widehat{\mathrm{A}}u|v\rangle \tag{8.39}$$

for all vectors $|u\rangle$ and $|v\rangle$. Since all inner products obey $\langle b|a\rangle = \langle a|b\rangle^*$, the Hermitian condition can also be expressed as

$$\langle u|\widehat{\mathrm{A}}|v\rangle = \langle v|\widehat{\mathrm{A}}|u\rangle^*. \tag{8.40}$$

Applying this condition in the special case where $|u\rangle = |e_i\rangle$ and $|v\rangle = |e_j\rangle$, are orthonormal basis vectors, we see that a Hermitian operator obeys

$$\langle e_i|\widehat{\mathrm{A}}|e_j\rangle = \langle e_j|\widehat{\mathrm{A}}|e_i\rangle^*$$

so the matrix elements of a Hermitian operator obey the condition

$$A_{ij} = A_{ji}^* \tag{8.41}$$

Any matrix for which this applies is said to be a **Hermitian matrix**.

A Hermitian matrix is unchanged by the operation of **Hermitian conjugation**, which converts rows into columns and takes the complex conjugate of all matrix elements.

For example,

$$\begin{bmatrix} 2 & 1+\mathrm{i} \\ 1-\mathrm{i} & 3 \end{bmatrix},$$

is a Hermitian matrix. The tell-tale signs are that the matrix elements along the main diagonal ($A_{11}$ and $A_{22}$) are real, and pairs of matrix elements reflected across the main diagonal ($A_{12}$ and $A_{21}$) are complex conjugates of one another.

Although we shall not prove it, it is possible to show that any Hermitian matrix acts as a Hermitian operator on vectors (that is Equation 8.40 follows from Equation 8.41).

### 8.3.5 The determinant of a square matrix

Each square $n \times n$ matrix

$$\mathrm{A} = \begin{bmatrix} A_{11} & A_{12} & \dots & A_{1n} \\ A_{21} & A_{22} & \dots & A_{2n} \\ \cdot & \cdot & & \cdot \\ \cdot & \cdot & & \cdot \\ A_{n1} & A_{n2} & \dots & A_{nn} \end{bmatrix}$$

has a corresponding *determinant*

$$\det \mathrm{A} = \begin{vmatrix} A_{11} & A_{12} & \dots & A_{1n} \\ A_{21} & A_{22} & \dots & A_{2n} \\ \cdot & \cdot & & \cdot \\ \cdot & \cdot & & \cdot \\ A_{n1} & A_{n2} & \dots & A_{nn} \end{vmatrix}. \tag{8.42}$$

Note the subtle difference in notation: the matrix uses a square bracket, while the determinant uses vertical lines. However, there is a immense difference in meaning between these two concepts. The matrix A is an array of $n^2$ elements, but the determinant $\det \mathrm{A}$ is a particular combination of these elements that reduces to a single scalar quantity.

For a $2 \times 2$ matrix, we define

$$\begin{vmatrix} A_{11} & A_{12} \\ A_{21} & A_{22} \end{vmatrix} = A_{11}A_{22} - A_{12}A_{21}.$$

Although not needed in this book, we shall briefly indicate how larger determinants are calculated. To do this, we need the following definition:

The **cofactor** of a given matrix element $A_{ij}$ is found by striking out the row and column that contain the given element, forming the determinant of the remaining elements in the order that they appear in the matrix, and then multiplying the result by $(-1)^{i+j}$, where $i$ and $j$ are the row and column numbers of the given matrix element. For example, the cofactor of $A_{11}$ in Equation 8.42 is

$$\mathrm{cof}\,(A_{11}) = (-1)^{1+1} \begin{vmatrix} A_{22} & A_{23} & \dots & A_{2n} \\ A_{32} & A_{33} & \dots & A_{3n} \\ \cdot & \cdot & & \cdot \\ \cdot & \cdot & & \cdot \\ A_{n2} & A_{n3} & \dots & A_{nn} \end{vmatrix}.$$

The **determinant** of a matrix is evaluated by selecting any complete row or column and taking the sum of all the elements in that row or column, multiplied by their corresponding cofactors.

Applying this procedure to a $3 \times 3$ matrix, we see that

$$\begin{aligned} \det \mathrm{A} &= \begin{vmatrix} a_1 & a_2 & a_3 \\ b_1 & b_2 & b_3 \\ c_1 & c_2 & c_3 \end{vmatrix} \\ &= a_1 \begin{vmatrix} b_2 & b_3 \\ c_2 & c_3 \end{vmatrix} - a_2 \begin{vmatrix} b_1 & b_3 \\ c_1 & c_3 \end{vmatrix} + a_3 \begin{vmatrix} b_1 & b_2 \\ c_1 & c_2 \end{vmatrix} \\ &= a_1(b_2c_3 - b_3c_2) - a_2(b_1c_3 - b_3c_1) + a_3(b_1c_2 - b_2c_1). \end{aligned}$$

One application of this result is the vector product of two vectors in three-dimensional space, which is given by

$$\mathbf{b}\times\mathbf{c} = \begin{vmatrix} \mathbf{e}_x & \mathbf{e}_y & \mathbf{e}_z \\ b_x & b_y & b_z \\ c_x & c_y & c_z \end{vmatrix},$$

and can be expanded to give

$$\mathbf{b}\times\mathbf{c} = (b_y c_z - b_z c_y)\,\mathbf{e}_x + (b_z c_x - b_x c_z)\,\mathbf{e}_y + (b_x c_y - b_y c_x)\,\mathbf{e}_z,$$

in agreement with Equation 8.14.

### 8.3.6 The inverse of a matrix

For a square matrix A, it is sometimes possible to find a matrix $\mathrm{A}^{-1}$ such that

$$\mathrm{AA}^{-1} = \mathrm{A}^{-1}\mathrm{A} = \mathrm{I}, \tag{8.43}$$

where I is a unit matrix. In this case, $\mathrm{A}^{-1}$ is called the **inverse matrix** of A. For example, if

$$\mathrm{A} = \begin{bmatrix} 1 & 1 \\ 1 & 2 \end{bmatrix} \quad \text{then} \quad \mathrm{A}^{-1} = \begin{bmatrix} 2 & -1 \\ -1 & 1 \end{bmatrix}$$

because

$$\mathrm{A}^{-1}\mathrm{A} = \begin{bmatrix} 2 & -1 \\ -1 & 1 \end{bmatrix}\begin{bmatrix} 1 & 1 \\ 1 & 2 \end{bmatrix} = \begin{bmatrix} 1 & 0 \\ 0 & 1 \end{bmatrix}$$

and

$$\mathrm{AA}^{-1} = \begin{bmatrix} 1 & 1 \\ 1 & 2 \end{bmatrix}\begin{bmatrix} 2 & -1 \\ -1 & 1 \end{bmatrix} = \begin{bmatrix} 1 & 0 \\ 0 & 1 \end{bmatrix}.$$

The general rule for constructing the inverse of a $2\times 2$ matrix is as follows. If

$$\mathrm{A} = \begin{bmatrix} A_{11} & A_{12} \\ A_{21} & A_{22} \end{bmatrix},$$

the inverse matrix $\mathrm{A}^{-1}$ is given by

$$\mathrm{A}^{-1} = \frac{1}{\det \mathrm{A}}\begin{bmatrix} A_{22} & -A_{12} \\ -A_{21} & A_{11} \end{bmatrix}. \tag{8.44}$$

provided that $\det \mathrm{A} \equiv A_{11}A_{22} - A_{12}A_{21} \neq 0$. If $\det \mathrm{A} = 0$, the matrix A has no inverse. Conversely, if A has no inverse, then $\det \mathrm{A} = 0$.

More generally, a square matrix A with matrix elements $A_{ij}$ and $\det \mathrm{A} \neq 0$ has an inverse matrix $\mathrm{A}^{-1}$, with matrix elements

$$(\mathrm{A}^{-1})_{ij} = \frac{\mathrm{cof}\,(A_{ji})}{\det \mathrm{A}}, \tag{8.45}$$

Note that the order of subscripts on the right-hand side of this equation is the reverse of that on the left; we use cofactors of the transpose of A.

where $\mathrm{cof}\,A_{ji}$ is the *cofactor* of matrix element $A_{ji}$, introduced in the context of determinants. But if $\det \mathrm{A} = 0$, no inverse matrix exists.

### 8.3.7 Eigenvalues and eigenvectors

For any square matrix A, we can set up the **matrix eigenvalue equation**

$$\mathrm{AX} = \lambda \mathrm{X}, \tag{8.46}$$

where X is a column matrix and $\lambda$ is a scalar.

Any non-zero column matrix X that satisfies this equation is called an **eigenvector** of A, and the corresponding value of $\lambda$ is called an **eigenvalue**. (We insist that X be non-zero, otherwise Equation 8.46 would be trivially satisfied by any value of $\lambda$.)

To find the eigenvectors and eigenvalues of a given $n \times n$ square matrix, we rearrange Equation 8.46 as follows:

$$(\mathrm{A} - \lambda \mathrm{I})\mathrm{X} = 0, \tag{8.47}$$

where I is an $n \times n$ unit matrix and 0 is an $n \times 1$ column matrix consisting entirely of zeros.

Now, let us suppose, that the matrix $\mathrm{A} - \lambda\mathrm{I}$ has an inverse, $(\mathrm{A} - \lambda\mathrm{I})^{-1}$. If this were so, we would be able to act with this inverse on both sides of Equation 8.47 to obtain

$$\mathrm{X} = (\mathrm{A} - \lambda\mathrm{I})^{-1}\, 0 = 0.$$

However, this possibility is ruled out by our assumption that X is a non-zero column matrix. We therefore conclude that $\mathrm{A} - \lambda\mathrm{I}$ has no inverse, and from our previous discussion of inverses, this implies that

$$\det(\mathrm{A} - \lambda\mathrm{I}) = 0. \tag{8.48}$$

This is called the **characteristic equation** of the matrix A. For an $n \times n$ matrix A, the characteristic equation is an $n$th-order polynomial equation in $\lambda$, which has $n$ (not necessarily distinct) solutions; these are the eigenvalues of A.

**Essential skill:**
Finding the eigenvalues and eigenvectors of a matrix

**Worked Example 8.1**

Find the eigenvalues and normalized eigenvectors of $\mathrm{A} = \begin{bmatrix} 1 & 1 \\ 1 & 1 \end{bmatrix}$.

**Solution**

In this case, the characteristic equation is

$$\det(\mathrm{A} - \lambda\mathrm{I}) = \begin{vmatrix} 1-\lambda & 1 \\ 1 & 1-\lambda \end{vmatrix} = 0,$$

which gives

$$(1-\lambda)^2 - 1 = 0,$$

so the two eigenvalues are $\lambda = 0$ and $\lambda = 2$.

To find the corresponding eigenvectors, we substitute each eigenvalue in turn back into the eigenvalue equation in the form of Equation 8.47.

For $\lambda = 0$, we obtain

$$\begin{bmatrix} 1 & 1 \\ 1 & 1 \end{bmatrix} \begin{bmatrix} x_1 \\ x_2 \end{bmatrix} = \begin{bmatrix} 0 \\ 0 \end{bmatrix},$$

which gives $x_1 = -x_2$, so the eigenvector corresponding to $\lambda = 0$ is

$$\mathrm{X}_1 = \alpha \begin{bmatrix} 1 \\ -1 \end{bmatrix} \quad \text{where } \alpha \text{ is a non-zero constant.}$$

For $\lambda = 2$, we obtain

$$\begin{bmatrix} -1 & 1 \\ 1 & -1 \end{bmatrix} \begin{bmatrix} x_1 \\ x_2 \end{bmatrix} = \begin{bmatrix} 0 \\ 0 \end{bmatrix},$$

which gives $x_1 = x_2$, so the eigenvector corresponding to $\lambda = 2$ is

$$\mathrm{X}_2 = \beta \begin{bmatrix} 1 \\ 1 \end{bmatrix} \quad \text{where } \beta \text{ is a non-zero constant.}$$

These eigenvectors can be normalized by taking $\alpha = \beta = 1/\sqrt{2}$.

**Exercise 8.12** Find the eigenvalues and eigenvectors of $\mathrm{A} = \begin{bmatrix} 0 & -\mathrm{i} \\ \mathrm{i} & 0 \end{bmatrix}$.

**Exercise 8.13** Find the eigenvalues and eigenvalues of $\mathrm{A} = \begin{bmatrix} 1 & 0 \\ 1 & 1 \end{bmatrix}$.

■

Exercise 8.13 shows that it is possible for an $n \times n$ square matrix to have fewer than $n$ independent eigenvectors. However, the Hermitian matrices that are important in quantum mechanics are special in this respect. All $n \times n$ Hermitian matrices have the following properties, which we state without proof:

### The eigenvalues and eigenvectors of Hermitian matrices

1. All their eigenvalues are real.
2. Eigenvectors with different eigenvalues are orthogonal.
3. It is always possible to find a set of $n$ mutually orthogonal eigenvectors, even if some of them share the same eigenvalue. These eigenvectors provide a basis for an $n$-dimensional vector space.
4. Given two $n \times n$ Hermitian matrices, it is possible to find a set of $n$ mutually orthogonal eigenvectors of both matrices if, and only if, the two matrices commute.

# Acknowledgements

Grateful acknowledgement is made to the following sources:

Fig 1.1.a: T. A. Savas, Lithography and microscopy, Nanostructures Laboratory, MIT; Fig 1.1b: Courtesy of J. P. Toennies, Max-Planck-Institut für Stromungsforschung, Göttingen, Germany; Fig 1.3: Ramsey et Musprat /AIP Emilio Segre Visual Archives; Fig 1.8: Science Photo Library; Fig 1.9: AIP Emilio Segre Visual Archives, *Physics Today* Collection;

Fig 2.10: Adapted from Spectrum, Bloor D., et al.,(1961), Proc. Roy.Soc. A, Vol 260, 51. Reprinted with permission of the Royal Society; Fig 2.8: Photo courtesy of Horst Schmidt-Bocking;

Fig 3.10: Larry Mulvehill/Science Photo Library;

Fig 4.4: Indian National Council of Science Museums, AIP Emilio Segre Visual Archives; Fig 4.5: Los Alamos National Laboratory/Science Photo Library; Fig 4.7: Science and Society Picture Library; Fig 4.9: Ketterle,W. et al, MITT 1995;

Fig 5.1: AIP/Emilio Segre Visual Archives;

Fig 6.1: AIP Emilio Segre Visual Archives, W. F. Meggers Gallery of Nobel Laureates; Fig 6.8: Pan, Jain-Wei, et al., (2000), 'Experimental test of quantum nonlocality in three-photon Greenberger-Horne-Zeilinger entanglement', NATURE, Vol 403, Feb 2000, Copyright ©Macmillan Magazines Ltd;

Fig 7.3: Photo ©Estate of Francis Bello/Science Photo Library; Fig 7.8: Jennewin, Thomas. (2000), 'Quantum cryptography with entangled photons', Physical Review Letters, The American Physical Society; Fig. 7.9: Courtesy of id Quantique SA; Fig 7.14: Wgsimon, English Wikipedia.

Every effort has been made to contact copyright holders. If any have been inadvertently overlooked the publishers will be pleased to make the necessary arrangements at the first opportunity.

# Solutions to exercises

**Ex 1.1** (a) The normalization condition is $\langle \Psi | \Psi \rangle = 1$.

(b) According to Chapter 4 of Book 1, the probability of measuring energy $E_i$ in a state described by the wave function $\Psi(x,t)$ is

$$\text{probability} = \left| \int_{-\infty}^{\infty} \psi_i^*(x)\, \Psi(x,t)\, \mathrm{d}x \right|^2,$$

where $\psi_i(x)$ is the energy eigenfunction corresponding to the eigenvalue $E_i$. In Dirac notation, this can be written as

$$\text{probability} = |\langle \psi_i | \Psi \rangle|^2.$$

Time is left out of this equation, being determined by the context. In this case, the appropriate time is the instant $t$ of the measurement; if you wish to be precise about this, you can write $|\langle \psi_i | \Psi \rangle_t|^2$.

**Ex 1.2** A complex number $z$ is real if $z^* = z$. Let $z_1 = \langle f|f \rangle$, $z_2 = \langle f|g \rangle \langle g|f \rangle$ and $z_3 = \langle f|g \rangle + \langle g|f \rangle$. Then Equation 1.21 gives

$$z_1^* = \langle f|f \rangle^* = \langle f|f \rangle = z_1,$$

$$\begin{aligned} z_2^* = \langle f|g \rangle^* \langle g|f \rangle^* &= \langle g|f \rangle \langle f|g \rangle \\ &= \langle f|g \rangle \langle g|f \rangle = z_2, \end{aligned}$$

$$\begin{aligned} z_3^* = \langle f|g \rangle^* + \langle g|f \rangle^* &= \langle g|f \rangle + \langle f|g \rangle \\ &= \langle f|g \rangle + \langle g|f \rangle = z_3. \end{aligned}$$

So all these quantities are real.

**Ex 1.3** Using Equations 1.22 and 1.23, we have

$$\langle f|f \rangle \equiv \langle \mathrm{e}^{\mathrm{i}\alpha} g | \mathrm{e}^{\mathrm{i}\alpha} g \rangle = \mathrm{e}^{-\mathrm{i}\alpha} \mathrm{e}^{\mathrm{i}\alpha} \langle g|g \rangle = \langle g|g \rangle.$$

**Ex 1.4** From Equations 1.24 and 1.22,

$$\begin{aligned} \langle f|f + \mathrm{i}g \rangle &= \langle f|f \rangle + \langle f|\mathrm{i}g \rangle \\ &= \langle f|f \rangle + \mathrm{i}\, \langle f|g \rangle. \end{aligned}$$

From Equations 1.25 and 1.23,

$$\begin{aligned} \langle g - \mathrm{i}f|g \rangle &= \langle g|g \rangle - \langle \mathrm{i}f|g \rangle \\ &= \langle g|g \rangle + \mathrm{i}\, \langle f|g \rangle. \end{aligned}$$

Subtracting these two results and using the fact that $\langle f|f \rangle = \langle g|g \rangle$, we conclude that

$$\langle f|f + \mathrm{i}g \rangle - \langle g - \mathrm{i}f|g \rangle = \langle f|f \rangle - \langle g|g \rangle = 0.$$

**Ex 1.5** The vectors $|a\rangle$ and $|c\rangle$ will be orthogonal if $\langle a|c \rangle = 0$. Taking the inner product of $|c\rangle = |a\rangle + \beta\, |b\rangle$ with $|a\rangle$ gives

$$\langle a|c \rangle = \langle a|a \rangle + \beta\, \langle a|b \rangle.$$

The requirement that $\langle a|c \rangle = 0$ is achieved by taking $\beta = -\langle a|a \rangle / \langle a|b \rangle$.

**Ex 1.6** (a) Given $|a\rangle = |u\rangle + |v\rangle$ and $|b\rangle = |u\rangle - |v\rangle$, we have

$$\begin{aligned} \langle a|b \rangle &= \big(\langle u| + \langle v|\big)\big(|u\rangle - |v\rangle\big) \\ &= \langle u|u \rangle + \langle v|u \rangle - \langle u|v \rangle - \langle v|v \rangle \\ &= 1 + 0 - 0 - 1 = 0. \end{aligned}$$

(b) Given $|c\rangle = |u\rangle + \mathrm{i}\, |v\rangle$ and $|d\rangle = \mathrm{i}\, |u\rangle + |v\rangle$, we have

$$\begin{aligned} \langle c|d \rangle &= \big(\langle u| - \mathrm{i}\, \langle v|\big)\big(\mathrm{i}\, |u\rangle + |v\rangle\big) \\ &= \mathrm{i}\, \langle u|u \rangle + \langle v|u \rangle + \langle u|v \rangle - \mathrm{i}\, \langle v|v \rangle \\ &= \mathrm{i} + 0 + 0 - \mathrm{i} = 0. \end{aligned}$$

**Ex 1.7** We are given the ket vector

$$|c\rangle = \langle b|b \rangle\, |a\rangle - \langle b|a \rangle\, |b\rangle,$$

and we know that $\langle b|b \rangle^* = \langle b|b \rangle$ and $\langle b|a \rangle^* = \langle a|b \rangle$, so the corresponding bra vector is

$$\begin{aligned} \langle c| &= \langle b|b \rangle^*\, \langle a| - \langle b|a \rangle^*\, \langle b| \\ &= \langle b|b \rangle\, \langle a| - \langle a|b \rangle\, \langle b|. \end{aligned}$$

Joining these bra and ket vectors together gives

$$\langle c|c \rangle = \Big(\langle b|b \rangle\, \langle a| - \langle a|b \rangle\, \langle b|\Big)\Big(\langle b|b \rangle\, |a\rangle - \langle b|a \rangle\, |b\rangle\Big).$$

When we multiply out the round brackets, three of the terms differ only in sign, so cancellations occur leading to

$$\begin{aligned} \langle c|c \rangle &= \langle b|b \rangle^2 \langle a|a \rangle - \langle a|b \rangle \langle b|a \rangle \langle b|b \rangle \\ &= \langle b|b \rangle \Big(\langle a|a \rangle \langle b|b \rangle - \big|\langle a|b \rangle\big|^2\Big). \end{aligned}$$

We must always have $\langle c|c \rangle \geq 0$, so

$$\langle b|b \rangle \Big(\langle a|a \rangle \langle b|b \rangle - \big|\langle a|b \rangle\big|^2\Big) \geq 0.$$

Assume for the moment that $|b\rangle$ is not the zero vector. Then we have $\langle b|b \rangle > 0$ and so

$$\langle a|a \rangle \langle b|b \rangle - \big|\langle a|b \rangle\big|^2 \geq 0,$$

which gives the Cauchy–Schwarz inequality

$$\langle a|a\rangle\langle b|b\rangle \geq \left|\langle a|b\rangle\right|^2.$$

If $|b\rangle$ is the zero vector, we have $\langle b|b\rangle = 0$ and $\langle a|b\rangle = 0$, so the Cauchy–Schwarz inequality is still satisfied, as the equality $0 = 0$, in this case.

**Ex 1.8** Explicitly,

$$\int_{-\infty}^{\infty} f^*(x)\big(\widehat{\mathrm{A}}g(x)\big)\,\mathrm{d}x = \int_{-\infty}^{\infty} \big(\widehat{\mathrm{A}}f(x)\big)^* g(x)\,\mathrm{d}x.$$

**Ex 1.9** We have

$$\begin{aligned}&\left\langle\frac{\partial f}{\partial x}\Big| g\right\rangle + \left\langle f\Big|\frac{\partial g}{\partial x}\right\rangle\\ &= \int_{-\infty}^{\infty}\left(\frac{\partial f^*}{\partial x}\,g(x) + f^*(x)\,\frac{\partial g}{\partial x}\right)\mathrm{d}x = 0,\end{aligned}$$

where the last step follows from the chain of reasoning leading to Equation 1.37. If the operator $\partial/\partial x$ were Hermitian, we would also have

$$\left\langle\frac{\partial f}{\partial x}\Big| g\right\rangle = \left\langle f\Big|\frac{\partial g}{\partial x}\right\rangle.$$

Taken together, these equations imply that

$$\left\langle f\Big|\frac{\partial g}{\partial x}\right\rangle = \int_{-\infty}^{\infty} f^*(x)\,\frac{\partial g}{\partial x}\,\mathrm{d}x = 0$$

for all normalizable functions $f(x)$ and $g(x)$. This is clearly not true. (For example, it is not true if $f(x) = x\mathrm{e}^{-x^2}$ and $g(x) = \mathrm{e}^{-x^2}$.) Hence $\partial/\partial x$ cannot be Hermitian; it cannot represent any observable quantity.

**Ex 1.10** Assuming that $\widehat{\mathrm{A}}$ and $\widehat{\mathrm{B}}$ are Hermitian, we have

$$\begin{aligned}\langle f|\widehat{\mathrm{A}}g\rangle &= \langle\widehat{\mathrm{A}}f|g\rangle,\\ \langle f|\widehat{\mathrm{B}}g\rangle &= \langle\widehat{\mathrm{B}}f|g\rangle,\end{aligned}$$

for all normalizable $f$ and $g$. So

$$\begin{aligned}\langle f|(\widehat{\mathrm{A}}+\widehat{\mathrm{B}})g\rangle &= \langle f|\widehat{\mathrm{A}}g\rangle + \langle f|\widehat{\mathrm{B}}g\rangle\\ &= \langle\widehat{\mathrm{A}}f|g\rangle + \langle\widehat{\mathrm{B}}f|g\rangle\\ &= \langle(\widehat{\mathrm{A}}+\widehat{\mathrm{B}})f|g\rangle,\end{aligned}$$

as required.

**Ex 1.11** For any functions $f(x)$ and $g(x)$, Equation 1.39 tells us that

$$\langle f|\widehat{\mathrm{A}}\widehat{\mathrm{B}}g\rangle = \langle\widehat{\mathrm{B}}\widehat{\mathrm{A}}f|g\rangle.$$

Similarly,

$$\langle f|\widehat{\mathrm{B}}\widehat{\mathrm{A}}g\rangle = \langle\widehat{\mathrm{A}}\widehat{\mathrm{B}}f|g\rangle.$$

Adding these two equations together gives

$$\begin{aligned}\langle f|(\widehat{\mathrm{A}}\widehat{\mathrm{B}}+\widehat{\mathrm{B}}\widehat{\mathrm{A}})g\rangle &= \langle(\widehat{\mathrm{B}}\widehat{\mathrm{A}}+\widehat{\mathrm{A}}\widehat{\mathrm{B}})f|g\rangle\\ &= \langle(\widehat{\mathrm{A}}\widehat{\mathrm{B}}+\widehat{\mathrm{B}}\widehat{\mathrm{A}})f|g\rangle.\end{aligned}$$

Hence $\widehat{\mathrm{A}}\widehat{\mathrm{B}}+\widehat{\mathrm{B}}\widehat{\mathrm{A}}$ is Hermitian.

Since $\widehat{\mathrm{x}}$ and $\widehat{\mathrm{p}}_x$ are both Hermitian operators and $\frac{1}{2}$ is a real number, we conclude that $\frac{1}{2}(\widehat{\mathrm{x}}\,\widehat{\mathrm{p}}_x + \widehat{\mathrm{p}}_x\widehat{\mathrm{x}})$ is a Hermitian operator.

**Ex 1.12** When $\widehat{\mathrm{A}} = \widehat{\mathrm{I}}$, the left-hand side of Equation 1.46 becomes

$$\frac{\mathrm{d}}{\mathrm{d}t}\langle\widehat{\mathrm{I}}\rangle \equiv \frac{\mathrm{d}}{\mathrm{d}t}\langle\Psi|\widehat{\mathrm{I}}\,\Psi\rangle = \frac{\mathrm{d}}{\mathrm{d}t}\langle\Psi|\Psi\rangle.$$

The identity operator commutes with any other operator, so the right-hand side of Equation 1.46 gives

$$\frac{1}{\mathrm{i}\hbar}\left\langle\left[\widehat{\mathrm{I}},\widehat{\mathrm{H}}\right]\right\rangle = 0.$$

So, in this case, the generalized Ehrenfest theorem tells us that $\mathrm{d}\langle\Psi|\Psi\rangle/\mathrm{d}t = 0$. This shows that the normalization of the wave function is preserved; if the wave function of an isolated system is normalized at any initial time, it will remain normalized at all future times.

**Ex 1.13** We have

$$\begin{aligned}\left[\widehat{\mathrm{A}},\widehat{\mathrm{B}}+\widehat{\mathrm{C}}\right] &= \widehat{\mathrm{A}}(\widehat{\mathrm{B}}+\widehat{\mathrm{C}}) - (\widehat{\mathrm{B}}+\widehat{\mathrm{C}})\widehat{\mathrm{A}}\\ &= \widehat{\mathrm{A}}\widehat{\mathrm{B}} - \widehat{\mathrm{B}}\widehat{\mathrm{A}} + \widehat{\mathrm{A}}\widehat{\mathrm{C}} - \widehat{\mathrm{C}}\widehat{\mathrm{A}}\\ &= \left[\widehat{\mathrm{A}},\widehat{\mathrm{B}}\right] + \left[\widehat{\mathrm{A}},\widehat{\mathrm{C}}\right].\end{aligned}$$

Hence $\left[\widehat{\mathrm{A}},\widehat{\mathrm{B}}+\widehat{\mathrm{C}}\right] = \left[\widehat{\mathrm{A}},\widehat{\mathrm{B}}\right]$ if $\left[\widehat{\mathrm{A}},\widehat{\mathrm{C}}\right] = 0$.

**Ex 1.14** Using $\widehat{\mathrm{p}}_x = -\mathrm{i}\hbar\,\partial/\partial x$ and $\widehat{\mathrm{V}}(x) = V(x)$, and applying the required commutator to an arbitrary function $f(x)$, gives

$$\begin{aligned}[\widehat{\mathrm{p}}_x,\widehat{\mathrm{V}}(x)]f(x) &= \left(-\mathrm{i}\hbar\,\frac{\partial}{\partial x}\right)\big(V(x)f(x)\big)\\ &\qquad - V(x)\left(-\mathrm{i}\hbar\,\frac{\partial}{\partial x}\right)f(x)\\ &= -\,\mathrm{i}\hbar\left(V\frac{\partial f}{\partial x} + \frac{\partial V}{\partial x}f - V\frac{\partial f}{\partial x}\right)\\ &= -\,\mathrm{i}\hbar\,\frac{\partial V}{\partial x}f(x).\end{aligned}$$

Since this equation is true for any $f(x)$, we are entitled to write it as an operator equation

$$[\widehat{\mathrm{p}}_x,\widehat{\mathrm{V}}(x)] = -\mathrm{i}\hbar\,\frac{\partial V}{\partial x},$$

where the right-hand side represents the action of multiplying by $-i\hbar\,\partial V/\partial x$. Combining this commutation relation with Equation 1.51, we obtain

$$\frac{d\langle p_x\rangle}{dt} = \frac{1}{i\hbar}\left\langle -i\hbar\frac{\partial V}{\partial x}\right\rangle = -\left\langle\frac{\partial V}{\partial x}\right\rangle,$$

which is Ehrenfest's second equation (Equation 1.43).

**Ex 1.15** The operator $\widehat{H}^2$ commutes with $\widehat{H}$ because

$$\widehat{H}^2\widehat{H} = \widehat{H}^3 = \widehat{H}\widehat{H}^2.$$

Hence $\langle H^2\rangle = \langle E^2\rangle$ remains constant in time. We already know that $\langle E\rangle$ remains constant in time, so the uncertainty in energy, $\Delta E = \sqrt{\langle E^2\rangle - \langle E\rangle^2}$, also remains constant in time.

**Ex 1.16** None. The operator $\widehat{x} = x$ commutes with the operator $\widehat{p}_y = -i\hbar\,\partial/\partial y$, so the right-hand side of Equation 1.57 is equal to zero.

**Ex 1.17** Taking the modulus of the generalized Ehrenfest theorem (Equation 1.46) gives

$$\left|\frac{d\langle A\rangle}{dt}\right| = \left|\frac{1}{i\hbar}\left\langle[\widehat{A},\widehat{H}]\right\rangle\right| = \frac{1}{\hbar}\left|\left\langle[\widehat{A},\widehat{H}]\right\rangle\right|.$$

Combining this with the generalized uncertainty principle (Equation 1.57), and recalling that the Hamiltonian operator $\widehat{H}$ is the energy operator of the system, we obtain

$$\left|\frac{d\langle A\rangle}{dt}\right| \le \frac{2}{\hbar}\Delta A\,\Delta H = \frac{2}{\hbar}\Delta A\,\Delta E,$$

as required.

**Ex 1.18** We have

$$\begin{aligned}&(\widehat{A} - \langle A\rangle)(\widehat{B} - \langle B\rangle)\\ &= \widehat{A}\widehat{B} - \langle A\rangle\widehat{B} - \langle B\rangle\widehat{A} + \langle A\rangle\langle B\rangle,\\ &(\widehat{B} - \langle B\rangle)(\widehat{A} - \langle A\rangle)\\ &= \widehat{B}\widehat{A} - \langle B\rangle\widehat{A} - \langle A\rangle\widehat{B} + \langle B\rangle\langle A\rangle,\end{aligned}$$

where we have used the fact that $\widehat{A}$ and $\widehat{B}$ are linear operators to bring the constants $\langle A\rangle$ and $\langle B\rangle$ to the front of each term. Subtracting the above two equations gives

$$[\widehat{A} - \langle A\rangle, \widehat{B} - \langle B\rangle] = \widehat{A}\widehat{B} - \widehat{B}\widehat{A} = [\widehat{A},\widehat{B}].$$

Finally, substituting this result into Equation 1.64, we obtain

$$\Delta A\,\Delta B \ge \tfrac{1}{2}\left|\left\langle[\widehat{A},\widehat{B}]\right\rangle\right|,$$

which is the generalized uncertainty principle, valid for any observables $A$ and $B$ represented by the linear Hermitian operators $\widehat{A}$ and $\widehat{B}$.

**Ex 2.1** In uniform circular motion, the vectors **r** and **p** are perpendicular to one another, so the magnitude of the angular momentum is $L = rp\sin(\pi/2) = mvr$. The direction of the angular momentum is perpendicular to both **r** and **p**, and so is perpendicular to the horizontal plane of motion. Using the right-hand rule, the direction of **L** is vertically *downwards*.

**Ex 2.2** Expanding the determinant gives

$$\mathbf{L} = \mathbf{e}_x\begin{vmatrix} y & z\\ p_y & p_z\end{vmatrix} - \mathbf{e}_y\begin{vmatrix} x & z\\ p_x & p_z\end{vmatrix} + \mathbf{e}_z\begin{vmatrix} x & y\\ p_x & p_y\end{vmatrix},$$

so the $y$-component is

$$L_y = -\begin{vmatrix} x & z\\ p_x & p_z\end{vmatrix} = -(xp_z - zp_x) = zp_x - xp_z,$$

as expected.

**Ex 2.3** Provided that $n \neq m$, we have

$$\begin{aligned}\int_0^{2\pi} f_m^*(\phi)\,f_n(\phi)\,d\phi &= \frac{1}{2\pi}\int_0^{2\pi} e^{-im\phi}\,e^{in\phi}\,d\phi\\ &= \frac{1}{2\pi}\int_0^{2\pi} e^{i(n-m)\phi}\,d\phi\\ &= \frac{1}{2\pi}\left[\frac{e^{i(n-m)\phi}}{i(n-m)}\right]_0^{2\pi} = 0,\end{aligned}$$

as required, (since $(n-m)$ is an integer).

**Ex 2.4** If the energies are proportional to $l(l+1)$, then the second excited state will be at energy

$$\begin{aligned}2(2+1)/1(1+1)\times 0.00256\,\text{eV} &= 3\times 0.00256\,\text{eV}\\ &= 0.00768\,\text{eV},\end{aligned}$$

and the next state will be at energy

$$3(3+1)/1(1+1)\times 0.00256\,\text{eV} = 0.01536\,\text{eV}.$$

These values agree with the energies shown in the figure and are consistent with the claim that the energy levels are proportional to $l(l+1)$, where $l = 0, 1, 2, \ldots$.

**Ex 2.5** (a) The operator $\widehat{L}_z$ commutes with $\widehat{V}(r,\theta)$ for exactly the same reason that it commutes with $\widehat{V}(r)$ (see main text); the derivative with respect to $\phi$ does not affect $V(r,\theta)$ at all. It follows that $\langle L_z\rangle$ is conserved; this is reasonable because the system has axial symmetry around the $z$-axis. (However, $\langle L_x\rangle$ and $\langle L_y\rangle$ will not be conserved in this case).

(b) The operator $\widehat{L}_z$ does *not* commute with $\widehat{V}(r, \phi)$ in general. For any function $f(r, \theta, \phi)$, we have

$$\begin{aligned}
&\widehat{L}_z\, \widehat{V}(r, \phi)\, f(r, \theta, \phi) \\
&= -i\hbar \frac{\partial}{\partial \phi}\big(V(r, \phi)\, f(r, \theta, \phi)\big) \\
&= -i\hbar\, V(r, \phi) \frac{\partial f}{\partial \phi} - i\hbar\, f(r, \theta, \phi) \frac{\partial V}{\partial \phi} \\
&= \widehat{V}(r, \phi)\widehat{L}_z f(r, \theta, \phi) - i\hbar\, f(r, \theta, \phi) \frac{\partial V}{\partial \phi}.
\end{aligned}$$

This is equal to $\widehat{V}(r, \phi)\, \widehat{L}_z\, f(r, \theta, \phi)$ only in the trivial case where $\partial V/\partial \phi = 0$, which corresponds to $V$ being independent of $\phi$. It follows that $\langle L_z \rangle$ is not conserved.

**Ex 2.6** (a) The possible kets are $|3, -3\rangle$, $|3, -2\rangle$, $|3, -1\rangle$, $|3, 0\rangle$, $|3, 1\rangle$, $|3, 2\rangle$ and $|3, 3\rangle$.

(b) The minimum possible value of $m$ is $-4$, and $l(l + 1) = 4(4 + 1) = 20$, so the appropriate eigenvalue equations are

$$\widehat{L}_z|4, -4\rangle = -4\hbar|4, -4\rangle$$

and

$$\widehat{L}^2|4, -4\rangle = 20\hbar^2|4, -4\rangle.$$

**Ex 3.1** The magnitudes of the deflections are the same as for the previous case, so the magnitude of the spin component must be the same. Hence we interpret the result by saying that the only possible outcomes of a measurement of $S_x$ are $\pm\hbar/2$.

**Ex 3.2** (a) In Figure 3.3, $\theta = 0°$ so $\cos^2(\theta/2) = 1$, in agreement with the fact that only an upper component is found by the analyzer.

In Figure 3.4, $\theta = 90°$ so

$$\cos^2(\theta/2) = \cos^2(45°) = (1/\sqrt{2})^2 = 1/2,$$

in agreement with the fact that two components of equal intensity are found.

(b) Rotating the analyzer of Figure 3.3 by 180° gives $\theta = 180°$ so

$$\cos^2(\theta/2) = \cos^2(90°) = 0,$$

showing that none of the beam is deflected towards the north pole of the inverted analyzer; all of the beam is deflected towards the south pole.

(c) Rotating the analyzer of Figure 3.4 by 180° gives $\theta = 270°$ so

$$\cos^2(\theta/2) = \cos^2(135°) = (-1/\sqrt{2})^2 = 1/2,$$

showing that equal intensities are again observed.

**Ex 3.3** The angle between successive orientations is $\frac{1}{n}\, 90°$. Applying the $\cos^2(\theta/2)$ rule $n$ times, we see that a fraction

$$f(n) = \left[\cos^2(\tfrac{1}{n}\, 90°/2)\right]^n = \cos^{2n}(90°/2n)$$

of the beam prepared by $P_1$ is deflected along the orientation vector of A. Evaluating this result for $n = 1$, $n = 2$ and $n = 3$ gives $f(1) = 0.50$, $f(2) = 0.73$ and $f(3) = 0.81$.

**Ex 3.4** (a) No definite prediction can be made for a single atom in the given state, except that a measurement of $S_z$ will give *either* $+\hbar/2$ *or* $-\hbar/2$. The probability of getting $+\hbar/2$ is $(\sqrt{3}/2)^2 = 3/4$, and the probability of getting $-\hbar/2$ is $(1/2)^2 = 1/4$, so the value $+\hbar/2$ is more likely, but the value $-\hbar/2$ would not be at all surprising.

(b) For a million atoms, we expect that close to 750 000 atoms will give $S_z = +\hbar/2$, and the remainder will give $S_z = -\hbar/2$.

**Ex 3.5** Using Equation 3.7, we have

$$\begin{aligned}
\langle A|B\rangle^* &= \left(a_1^* b_1 + a_2^* b_2\right)^* \\
&= a_1 b_1^* + a_2 b_2^* = b_1^* a_1 + b_2^* a_2 = \langle B|A\rangle.
\end{aligned}$$

This result illustrates the fact that the inner product in spin space obeys similar rules to the inner product in function space.

**Ex 3.6** Any vector $|a\rangle$ can be multiplied by a constant $\lambda$ to obtain $|A\rangle = \lambda|a\rangle$. To ensure that $|A\rangle$ is normalized, we require that

$$1 = \langle A|A\rangle = |\lambda|^2\langle a|a\rangle,$$

and this can be achieved by taking $\lambda = 1/\sqrt{\langle a|a\rangle}$.

(a) For $|a\rangle = |\uparrow_z\rangle + |\downarrow_z\rangle$, the coefficients are $a_1 = 1$ and $a_2 = 1$, so $\langle a|a\rangle = |a_1|^2 + |a_2|^2 = 2$. A suitable normalization factor is $\lambda = 1/\sqrt{2}$, and the corresponding normalized vector is $|A\rangle = (|\uparrow_z\rangle + |\downarrow_z\rangle)/\sqrt{2}$.

(b) For $|a\rangle = |\uparrow_z\rangle + i|\downarrow_z\rangle$, the coefficients are $a_1 = 1$ and $a_2 = i$, so we have $\langle a|a\rangle = |a_1|^2 + |a_2|^2 = 2$, and $\lambda = 1/\sqrt{2}$ is again suitable. The corresponding normalized vector is $|A\rangle = (|\uparrow_z\rangle + i|\downarrow_z\rangle)/\sqrt{2}$.

(c) For $|a\rangle = 5|\uparrow_z\rangle - 12|\downarrow_z\rangle$, the coefficients are $a_1 = 5$ and $a_2 = -12$, so $\langle a|a\rangle = |a_1|^2 + |a_2|^2 = 169$.

We can therefore take $\lambda = 1/13$, and the corresponding normalized vector is $|A\rangle = (5|\uparrow_z\rangle - 12|\downarrow_z\rangle)/13$.

**Ex 3.7** If $|C\rangle$ were a multiple of $|A\rangle$, the ratio of the coefficient of $|\uparrow_z\rangle$ to the coefficient of $|\downarrow_z\rangle$ would be the same for both vectors.

In $|C\rangle = (\mathrm{i}|\uparrow_z\rangle + |\downarrow_z\rangle)/\sqrt{2}$ this ratio has the value $\mathrm{i}/1 = \mathrm{i}$, but in $|A\rangle = (|\uparrow_z\rangle + \mathrm{i}|\downarrow_z\rangle)/\sqrt{2}$ it has a different value, $1/\mathrm{i} = -\mathrm{i}$.

**Ex 3.8** We have

$$\langle U|U\rangle = \frac{1}{2}\begin{bmatrix}1 & 1\end{bmatrix}\begin{bmatrix}1\\1\end{bmatrix} = \frac{1}{2}(1+1) = 1,$$

$$\langle V|V\rangle = \frac{1}{2}\begin{bmatrix}-1 & 1\end{bmatrix}\begin{bmatrix}-1\\1\end{bmatrix} = \frac{1}{2}(1+1) = 1,$$

$$\langle U|V\rangle = \frac{1}{2}\begin{bmatrix}1 & 1\end{bmatrix}\begin{bmatrix}-1\\1\end{bmatrix} = \frac{1}{2}(-1+1) = 0.$$

The vectors $|U\rangle$ and $|V\rangle$ are normalized and orthogonal to one another, so they are orthonormal.

**Ex 3.9** The question tells us that

$$|\uparrow_x\rangle = \frac{1}{\sqrt{2}}\begin{bmatrix}1\\1\end{bmatrix} \quad \text{and} \quad |\downarrow_x\rangle = \frac{1}{\sqrt{2}}\begin{bmatrix}-1\\1\end{bmatrix}.$$

Hence

$$\frac{1}{\sqrt{2}}|\uparrow_x\rangle - \frac{1}{\sqrt{2}}|\downarrow_x\rangle = \frac{1}{2}\begin{bmatrix}1\\1\end{bmatrix} - \frac{1}{2}\begin{bmatrix}-1\\1\end{bmatrix} = \begin{bmatrix}1\\0\end{bmatrix} = |\uparrow_z\rangle.$$

The coefficient of $|\uparrow_x\rangle$ in the expansion for $|\uparrow_z\rangle$ is $1/\sqrt{2}$. The probability of getting $S_x = +\hbar/2$ is given by the square of the modulus of this coefficient, and so is equal to $1/2$.

**Ex 3.10** Multiplying out the matrices,

$$\widehat{\mathrm{S}}_x\widehat{\mathrm{S}}_y = \frac{\hbar^2}{4}\begin{bmatrix}0 & 1\\1 & 0\end{bmatrix}\begin{bmatrix}0 & -\mathrm{i}\\\mathrm{i} & 0\end{bmatrix} = \frac{\hbar^2}{4}\begin{bmatrix}\mathrm{i} & 0\\0 & -\mathrm{i}\end{bmatrix}$$

and

$$\widehat{\mathrm{S}}_y\widehat{\mathrm{S}}_x = \frac{\hbar^2}{4}\begin{bmatrix}0 & -\mathrm{i}\\\mathrm{i} & 0\end{bmatrix}\begin{bmatrix}0 & 1\\1 & 0\end{bmatrix} = \frac{\hbar^2}{4}\begin{bmatrix}-\mathrm{i} & 0\\0 & \mathrm{i}\end{bmatrix}.$$

Subtracting these two results, we obtain

$$\widehat{\mathrm{S}}_x\widehat{\mathrm{S}}_y - \widehat{\mathrm{S}}_y\widehat{\mathrm{S}}_x = \frac{\hbar^2}{2}\begin{bmatrix}\mathrm{i} & 0\\0 & -\mathrm{i}\end{bmatrix} = \mathrm{i}\hbar\frac{\hbar}{2}\begin{bmatrix}1 & 0\\0 & -1\end{bmatrix} = \mathrm{i}\hbar\,\widehat{\mathrm{S}}_z,$$

as required.

**Ex 3.11** Operating with $\widehat{\mathrm{S}}_y$ on the two vectors given in the question, we obtain

$$\widehat{\mathrm{S}}_y\frac{1}{\sqrt{2}}\begin{bmatrix}1\\\mathrm{i}\end{bmatrix} = \frac{\hbar}{2\sqrt{2}}\begin{bmatrix}0 & -\mathrm{i}\\\mathrm{i} & 0\end{bmatrix}\begin{bmatrix}1\\\mathrm{i}\end{bmatrix} = \frac{\hbar}{2}\frac{1}{\sqrt{2}}\begin{bmatrix}1\\\mathrm{i}\end{bmatrix}$$

and

$$\widehat{\mathrm{S}}_y\frac{1}{\sqrt{2}}\begin{bmatrix}\mathrm{i}\\1\end{bmatrix} = \frac{\hbar}{2\sqrt{2}}\begin{bmatrix}0 & -\mathrm{i}\\\mathrm{i} & 0\end{bmatrix}\begin{bmatrix}\mathrm{i}\\1\end{bmatrix} = -\frac{\hbar}{2}\frac{1}{\sqrt{2}}\begin{bmatrix}\mathrm{i}\\1\end{bmatrix}.$$

So these vectors are eigenvectors of $\widehat{\mathrm{S}}_y$, with eigenvalues $+\hbar/2$ and $-\hbar/2$, respectively.

The physical interpretation is that, when a measurement of $S_y$ is made, $\frac{1}{\sqrt{2}}\begin{bmatrix}1\\\mathrm{i}\end{bmatrix}$ describes a state that is certain to give the value $+\hbar/2$, and $\frac{1}{\sqrt{2}}\begin{bmatrix}\mathrm{i}\\1\end{bmatrix}$ describes a state that is certain to give the value $-\hbar/2$.

*Comment*: Exercise 8.12 in the *Mathematical toolkit* shows that these are the only eigenvectors and eigenvalues of $\widehat{\mathrm{S}}_y$.

**Ex 3.12** Taking the inner products of vectors using spinor notation, we obtain

$$\langle\uparrow_\mathbf{n}|\uparrow_\mathbf{n}\rangle = \begin{bmatrix}\cos(\theta/2) & \mathrm{e}^{-\mathrm{i}\phi}\sin(\theta/2)\end{bmatrix}\begin{bmatrix}\cos(\theta/2)\\\mathrm{e}^{\mathrm{i}\phi}\sin(\theta/2)\end{bmatrix} = \cos^2(\theta/2) + \sin^2(\theta/2) = 1,$$

$$\langle\downarrow_\mathbf{n}|\downarrow_\mathbf{n}\rangle = \begin{bmatrix}-\mathrm{e}^{\mathrm{i}\phi}\sin(\theta/2) & \cos(\theta/2)\end{bmatrix}\begin{bmatrix}-\mathrm{e}^{-\mathrm{i}\phi}\sin(\theta/2)\\\cos(\theta/2)\end{bmatrix} = \sin^2(\theta/2) + \cos^2(\theta/2) = 1,$$

$$\begin{aligned}\langle\uparrow_\mathbf{n}|\downarrow_\mathbf{n}\rangle &= \begin{bmatrix}\cos(\theta/2) & \mathrm{e}^{-\mathrm{i}\phi}\sin(\theta/2)\end{bmatrix}\begin{bmatrix}-\mathrm{e}^{-\mathrm{i}\phi}\sin(\theta/2)\\\cos(\theta/2)\end{bmatrix}\\&= -\mathrm{e}^{-\mathrm{i}\phi}\cos(\theta/2)\sin(\theta/2)\\&\quad + \mathrm{e}^{-\mathrm{i}\phi}\sin(\theta/2)\cos(\theta/2)\\&= 0.\end{aligned}$$

This shows that the eigenvectors are normalized and mutually orthogonal.

*Comment*: The orthogonality of these eigenfunctions also follows from general quantum-mechanical principles. Because it represents an observable, the general spin matrix behaves as a Hermitian operator. This implies that different eigenvectors, corresponding to different eigenvalues, are orthogonal.

**Ex 3.13** The first step in any exercise like this is to write down what $\theta$ and $\phi$ are.

(a) We require $|\uparrow_{\mathbf{n}}\rangle$ with $\theta = 90°$ and $\phi = 0$. This gives

$$|\uparrow_x\rangle = \begin{bmatrix}\cos 45°\\ \sin 45°\end{bmatrix} = \frac{1}{\sqrt{2}}\begin{bmatrix}1\\ 1\end{bmatrix}.$$

(b) We require $|\downarrow_{\mathbf{n}}\rangle$ with $\theta = 90°$ and $\phi = 90°$. Noting that $e^{-i\pi/2} = -i$, we have

$$|\downarrow_y\rangle = \begin{bmatrix}i\sin 45°\\ \cos 45°\end{bmatrix} = \frac{1}{\sqrt{2}}\begin{bmatrix}i\\ 1\end{bmatrix}.$$

(c) We require $|\uparrow_{\mathbf{n}}\rangle$ with $\theta = 60°$ and $\phi = 0$. This gives

$$|\uparrow_{\mathbf{n}}\rangle = \begin{bmatrix}\cos 30°\\ \sin 30°\end{bmatrix} = \tfrac{1}{2}\begin{bmatrix}\sqrt{3}\\ 1\end{bmatrix}.$$

**Ex 3.14** Using Equations 3.22 and 3.24, we have

$$\widehat{S}_{\mathbf{n}}|\uparrow_{\mathbf{n}}\rangle = \frac{\hbar}{2}\begin{bmatrix}\cos\theta & e^{-i\phi}\sin\theta\\ e^{i\phi}\sin\theta & -\cos\theta\end{bmatrix}\begin{bmatrix}\cos(\theta/2)\\ e^{i\phi}\sin(\theta/2)\end{bmatrix}.$$

Multiplying out the matrices gives

$$\widehat{S}_{\mathbf{n}}|\uparrow_{\mathbf{n}}\rangle = \frac{\hbar}{2}\begin{bmatrix}\cos\theta\cos(\theta/2) + \sin\theta\sin(\theta/2)\\ e^{i\phi}(\sin\theta\cos(\theta/2) - \cos\theta\sin(\theta/2))\end{bmatrix}.$$

The standard trigonometric identities

$$\cos(A - B) = \cos A\cos B + \sin A\sin B,$$
$$\sin(A - B) = \sin A\cos B - \cos A\sin B$$

can then be used to obtain

$$\widehat{S}_{\mathbf{n}}|\uparrow_{\mathbf{n}}\rangle = \frac{\hbar}{2}\begin{bmatrix}\cos(\theta/2)\\ e^{i\phi}\sin(\theta/2)\end{bmatrix} = \frac{\hbar}{2}|\uparrow_{\mathbf{n}}\rangle,$$

as required.

*Comment*: A similar calculation would show that $|\downarrow_{\mathbf{n}}\rangle$ in Equations 3.24 is an eigenvector of $\widehat{S}_{\mathbf{n}}$ with eigenvalue $-\hbar/2$.

**Ex 3.15** The eigenvectors $|\uparrow_y\rangle$ and $|\downarrow_y\rangle$ are obtained by setting $\theta = \pi/2$ and $\phi = \pi/2$ in Equations 3.24. This gives

$$|\uparrow_y\rangle = \frac{1}{\sqrt{2}}\begin{bmatrix}1\\ i\end{bmatrix} \quad\text{and}\quad |\downarrow_y\rangle = \frac{1}{\sqrt{2}}\begin{bmatrix}i\\ 1\end{bmatrix}.$$

These vectors provide an orthonormal basis in spin space, so we can write

$$|\uparrow_z\rangle = a_{\rm u}|\uparrow_y\rangle + a_{\rm d}|\downarrow_y\rangle,$$

where

$$a_{\rm u} = \frac{1}{\sqrt{2}}\begin{bmatrix}1 & -i\end{bmatrix}\begin{bmatrix}1\\ 0\end{bmatrix} = \frac{1}{\sqrt{2}},$$
$$a_{\rm d} = \frac{1}{\sqrt{2}}\begin{bmatrix}-i & 1\end{bmatrix}\begin{bmatrix}1\\ 0\end{bmatrix} = -\frac{i}{\sqrt{2}}.$$

Hence

$$|\uparrow_z\rangle = \frac{1}{\sqrt{2}}|\uparrow_y\rangle - \frac{i}{\sqrt{2}}|\downarrow_y\rangle.$$

When $S_y$ is measured, the probability of getting $+\hbar/2$ is

$$|a_{\rm u}|^2 = \left|\frac{1}{\sqrt{2}}\right|^2 = \frac{1}{2},$$

and the probability of getting $-\hbar/2$ is

$$|a_{\rm d}|^2 = \left|\frac{-i}{\sqrt{2}}\right|^2 = \frac{1}{2}.$$

**Ex 3.16** The state in question is that represented by $|\uparrow_z\rangle$, so Equation 3.34 gives

$$\langle\uparrow_z|\widehat{S}_y|\uparrow_z\rangle = \frac{\hbar}{2}\begin{bmatrix}1 & 0\end{bmatrix}\begin{bmatrix}0 & -i\\ i & 0\end{bmatrix}\begin{bmatrix}1\\ 0\end{bmatrix}$$
$$= \frac{\hbar}{2}\begin{bmatrix}1 & 0\end{bmatrix}\begin{bmatrix}0\\ i\end{bmatrix} = \frac{\hbar}{2}(0 + 0) = 0,$$

thus the required expectation value is zero.

An alternative method is based on Equation 3.32. Repeating the calculation in Exercise 3.15, we see that the spin-up probability $p_{\rm u}$ is equal to $1/2$, and the spin-down probability $p_{\rm d}$ is also equal to $1/2$. Hence

$$\langle S_{\mathbf{n}}\rangle = p_{\rm u}\left(\frac{\hbar}{2}\right) + p_{\rm d}\left(-\frac{\hbar}{2}\right) = \frac{\hbar}{2}\left(\frac{1}{2} - \frac{1}{2}\right) = 0.$$

**Ex 3.17** The transition is produced by photons of energy $E_{\rm phot} = hf$, where $f$ is the frequency required. The separation between the two energy levels is $\Delta E = \hbar\omega$. We equate $E_{\rm phot}$ to $\Delta E$ to obtain

$$f = \frac{\hbar\omega}{h} = \frac{\omega}{2\pi} = \frac{\gamma_{\rm s}B}{2\pi}$$
$$= \frac{4.26\times 10^7\,{\rm Hz\,T^{-1}}\times 3.00\,{\rm T}}{2\pi} = 2.03\times 10^7\,{\rm Hz},$$

a frequency in the short-wave radio part of the electromagnetic spectrum.

**Ex 3.18** In the time-dependent spin state obtained in Worked Example 3.4,

$$\langle S_y\rangle = \frac{\hbar}{2}\begin{bmatrix}\cos(\omega t/2) & i\sin(\omega t/2)\end{bmatrix}\begin{bmatrix}0 & -i\\ i & 0\end{bmatrix}\begin{bmatrix}\cos(\omega t/2)\\ -i\sin(\omega t/2)\end{bmatrix}$$
$$= \frac{\hbar}{2}\begin{bmatrix}\cos(\omega t/2) & i\sin(\omega t/2)\end{bmatrix}\begin{bmatrix}-\sin(\omega t/2)\\ i\cos(\omega t/2)\end{bmatrix}$$
$$= \frac{\hbar}{2}(-2\cos(\omega t/2)\sin(\omega t/2))$$
$$= -\frac{\hbar}{2}\sin(\omega t).$$

*Comment*: Combining this result with that obtained in Worked Example 3.4, we see that the spin components $S_z$ and $S_y$ that are perpendicular to the magnetic field have expectation values that vary sinusoidally in time and are $\pi/2$ out of phase with one another. The angular frequency of oscillation is equal to the Larmor frequency. This phenomenon is called **spin precession**; in an MRI scanner, it produces the signals that are used to distinguish one type of tissue from another.

**Ex 3.19** The eigenvectors of the Hamiltonian matrix are the eigenvectors of $\widehat{\mathrm{S}}_y$. Using Equations 3.24 with $\theta = \pi/2$ and $\phi = \pi/2$, these are

$$|\uparrow_y\rangle = \frac{1}{\sqrt{2}}\begin{bmatrix}1\\ \mathrm{i}\end{bmatrix} \quad \text{and} \quad |\downarrow_y\rangle = \frac{1}{\sqrt{2}}\begin{bmatrix}\mathrm{i}\\ 1\end{bmatrix}.$$

Because the particle has $\gamma_\mathrm{s} > 0$, the corresponding energy eigenvalues are $E_\mathrm{u} = -\hbar\omega/2$ and $E_\mathrm{d} = +\hbar\omega/2$.

Using the results of Exercise 3.15, the initial state can be written as

$$|A\rangle_\text{initial} = |\uparrow_z\rangle = \frac{1}{\sqrt{2}}\Big(|\uparrow_y\rangle - \mathrm{i}|\downarrow_y\rangle\Big),$$

so the required time-dependent spinor is

$$\begin{aligned}|A\rangle &= \frac{1}{\sqrt{2}}\Big(\mathrm{e}^{+\mathrm{i}\omega t/2}|\uparrow_y\rangle - \mathrm{i}\,\mathrm{e}^{-\mathrm{i}\omega t/2}|\downarrow_y\rangle\Big)\\ &= \frac{1}{2}\mathrm{e}^{+\mathrm{i}\omega t/2}\begin{bmatrix}1\\ \mathrm{i}\end{bmatrix} - \frac{\mathrm{i}}{2}\mathrm{e}^{-\mathrm{i}\omega t/2}\begin{bmatrix}\mathrm{i}\\ 1\end{bmatrix}\\ &= \frac{1}{2}\begin{bmatrix}\mathrm{e}^{+\mathrm{i}\omega t/2} + \mathrm{e}^{-\mathrm{i}\omega t/2}\\ \mathrm{i}\big(\mathrm{e}^{+\mathrm{i}\omega t/2} - \mathrm{e}^{-\mathrm{i}\omega t/2}\big)\end{bmatrix}\\ &= \begin{bmatrix}\cos(\omega t/2)\\ -\sin(\omega t/2)\end{bmatrix}.\end{aligned}$$

**Ex 4.1** For simplicity we denote the $x$-components of the momenta of the two particles by $p_1$ and $p_2$. The kinetic energies of the particles are $p_1^2/2m_1$ and $p_2^2/2m_2$, and the potential energies are those given: $\frac{1}{2}C_1x_1^2$ and $\frac{1}{2}C_2x_2^2$. The classical Hamiltonian function of the system is then

$$H = \frac{p_1^2}{2m_1} + \frac{p_2^2}{2m_2} + \tfrac{1}{2}C_1x_1^2 + \tfrac{1}{2}C_2x_2^2.$$

Hence, recalling that the momentum operator has the form $\widehat{\mathrm{p}}_x = -\mathrm{i}\hbar\,\partial/\partial x$, the Hamiltonian operator for the system is

$$\widehat{\mathrm{H}} = -\frac{\hbar^2}{2m_1}\frac{\partial^2}{\partial x_1^2} - \frac{\hbar^2}{2m_2}\frac{\partial^2}{\partial x_2^2} + \tfrac{1}{2}C_1x_1^2 + \tfrac{1}{2}C_2x_2^2.$$

The Schrödinger equation is always of the form

$$\mathrm{i}\hbar\frac{\partial\Psi(x_1,x_2,t)}{\partial t} = \widehat{\mathrm{H}}\,\Psi(x_1,x_2,t),$$

which in this case is

$$\begin{aligned}\mathrm{i}\hbar&\frac{\partial\Psi(x_1,x_2,t)}{\partial t}\\ &= \left[-\frac{\hbar^2}{2m_1}\frac{\partial^2}{\partial x_1^2} - \frac{\hbar^2}{2m_2}\frac{\partial^2}{\partial x_2^2} + \tfrac{1}{2}C_1x_1^2 + \tfrac{1}{2}C_2x_2^2\right]\\ &\quad\times\Psi(x_1,x_2,t).\end{aligned}$$

**Ex 4.2** (a) The expectation value $\langle p_1\rangle$ is obtained by inserting the operator $-\mathrm{i}\hbar\,\partial/\partial x_1$ representing $\widehat{\mathrm{p}}_1$ into the sandwich integral:

$$\langle p_1\rangle = -\mathrm{i}\hbar\int_{-\infty}^{\infty}\int_{-\infty}^{\infty}\psi^*(x_1,x_2)\frac{\partial\psi(x_1,x_2)}{\partial x_1}\,\mathrm{d}x_1\,\mathrm{d}x_2,$$

where

$$\psi(x_1,x_2) = \left(\frac{1}{\pi a_1a_2}\right)^{1/2}\mathrm{e}^{-x_1^2/2a_1^2}\,\mathrm{e}^{-x_2^2/2a_2^2}.$$

Differentiating and then separating the integrals, we obtain

$$\begin{aligned}\langle p_1\rangle &= \left(\frac{-\mathrm{i}\hbar}{\pi a_1a_2}\right)\left(\frac{-2}{2a_1^2}\right)\\ &\quad\times\int_{-\infty}^{\infty}x_1\,\mathrm{e}^{-x_1^2/a_1^2}\,\mathrm{d}x_1\times\int_{-\infty}^{\infty}\mathrm{e}^{-x_2^2/a_2^2}\,\mathrm{d}x_2,\end{aligned}$$

which is equal to 0 because the integrand in the first integral is an odd function, and the range of integration is symmetrical about $x_1 = 0$.

(b) The expectation value of $(x_1 - x_2)^2$ is

$$\begin{aligned}&\int_{-\infty}^{\infty}\int_{-\infty}^{\infty}\psi^*(x_1,x_2)\,(x_1-x_2)^2\,\psi(x_1,x_2)\,\mathrm{d}x_1\,\mathrm{d}x_2\\ &= \frac{1}{\pi a_1a_2}\int_{-\infty}^{\infty}\int_{-\infty}^{\infty}(x_1^2 - 2x_1x_2 + x_2^2)\\ &\qquad\qquad\times\mathrm{e}^{-x_1^2/a_1^2}\,\mathrm{e}^{-x_2^2/a_2^2}\,\mathrm{d}x_1\,\mathrm{d}x_2.\end{aligned}$$

The integral is a sum of three terms corresponding to the three terms in $x_1^2 - 2x_1x_2 + x_2^2$. Let us consider the integral involving $x_1^2$:

$$I_1 = \frac{1}{\pi a_1a_2}\int_{-\infty}^{\infty}x_1^2\,\mathrm{e}^{-x_1^2/a_1^2}\,\mathrm{d}x_1\int_{-\infty}^{\infty}\mathrm{e}^{-x_2^2/a_2^2}\,\mathrm{d}x_2.$$

Using standard integrals inside the back cover, the first integral is $\frac{1}{2}a_1^3\sqrt{\pi}$ and the second is $a_2\sqrt{\pi}$, so

$$I_1 = \frac{1}{\pi a_1a_2}\times\tfrac{1}{2}a_1^3\sqrt{\pi}\times a_2\sqrt{\pi} = \tfrac{1}{2}a_1^2.$$

The integral involving $x_1x_2$ is a product of two integrals that are both integrals from $-\infty$ to $\infty$ of odd functions and are therefore equal to zero. Finally, the integral involving $x_2^2$ is equal to $\frac{1}{2}a_2^2$ by an argument similar to that given above for $I_1$. It follows that

$$\langle (x_1 - x_2)^2 \rangle = \tfrac{1}{2}a_1^2 + \tfrac{1}{2}a_2^2.$$

This expectation value is the quantum-mechanical prediction for the average value of the square of the separation of the particles.

**Ex 4.3** (a) The single-particle eigenfunctions in Equations 4.18 and 4.19 are real, so we simply take the product of their squares:

$$\text{probability density} = \frac{4}{L^2}\sin^2\left(\frac{\pi x_1}{L}\right)\sin^2\left(\frac{2\pi x_2}{L}\right).$$

(b) At $(x_1, x_2) = (L/2, L/4)$, the arguments of both sine functions in the probability density are equal to $\pi/2$, so the sine functions reach their maximum values, and so does the probability density.

At $(x_1, x_2) = (L/2, 3L/4)$, one sine function is equal to $+1$ and the other is equal to $-1$. Since both sine functions are squared, this also corresponds to a maximum in the probability density.

**Ex 4.4** (a) The spin component of particle 1 in the $z$-direction is $-\frac{1}{2}\hbar$, so $m_{s_1} = -\frac{1}{2}$; likewise, for particle 2, $m_{s_2} = +\frac{1}{2}$, so the spin state can be represented by the ket $|-\frac{1}{2}, +\frac{1}{2}\rangle$.

(b) Following the same principles, the spin state can be represented by the ket $|-\frac{1}{2}, -\frac{1}{2}\rangle$.

**Ex 4.5** To see whether a given ket is an eigenvector of an operator, we let the operator act on the ket and see if we get the same ket back, multiplied by a constant.

(a) We have

$$\begin{aligned}\widehat{S}_{z1}|\uparrow\uparrow\rangle &= \left(\widehat{S}_{z1}|\uparrow\rangle_1\right)|\uparrow\rangle_2\\ &= \left(\tfrac{1}{2}\hbar|\uparrow\rangle_1\right)|\uparrow\rangle_2\\ &= \tfrac{1}{2}\hbar|\uparrow\uparrow\rangle,\\ \widehat{S}_{z2}|\uparrow\uparrow\rangle &= |\uparrow\rangle_1\left(\widehat{S}_{z2}|\uparrow\rangle_2\right)\\ &= |\uparrow\rangle_1\left(\tfrac{1}{2}\hbar|\uparrow\rangle_2\right)\\ &= \tfrac{1}{2}\hbar|\uparrow\uparrow\rangle.\end{aligned}$$

Adding these equations together gives

$$(\widehat{S}_{z1} + \widehat{S}_{z2})|\uparrow\uparrow\rangle = \hbar|\uparrow\uparrow\rangle,$$

so $|\uparrow\uparrow\rangle$ is an eigenvector of $\widehat{S}_{z1} + \widehat{S}_{z2}$, with eigenvalue $\hbar$.

(b) Similar calculations give

$$\begin{aligned}\widehat{S}_{z1}|\uparrow\downarrow\rangle &= +\tfrac{1}{2}\hbar|\uparrow\downarrow\rangle,\\ \widehat{S}_{z1}|\downarrow\uparrow\rangle &= -\tfrac{1}{2}\hbar|\downarrow\uparrow\rangle,\\ \widehat{S}_{z2}|\uparrow\downarrow\rangle &= -\tfrac{1}{2}\hbar|\uparrow\downarrow\rangle,\\ \widehat{S}_{z2}|\downarrow\uparrow\rangle &= +\tfrac{1}{2}\hbar|\downarrow\uparrow\rangle,\end{aligned}$$

so

$$\begin{aligned}(\widehat{S}_{z1} + \widehat{S}_{z2})|\uparrow\downarrow\rangle &= (+\tfrac{1}{2}\hbar - \tfrac{1}{2}\hbar)|\uparrow\downarrow\rangle = 0|\uparrow\downarrow\rangle,\\ (\widehat{S}_{z1} + \widehat{S}_{z2})|\downarrow\uparrow\rangle &= (-\tfrac{1}{2}\hbar + \tfrac{1}{2}\hbar)|\downarrow\uparrow\rangle = 0|\downarrow\uparrow\rangle.\end{aligned}$$

Hence

$$(\widehat{S}_{z1} + \widehat{S}_{z2})(|\uparrow\downarrow\rangle + |\downarrow\uparrow\rangle) = 0(|\uparrow\downarrow\rangle + |\downarrow\uparrow\rangle).$$

Thus $|\uparrow\downarrow\rangle + |\downarrow\uparrow\rangle$ is an eigenvector of $\widehat{S}_{z1} + \widehat{S}_{z2}$, with eigenvalue 0.

(c) The working follows that of part (b) until the last line. Then

$$(\widehat{S}_{z1} + \widehat{S}_{z2})(|\uparrow\downarrow\rangle - |\downarrow\uparrow\rangle) = 0(|\uparrow\downarrow\rangle - |\downarrow\uparrow\rangle).$$

So $|\uparrow\downarrow\rangle - |\downarrow\uparrow\rangle$ is an eigenvector of $\widehat{S}_{z1} + \widehat{S}_{z2}$, with eigenvalue 0.

**Ex 4.6** (a) We consider

$$\psi^+(x_1, x_2) = \frac{1}{\sqrt{2}}\left[\psi_n(x_1)\,\psi_k(x_2) + \psi_k(x_1)\,\psi_n(x_2)\right].$$

Swapping particle labels,

$$\begin{aligned}\psi^+(x_2, x_1) &= \frac{1}{\sqrt{2}}\left[\psi_n(x_2)\,\psi_k(x_1) + \psi_k(x_2)\,\psi_n(x_1)\right]\\ &= \frac{1}{\sqrt{2}}\left[\psi_k(x_2)\,\psi_n(x_1) + \psi_n(x_2)\,\psi_k(x_1)\right]\\ &= \psi^+(x_1, x_2),\end{aligned}$$

so the function is symmetric.

(b) The normalization integral for $\psi^+(x_1, x_2)$ is

$$\begin{aligned}I &= \int_{-\infty}^{\infty}\int_{-\infty}^{\infty}|\psi^+(x_1, x_2)|^2\,\mathrm{d}x_1\,\mathrm{d}x_2\\ &= \frac{1}{2}\left[\int_{-\infty}^{\infty}\psi_n^*(x_1)\psi_n(x_1)\,\mathrm{d}x_1\int_{-\infty}^{\infty}\psi_k^*(x_2)\psi_k(x_2)\,\mathrm{d}x_2\right.\\ &\quad + \int_{-\infty}^{\infty}\psi_n^*(x_1)\psi_k(x_1)\,\mathrm{d}x_1\int_{-\infty}^{\infty}\psi_k^*(x_2)\psi_n(x_2)\,\mathrm{d}x_2\\ &\quad + \int_{-\infty}^{\infty}\psi_k^*(x_1)\psi_n(x_1)\,\mathrm{d}x_1\int_{-\infty}^{\infty}\psi_n^*(x_2)\psi_k(x_2)\,\mathrm{d}x_2\\ &\quad \left.+ \int_{-\infty}^{\infty}\psi_k^*(x_1)\psi_k(x_1)\,\mathrm{d}x_1\int_{-\infty}^{\infty}\psi_n^*(x_2)\psi_n(x_2)\,\mathrm{d}x_2\right].\end{aligned}$$

This can be expressed more compactly using Dirac bracket notation:

$$I = \tfrac{1}{2}\big[\langle\psi_n|\psi_n\rangle\langle\psi_k|\psi_k\rangle + \langle\psi_n|\psi_k\rangle\langle\psi_k|\psi_n\rangle + \langle\psi_k|\psi_n\rangle\langle\psi_n|\psi_k\rangle + \langle\psi_k|\psi_k\rangle\langle\psi_n|\psi_n\rangle\big].$$

However, the single-particle eigenfunctions are orthogonal and normalized, so $\langle\psi_i|\psi_j\rangle = \delta_{ij}$, allowing us to conclude that

$$I = \tfrac{1}{2}[1\times 1 + 0\times 0 + 0\times 0 + 1\times 1] = 1.$$

The total probability of the two particles being somewhere in the whole of space is unity.

**Ex 4.7** In the antisymmetric function given by Equation 4.37,

$$\psi^-(x_1,x_2) = \frac{1}{\sqrt{2}}\big[\psi_n(x_1)\,\psi_k(x_2) - \psi_k(x_1)\,\psi_n(x_2)\big].$$

Since $\psi_n(x) = \psi_k(x)$, we can replace $\psi_n$ by $\psi_k$, to obtain

$$\begin{aligned}\psi^-(x_1,x_2) &= \frac{1}{\sqrt{2}}\big[\psi_k(x_1)\,\psi_k(x_2) - \psi_k(x_1)\,\psi_k(x_2)\big]\\ &= 0.\end{aligned}$$

Thus the antisymmetric eigenfunction with two identical particles in the same spatial state is equal to zero *everywhere*.

**Ex 4.8** (a) Using the single-particle eigenfunctions given in the question, the symmetric two-particle eigenfunction is

$$\begin{aligned}\psi^+(x_1,x_2) &= \frac{1}{\sqrt{2}}\big[\psi_0(x_1)\,\psi_1(x_2) + \psi_1(x_1)\,\psi_0(x_2)\big]\\ &= \frac{1}{a^2\sqrt{\pi}}(x_1+x_2)\,\mathrm{e}^{-x_1^2/2a^2}\,\mathrm{e}^{-x_2^2/2a^2}\\ &= \frac{1}{a^2\sqrt{\pi}}(x_1+x_2)\,\mathrm{e}^{-(x_1^2+x_2^2)/2a^2},\end{aligned}$$

and the antisymmetric two-particle eigenfunction is

$$\begin{aligned}\psi^-(x_1,x_2) &= \frac{1}{\sqrt{2}}\big[\psi_0(x_1)\,\psi_1(x_2) - \psi_1(x_1)\,\psi_0(x_2)\big]\\ &= \frac{1}{a^2\sqrt{\pi}}(x_2-x_1)\,\mathrm{e}^{-(x_1^2+x_2^2)/2a^2}.\end{aligned}$$

(b) Because the particles do not interact with one another, the total Hamiltonian operator describing the two-particle system can be expressed as a sum of Hamiltonians associated with each particle: $\widehat{\mathrm{H}} = \widehat{\mathrm{H}}_1 + \widehat{\mathrm{H}}_2$, where $\widehat{\mathrm{H}}_1\,\psi_n(x_1) = E_n\,\psi_n(x_1)$ and $\widehat{\mathrm{H}}_2\,\psi_n(x_2) = E_n\,\psi_n(x_2)$.

The operator $\widehat{\mathrm{H}}_1$ does nothing to $\psi_n(x_2)$, so $\widehat{\mathrm{H}}_1$ acting on $\psi^\pm(x_1,x_2)$ treats $\psi_n(x_2)$ like a constant. Thus

$$\begin{aligned}&\widehat{\mathrm{H}}_1\,\psi^\pm(x_1,x_2)\\ &= \widehat{\mathrm{H}}_1\frac{1}{\sqrt{2}}\big[\psi_0(x_1)\,\psi_1(x_2) \pm \psi_1(x_1)\,\psi_0(x_2)\big]\\ &= \frac{1}{\sqrt{2}}\Big[\big(\widehat{\mathrm{H}}_1\,\psi_0(x_1)\big)\psi_1(x_2) \pm \big(\widehat{\mathrm{H}}_1\,\psi_1(x_1)\big)\psi_0(x_2)\Big]\\ &= \frac{1}{\sqrt{2}}\big[E_0\,\psi_0(x_1)\,\psi_1(x_2) \pm E_1\,\psi_1(x_1)\,\psi_0(x_2)\big].\end{aligned}$$

In a similar way,

$$\begin{aligned}&\widehat{\mathrm{H}}_2\psi^\pm(x_1,x_2)\\ &= \frac{1}{\sqrt{2}}\big[E_1\,\psi_0(x_1)\,\psi_1(x_2) \pm E_0\,\psi_1(x_1)\,\psi_0(x_2)\big].\end{aligned}$$

Adding these two results together, we find that

$$\widehat{\mathrm{H}}\,\psi^\pm(x_1,x_2) = (E_0+E_1)\,\psi^\pm(x_1,x_2),$$

so $\psi^+(x_1,x_2)$ and $\psi^-(x_1,x_2)$ are eigenfunctions of $\widehat{\mathrm{H}}$, both with eigenvalue $E_0 + E_1 = (\frac{1}{2}+\frac{3}{2})\hbar\omega_0 = 2\hbar\omega_0$.

**Ex 4.9** Starting with

$$\begin{aligned}&\frac{1}{\sqrt{2}}(|\uparrow\downarrow\rangle + |\downarrow\uparrow\rangle)\\ &= \frac{1}{\sqrt{2}}(|\uparrow\rangle_1|\downarrow\rangle_2 + |\downarrow\rangle_1|\uparrow\rangle_2),\end{aligned}$$

we exchange the particle labels and then rearrange. This gives

$$\begin{aligned}&\frac{1}{\sqrt{2}}(|\uparrow\rangle_2|\downarrow\rangle_1 + |\downarrow\rangle_2|\uparrow\rangle_1)\\ &= \frac{1}{\sqrt{2}}(|\downarrow\rangle_1|\uparrow\rangle_2 + |\uparrow\rangle_1|\downarrow\rangle_2)\\ &= \frac{1}{\sqrt{2}}(|\uparrow\rangle_1|\downarrow\rangle_2 + |\downarrow\rangle_1|\uparrow\rangle_2)\\ &= \frac{1}{\sqrt{2}}(|\uparrow\downarrow\rangle + |\downarrow\uparrow\rangle),\end{aligned}$$

as required.

For $|\uparrow\uparrow\rangle = |\uparrow\rangle_1|\uparrow\rangle_2$ and $|\downarrow\downarrow\rangle = |\downarrow\rangle_1|\downarrow\rangle_2$, we simply interchange the particle labels and then re-order (perfectly legal!) to get the same expressions as we started with.

**Ex 4.10** Using a method similar to that in Exercise 4.5, we have

$$\begin{aligned}\widehat{S}_{z1}\,|\downarrow\downarrow\rangle &= \left(\widehat{S}_{z1}\,|\downarrow\rangle_1\right)|\downarrow\rangle_2\\ &= \left(-\tfrac{1}{2}\hbar\,|\downarrow\rangle_1\right)|\downarrow\rangle_2\\ &= -\tfrac{1}{2}\hbar\,|\downarrow\downarrow\rangle,\\ \widehat{S}_{z2}\,|\downarrow\downarrow\rangle &= |\downarrow\rangle_1\left(\widehat{S}_{z2}\,|\downarrow\rangle_2\right)\\ &= |\downarrow\rangle_1\left(-\tfrac{1}{2}\hbar\,|\downarrow\rangle_2\right)\\ &= -\tfrac{1}{2}\hbar\,|\downarrow\downarrow\rangle.\end{aligned}$$

Adding these equations together gives

$$\widehat{S}_z\,|\downarrow\downarrow\rangle = (\widehat{S}_{z1}+\widehat{S}_{z2})\,|\downarrow\downarrow\rangle = -\hbar\,|\downarrow\downarrow\rangle,$$

so $|\downarrow\downarrow\rangle$ is an eigenvector of $\widehat{S}_z$, with eigenvalue $-\hbar$ and the quantum number $M_S = -1$.

**Ex 4.11** Identical bosons are described by a symmetric total wave function. Spinless particles are counted as having symmetric spin states, so the spatial wave function must be symmetric too. The only possibility is

$$\psi^+(x_1,x_2) = \frac{1}{\sqrt{2}}\big[\psi_n(x_1)\,\psi_k(x_2)+\psi_k(x_1)\,\psi_n(x_2)\big].$$

**Ex 4.12** For the first excited level, one particle must be in the ground state of the harmonic oscillator and the other one in the first state. Using the solution to Exercise 4.8, the single-particle eigenfunctions can be combined to form symmetric and antisymmetric functions:

$$\psi^\pm(x_1,x_2) = \frac{1}{a^2\sqrt{\pi}}(x_1 \pm x_2)\,\mathrm{e}^{-(x_1^2+x_2^2)/2a^2},$$

where $a = \sqrt{\hbar/m\omega_0}$ and $\omega_0$ is the classical angular frequency.

These must be combined with the triplet and singlet spin functions $|\uparrow\uparrow\rangle$, $\frac{1}{\sqrt{2}}\big(|\uparrow\downarrow\rangle + |\downarrow\uparrow\rangle\big)$, $|\downarrow\downarrow\rangle$ and $\frac{1}{\sqrt{2}}\big(|\uparrow\downarrow\rangle - |\downarrow\uparrow\rangle\big)$.

Since the particles are fermions, their total wave function must be antisymmetric. We therefore combine $\psi^-(x_1,x_2)$ with the symmetric triplet spin kets and $\psi^+(x_1,x_2)$ with the antisymmetric singlet spin ket. The four possibilities are

$$\begin{aligned}&\frac{1}{a^2\sqrt{\pi}}(x_1-x_2)\,\mathrm{e}^{-(x_1^2+x_2^2)/2a^2}\,|\uparrow\uparrow\rangle,\\ &\frac{1}{a^2\sqrt{2\pi}}(x_1-x_2)\,\mathrm{e}^{-(x_1^2+x_2^2)/2a^2}\big(|\uparrow\downarrow\rangle + |\downarrow\uparrow\rangle\big),\\ &\frac{1}{a^2\sqrt{\pi}}(x_1-x_2)\,\mathrm{e}^{-(x_1^2+x_2^2)/2a^2}\,|\downarrow\downarrow\rangle,\\ &\frac{1}{a^2\sqrt{2\pi}}(x_1+x_2)\,\mathrm{e}^{-(x_1^2+x_2^2)/2a^2}\big(|\uparrow\downarrow\rangle - |\downarrow\uparrow\rangle\big).\end{aligned}$$

These states all have the same energy, $\frac{1}{2}\hbar\omega_0 + \frac{3}{2}\hbar\omega_0 = 2\hbar\omega_0$, corresponding to one particle in the ground state and the other in the first excited state. So, in the absence of any interactions between the particles, the first excited level of two identical fermions in a simple harmonic oscillator well has four-fold degeneracy.

**Ex 4.13** A hydrogen atom consists of a proton and an electron (2 fermions), so is a boson.

A deuterium atom consists of a proton, a neutron and an electron (3 fermions), so is a fermion.

A singly-ionized helium atom consists of 2 protons, 2 neutrons and 1 electron (5 fermions), so is a fermion.

A $^{238}_{92}$U nucleus consists of 238 protons plus neutrons (238 fermions), so is a boson.

A $^{235}_{92}$U nucleus consists of 235 protons plus neutrons (235 fermions), so is a fermion.

A $^{235}_{92}$U atom consists of 235 protons plus neutrons and 92 electrons (327 fermions), so is a fermion.

**Ex 4.14** Protons are spin-$\frac{1}{2}$ fermions, so they are described by an antisymmetric total wave function. The protons are in a spatially symmetric state, so they must be in an antisymmetric spin state, that is, the singlet state represented by $|0,0\rangle = \frac{1}{2}\big(|\uparrow\downarrow\rangle - |\downarrow\uparrow\rangle\big)$. The two-proton system therefore has $S = 0$ and $M_S = 0$.

**Ex 4.15** No, it is incorrect. The Pauli exclusion principle states that there can only be two electrons in the same quantum state. But quantum states can be degenerate: different states may have the same energy. This is the case in a three-dimensional box, where different combinations of the quantum numbers $n_x$, $n_y$ and $n_z$ can give the same energy.

**Ex 5.1** The wave functions $\Psi_1$ and $\Psi_3$ represent the same state, because $\Psi_3 = \mathrm{i}\Psi_1$, and $\mathrm{i} = \mathrm{e}^{\mathrm{i}\pi/2}$ is a phase factor (a complex number of unit modulus). The wave function $\Psi_2$ represents an entirely different state, because it cannot be expressed as a multiple of $\Psi_1$ or $\Psi_3$.

**Ex 5.2** A silver atom is a boson. It has 107 or 109 nucleons (protons or neutrons, all fermions) and 47 electrons, an even number of fermions in all.

*Comment*: In Chapters 2 and 3 of this book, a silver atom was used as a prime example of a spin-$\frac{1}{2}$ particle. Given that spin-$\frac{1}{2}$ particles are fermions, you might wonder what is going on! The answer is that the Stern–Gerlach experiment measures the magnetic dipole moment, and this is dominated by the contribution of the electrons (the nuclear contribution is roughly a thousand times smaller). The deflection of a silver atom depends only on the magnetic moment of the electrons; many contributions cancel out, and the magnetic moment is essentially determined by the spin of a single electron in the atom — a spin-$\frac{1}{2}$ particle.

**Ex 5.3** Using rules give in Chapter 1, we see that $\widehat{\mathrm{y}}\,\widehat{\mathrm{p}}_z$ is Hermitian because it is the product of two *commuting* Hermitian operators. For the same reason, $\widehat{\mathrm{z}}\,\widehat{\mathrm{p}}_y$ is Hermitian, and so is $-\widehat{\mathrm{z}}\,\widehat{\mathrm{p}}_y$, being the product of a Hermitian operator and a real constant $(-1)$. Finally, $\widehat{\mathrm{L}}_x = \widehat{\mathrm{y}}\,\widehat{\mathrm{p}}_z - \widehat{\mathrm{z}}\,\widehat{\mathrm{p}}_y$ is Hermitian because it is the sum of two Hermitian operators. This is to be expected, because $L_x$ is an observable quantity, and so must be represented by a linear Hermitian operator.

**Ex 5.4** The probability is

$$\begin{aligned}|\langle\uparrow_y \mid \uparrow_x\rangle|^2 &= \left|\frac{1}{\sqrt{2}}\begin{bmatrix}1 & -\mathrm{i}\end{bmatrix}\frac{1}{\sqrt{2}}\begin{bmatrix}1\\1\end{bmatrix}\right|^2\\ &= \tfrac{1}{4}|1-\mathrm{i}|^2\\ &= \tfrac{1}{4}(1-\mathrm{i})(1+\mathrm{i}) = \tfrac{1}{2}.\end{aligned}$$

**Ex 5.5** Multiplying out the matrices gives

$$\begin{aligned}\langle S_z\rangle &= \frac{1}{\sqrt{2}}\begin{bmatrix}1 & -\mathrm{i}\end{bmatrix}\frac{\hbar}{2}\begin{bmatrix}1 & 0\\0 & -1\end{bmatrix}\frac{1}{\sqrt{2}}\begin{bmatrix}1\\ \mathrm{i}\end{bmatrix}\\ &= \frac{\hbar}{4}\begin{bmatrix}1 & -\mathrm{i}\end{bmatrix}\begin{bmatrix}1\\ -\mathrm{i}\end{bmatrix}\\ &= \frac{\hbar}{4}(1-1) = 0.\end{aligned}$$

If $p_1$ is the probability of getting $S_z = +\hbar/2$, and $p_2$ is the probability of getting $-\hbar/2$, the expectation value of $S_z$ is

$$\langle S_z\rangle = p_1 \times \left(+\frac{\hbar}{2}\right) + p_2 \times \left(-\frac{\hbar}{2}\right) = \frac{\hbar}{2}(p_1 - p_2).$$

We have found $\langle S_z\rangle = 0$ in the state represented by $|\uparrow_y\rangle$, so it follows that $p_1 = p_2$. The normalization rule for probability, $p_1 + p_2 = 1$, then gives $p_1 = p_2 = 1/2$.

**Ex 5.6** The position measurement causes the initial ground-state wave function to collapse into a narrow wave packet that is strongly peaked around the measured position $x_0$. This wave packet is a linear superposition of different harmonic oscillator energy eigenfunctions. Evidently, this linear superposition includes the tenth excited state, so when the energy of the particle is measured, there is a non-zero probability of getting the corresponding energy, $E_{10}$. When this energy value is obtained, the wave function collapses into the corresponding energy eigenfunction, $\psi_{10}(x)$. This eigenfunction evolves as the stationary state $\Psi_{10}(x,t) = \psi_{10}(x)\,\mathrm{e}^{-\mathrm{i}E_{10}t/\hbar}$, so a measurement of energy taken at a later time still gives the value $E_{10}$.

**Ex 5.7** The state $|\Psi\rangle$ must be normalized, so

$$\begin{aligned}1 &= \langle\Psi|\Psi\rangle\\ &= \big(c_1^*\langle\Psi_1| + c_2^*\langle\Psi_2|\big)\big(c_1|\Psi_1\rangle + c_2|\Psi_2\rangle\big).\end{aligned}$$

Multiplying out the brackets and using the orthonormality of $|\Psi_1\rangle$ and $|\Psi_2\rangle$ then gives

$$1 = c_1^*c_1\langle\Psi_1|\Psi_1\rangle + c_2^*c_2\langle\Psi_2|\Psi_2\rangle = |c_1|^2 + |c_2|^2.$$

**Ex 5.8** (a) The probability of getting the eigenvalue $b_j$ is

$$\text{probability} = \big|\langle b_j|b_i\rangle\big|^2 = |\delta_{ji}|^2 = \delta_{ji},$$

so the probability is equal to 1 if $b_j = b_i$, and is equal to 0 otherwise.

(b) The probability of getting the eigenvalue $a_j$ is

$$\text{probability} = \big|\langle a_j|b_i\rangle\big|^2.$$

The $\cos^2(\theta/2)$ rule was an exemplar of this situation in Chapter 3, with $\widehat{\mathrm{S}}_z$ playing the role of $\widehat{\mathrm{B}}$, and $\widehat{\mathrm{S}}_{\mathbf{n}}$ (with $\mathbf{n}$ corresponding to the polar angle $\theta$) playing the role of $\widehat{\mathrm{A}}$.

**Ex 6.1** The first measurement will place the second particle in the state $|\downarrow_{\mathbf{n}}\rangle$, which, from Equation 6.9, is

$$-\sin 30^\circ|\uparrow\rangle + \cos 30^\circ|\downarrow\rangle.$$

The probability amplitude for the particle to be found in the $|\uparrow\rangle$ state is

$$\begin{aligned}\langle\uparrow \mid \downarrow_{\mathbf{n}}\rangle &= -\sin 30^\circ\langle\uparrow\mid\uparrow\rangle + \cos 30^\circ\langle\uparrow\mid\downarrow\rangle\\ &= -\sin 30^\circ = -\tfrac{1}{2},\end{aligned}$$

using the orthonormality of the spin kets $|\uparrow\rangle$ and $|\downarrow\rangle$. The required probability is the modulus squared of the probability amplitude, $|-\frac{1}{2}|^2 = 0.25$.

*Comment*: It would be legitimate simply to spot that the amplitude for the $|\uparrow\rangle$ term is $-\sin 30°$, and square to obtain the probability.

**Ex 6.2** From the expression for a spin state in the $-\mathbf{n}$-direction, Equation 6.9 with $\phi = 0$, we have

$$\langle\downarrow_{\mathbf{n}}| = -\sin(\theta/2)\,\langle\uparrow| + \cos(\theta/2)\,\langle\downarrow|.$$

Using the orthonormality of $|\uparrow\rangle$ and $|\downarrow\rangle$, we obtain the probability amplitude $\langle\downarrow_{\mathbf{n}}|\uparrow\rangle = -\sin(\theta/2)$. Taking the modulus and squaring, to get the probability, we obtain the desired equation.

*Comment*: This result also follows from $\sin^2(\theta/2) + \cos^2(\theta/2) = 1$ and the fact that the total probability is 1.

**Ex 6.3** First, the ket: the two particles are in a singlet state, with $S = 0$ and $m_S = 0$: hence $\langle * * |S = 0, M_S = 0\rangle$. Secondly, particle 1 is to be measured spin-up in the $z$-direction, hence $\langle\uparrow *|S = 0, M_S = 0\rangle$, and particle 2 is to be measured spin-down in direction $\mathbf{n}$, so finally we have $\langle\uparrow\downarrow_{\mathbf{n}}|S = 0, M_S = 0\rangle$.

**Ex 6.4** With both detectors aligned in the same direction, we have $\theta = 0$ and so Equation 6.17 gives

$$\text{probability(up, down)} = \tfrac{1}{2}\cos^2(0) = \tfrac{1}{2}.$$

Similarly, we find that

$$\text{probability(down, up)} = \tfrac{1}{2}\cos^2(0) = \tfrac{1}{2}.$$

So the total probability of finding the particles with opposite spin components in a given direction is $\frac{1}{2} + \frac{1}{2} = 1$.

**Ex 6.5** Since $\theta_1 - \theta_2 = \pi/2$, we know that $\frac{1}{2}\cos^2[(\theta_1 - \theta_2)/2] = \frac{1}{2}\sin^2[(\theta_1 - \theta_2)/2] = 1/4$, so the prediction is that there will be equal numbers in each of the four categories.

*Comment*: Alternatively, the answer follows by applying the fact that a singlet state has the symmetry property described in Section 6.2.3. Because a singlet state appears the same from all angles, the result follows since any one of the four cases is the same as any other case from a different perspective, so the numbers must be equal, i.e. $1/4$.

**Ex 6.6** The quantum prediction for $D(\theta_1 - \theta_2)$ is $C(\theta_1 - \theta_2) = -\cos(\theta_1 - \theta_2)$. Hence the prediction is that, for these particular angles, $\Sigma = -3\cos 45° + \cos 135° = -2\sqrt{2}$.

**Ex 6.7** We must verify normalization (that $\langle L|L\rangle = \langle R|R\rangle = 1$) and orthogonality (that $\langle L|R\rangle = \langle R|L\rangle = 0$).

Remember that the bra corresponding to $|R\rangle$ has the complex conjugate of all the coefficients in $|R\rangle$, leading to

$$\begin{aligned}\langle R|R\rangle &= \tfrac{1}{2}\big(\langle H| - i\,\langle V|\big)\big(|H\rangle + i|V\rangle\big)\\ &= \tfrac{1}{2}\big(\langle H|H\rangle + \langle V|V\rangle - i\,\langle V|H\rangle + i\,\langle H|V\rangle\big).\end{aligned}$$

The first two bra-kets are unity, and the third and fourth are zero, by the orthonormality of $|V\rangle$ and $|H\rangle$. Hence $\langle R|R\rangle = 1$, and the same argument can be used to show that $|L\rangle$ is normalized. We also have

$$\begin{aligned}\langle R|L\rangle &= -\tfrac{1}{2}\big(\langle H| - i\,\langle V|\big)\big(|H\rangle - i|V\rangle\big)\\ &= -\tfrac{1}{2}\big(\langle H|H\rangle - \langle V|V\rangle - i\,\langle V|H\rangle - i\,\langle H|V\rangle\big)\\ &= 0,\end{aligned}$$

so $|R\rangle$ and $|L\rangle$ are orthogonal. Note that since $\langle a|b\rangle = \langle b|a\rangle^*$ for any $|a\rangle$ and $|b\rangle$, $\langle L|R\rangle = 0$ too.

**Ex 6.8** First, $|V_\theta V_\theta\rangle$ is just $|V_\theta\rangle_1\,|V_\theta\rangle_2$ etc. From Equations 6.23 and 6.24, the left-hand side becomes

$$\begin{aligned}&\tfrac{1}{\sqrt{2}}\big[\big(\cos\theta|V\rangle_1 + \sin\theta|H\rangle_1\big)\big(\cos\theta|V\rangle_2 + \sin\theta|H\rangle_2\big)\\ &\quad + \big(-\sin\theta|V\rangle_1 + \cos\theta|H\rangle_1\big)\\ &\qquad \times \big(-\sin\theta|V\rangle_2 + \cos\theta|H\rangle_2\big)\big].\end{aligned}$$

Multiplying out, the two $|V\rangle_1|H\rangle_2$ terms cancel, as do the two $|H\rangle_1|V\rangle_2$ terms. Then, using $\cos^2\theta + \sin^2\theta = 1$, this becomes $\frac{1}{\sqrt{2}}\big[|V\rangle_1|V\rangle_2 + |H\rangle_1|H\rangle_2\big] = \frac{1}{\sqrt{2}}\big[|VV\rangle + |HH\rangle\big]$. Note that $|H\rangle_1|V\rangle_2$ is not the same as $|V\rangle_1|H\rangle_2$, since the first ket is the state of photon 1 and the second that of photon 2.

**Ex 6.9** (a) The 'near' measurement will collapse the entangled state vector Equation 6.28 onto the term $|VV\rangle$, so that the 'far' detector will receive a photon in the $|V\rangle$ state. Such a photon is certain to be stopped by a Polaroid sheet oriented in the $x$-direction.

(b) The state will be collapsed by the 'near' measurement onto the non-entangled term with both photons in the $|H\rangle$ state. The second photon is therefore certain to pass through the 'far' Polaroid.

(c) The photon approaching the 'far' Polaroid will certainly be in the state $|V\rangle$. Since the second detector is oriented with its vertical axis at $45° = \pi/4$ radians to the $z$-axis, Malus's law tells us that a fraction equal to $\cos^2(\pi/4) = 0.5$ will be detected on the far side of the 'far' Polaroid.

**Ex 6.10** If the first particle were to have a positive value of $S_z$ in a measurement, then the state vector would collapse onto the first term of Equation 6.31, for which $S_z$ is positive for both of the other two particles. Likewise, if the first particle were to have a negative value of $S_z$ in a measurement, the other two particles must also have negative $S_z$.

**Ex 7.1** In order to show that $|\mathrm{V}_\theta\rangle$ and $|\mathrm{H}_\theta\rangle$ are orthogonal for any value of $\theta$, we need to calculate the inner product $\langle \mathrm{V}_\theta|\mathrm{H}_\theta\rangle$:

$$\begin{aligned}\langle \mathrm{V}_\theta|\mathrm{H}_\theta\rangle &= \begin{bmatrix}-\sin\theta & \cos\theta\end{bmatrix}\begin{bmatrix}\cos\theta \\ \sin\theta\end{bmatrix} \\ &= -\sin\theta\cos\theta + \sin\theta\cos\theta = 0.\end{aligned}$$

Since this inner product is zero for any $\theta$, the two eigenvectors are orthogonal. This could also be shown by considering the inner product $\langle \mathrm{H}_\theta|\mathrm{V}_\theta\rangle$. (Remember that $\langle a|b\rangle = \langle b|a\rangle^*$ always.)

**Ex 7.2** To show that $|\mathrm{V}_\theta\rangle$ and $|\mathrm{H}_\theta\rangle$ are normalized, we need to calculate $\langle \mathrm{V}_\theta|\mathrm{V}_\theta\rangle$ and $\langle \mathrm{H}_\theta|\mathrm{H}_\theta\rangle$:

$$\begin{aligned}\langle \mathrm{V}_\theta|\mathrm{V}_\theta\rangle &= \begin{bmatrix}\cos\theta & \sin\theta\end{bmatrix}\begin{bmatrix}\cos\theta \\ \sin\theta\end{bmatrix} \\ &= \cos^2\theta + \sin^2\theta = 1,\end{aligned}$$

$$\begin{aligned}\langle \mathrm{H}_\theta|\mathrm{H}_\theta\rangle &= \begin{bmatrix}-\sin\theta & \cos\theta\end{bmatrix}\begin{bmatrix}-\sin\theta \\ \cos\theta\end{bmatrix} \\ &= \sin^2\theta + \cos^2\theta = 1.\end{aligned}$$

So $|\mathrm{V}_\theta\rangle$ and $|\mathrm{H}_\theta\rangle$ are normalized to unity.

**Ex 7.3** We use Equations 7.2 and 7.3:

$$\begin{aligned}\widehat{\mathcal{P}}(\theta)\,|\mathrm{V}_\theta\rangle &= \begin{bmatrix}\cos 2\theta & \sin 2\theta \\ \sin 2\theta & -\cos 2\theta\end{bmatrix}\begin{bmatrix}\cos\theta \\ \sin\theta\end{bmatrix} \\ &= \begin{bmatrix}\cos 2\theta\cos\theta + \sin 2\theta\sin\theta \\ \sin 2\theta\sin\theta - \cos 2\theta\sin\theta\end{bmatrix} \\ &= \begin{bmatrix}\cos(2\theta-\theta) \\ \sin(2\theta-\theta)\end{bmatrix} = |\mathrm{V}_\theta\rangle\end{aligned}$$

and

$$\begin{aligned}\widehat{\mathcal{P}}(\theta)\,|\mathrm{H}_\theta\rangle &= \begin{bmatrix}\cos 2\theta & \sin 2\theta \\ \sin 2\theta & -\cos 2\theta\end{bmatrix}\begin{bmatrix}-\sin\theta \\ \cos\theta\end{bmatrix} \\ &= \begin{bmatrix}-\cos 2\theta\sin\theta + \sin 2\theta\cos\theta \\ -\sin 2\theta\sin\theta - \cos 2\theta\cos\theta\end{bmatrix} \\ &= \begin{bmatrix}\sin(2\theta-\theta) \\ -\cos(2\theta-\theta)\end{bmatrix} = -|\mathrm{H}_\theta\rangle.\end{aligned}$$

**Ex 7.4** A photon polarized along the $z$-axis is represented by $|\psi\rangle = |\mathrm{V}\rangle = \begin{bmatrix}1 \\ 0\end{bmatrix}$, and the probability of a measurement yielding $|\mathrm{V}_\theta\rangle$ is given by

$$\begin{aligned}P_+(\theta) = |\langle \mathrm{V}_\theta|\mathrm{V}\rangle|^2 &= \left|\begin{bmatrix}\cos\theta & \sin\theta\end{bmatrix}\begin{bmatrix}1 \\ 0\end{bmatrix}\right|^2 \\ &= \cos^2\theta.\end{aligned}$$

This result for single photons is the quantum-mechanical explanation of Malus's law.

**Ex 7.5**

| | | | | |
|---|---|---|---|---|
| Alice's basis | H/V | H/V | H/V | H/V |
| Alice's sent bit | 1 | 0 | 1 | 0 |
| Bob's basis | H/V | H/V | D | D |
| Bob's detected bit | 1 | 0 | 1 or 0 | 1 or 0 |

| | | | | |
|---|---|---|---|---|
| Alice's basis | D | D | D | D |
| Alice's sent bit | 1 | 0 | 1 | 0 |
| Bob's basis | H/V | H/V | D | D |
| Bob's detected bit | 1 or 0 | 1 or 0 | 1 | 0 |

In the first two and last two columns, Alice and Bob employ the same bases and so Bob necessarily finds the photon in the state sent by Alice. In the other four cases, the bases are different and Bob will find a 0 or 1 with equal probability.

**Ex 7.6** Start by constructing a table similar to the one in the previous exercise, to cover all the different combinations of the common basis chosen by Alice and Bob, and the basis chosen by Eve, as shown below.

| | | | | |
|---|---|---|---|---|
| Alice & Bob basis | H/V | H/V | H/V | H/V |
| Alice's sent bit | 1 | 0 | 1 | 0 |
| Eve's basis | H/V | H/V | D | D |
| Bob's detected bit | 1 | 0 | 1 or 0 | 1 or 0 |

| | | | | |
|---|---|---|---|---|
| Alice & Bob basis | D | D | D | D |
| Alice's sent bit | 1 | 0 | 1 | 0 |
| Eve's basis | H/V | H/V | D | D |
| Bob's detected bit | 1 or 0 | 1 or 0 | 1 | 0 |

Through examination of this table, you should be able to see that, on average, Eve will choose the wrong basis for her measurement 50% of the time. Of those times, on half of the occasions, Bob will measure the wrong bit value. So in Bob's resulting string, 25% of the bits will differ from Alice's. The answer can also be seen, more simply perhaps, by noting that half the time, Eve chooses the 'wrong' basis, and on half of those occasions she will transmit the 'wrong' value to Bob. Hence 25% of the bits received by Bob will differ from what Alice sent.

**Ex 7.7** Using the relationships in Equations 7.10,

$$\begin{aligned}|\Psi^-\rangle = \frac{1}{\sqrt{2}}\Big[&\big(\cos\theta\,|\mathrm{V}_\theta\rangle_\mathrm{A} - \sin\theta\,|\mathrm{H}_\theta\rangle_\mathrm{A}\big)\\ &\times\big(\sin\theta\,|\mathrm{V}_\theta\rangle_\mathrm{B} + \cos\theta\,|\mathrm{H}_\theta\rangle_\mathrm{B}\big)\\ &-\big(\sin\theta\,|\mathrm{V}_\theta\rangle_\mathrm{A} + \cos\theta\,|\mathrm{H}_\theta\rangle_\mathrm{A}\big)\\ &\times\big(\cos\theta\,|\mathrm{V}_\theta\rangle_\mathrm{B} - \sin\theta\,|\mathrm{H}_\theta\rangle_\mathrm{B}\big)\Big].\end{aligned}$$

Multiplying out the terms in this equation, we obtain

$$\begin{aligned}|\Psi^-\rangle = \frac{1}{\sqrt{2}}\Big[&\big(\cos\theta\sin\theta\,|\mathrm{V}_\theta\rangle_\mathrm{A}\,|\mathrm{V}_\theta\rangle_\mathrm{B}\\ &+\cos\theta\cos\theta\,|\mathrm{V}_\theta\rangle_\mathrm{A}\,|\mathrm{H}_\theta\rangle_\mathrm{B}\\ &-\sin\theta\sin\theta\,|\mathrm{H}_\theta\rangle_\mathrm{A}\,|\mathrm{V}_\theta\rangle_\mathrm{B}\\ &-\sin\theta\cos\theta\,|\mathrm{H}_\theta\rangle_\mathrm{A}\,|\mathrm{H}_\theta\rangle_\mathrm{B}\big)\\ &-\big(\sin\theta\cos\theta\,|\mathrm{V}_\theta\rangle_\mathrm{A}\,|\mathrm{V}_\theta\rangle_\mathrm{B}\\ &-\sin\theta\sin\theta\,|\mathrm{V}_\theta\rangle_\mathrm{A}\,|\mathrm{H}_\theta\rangle_\mathrm{B}\\ &+\cos\theta\cos\theta\,|\mathrm{H}_\theta\rangle_\mathrm{A}\,|\mathrm{V}_\theta\rangle_\mathrm{B}\\ &-\cos\theta\sin\theta\,|\mathrm{H}_\theta\rangle_\mathrm{A}\,|\mathrm{H}_\theta\rangle_\mathrm{B}\big)\Big].\end{aligned}$$

Collecting terms, the two $|\mathrm{V}_\theta\rangle_\mathrm{A}\,|\mathrm{V}_\theta\rangle_\mathrm{B}$ terms cancel, and so do the two $|\mathrm{H}_\theta\rangle_\mathrm{A}\,|\mathrm{H}_\theta\rangle_\mathrm{B}$ terms. Using $\sin^2\theta + \cos^2\theta = 1$ twice, once for the $|\mathrm{V}_\theta\rangle_\mathrm{A}\,|\mathrm{H}_\theta\rangle_\mathrm{B}$ term and once for the $|\mathrm{H}_\theta\rangle_\mathrm{A}\,|\mathrm{V}_\theta\rangle_\mathrm{B}$ term, we find that this equation simplifies to Equation 7.15.

**Ex 7.8** $P_{++}(\alpha,\beta)$ is the probability that, for a pair of photons, Alice finds a vertically-polarized photon when her analyzer is set at angle $\alpha$, and Bob finds a vertically-polarized photon with his analyzer at angle $\beta$. This probability is found by calculating the modulus squared of the inner product of $|\mathrm{V}_\alpha\rangle_\mathrm{A}|\mathrm{V}_\beta\rangle_\mathrm{B}$ (in which we temporarily restore the A and B labels before reverting to the positional convention) with the Bell state described by Equation 7.14:

$$\begin{aligned}P_{++}(\alpha,\beta) &= |\langle\mathrm{V}_\alpha\mathrm{V}_\beta|\Psi^-\rangle|^2\\ &= \left|\frac{1}{\sqrt{2}}\langle\mathrm{V}_\alpha\mathrm{V}_\beta|\Big(|\mathrm{VH}\rangle - |\mathrm{HV}\rangle\Big)\right|^2.\end{aligned}$$

(Remember that on each side of the inner product, the first term refers to particle A, the second to particle B, so that the kets on the right could be written $|\mathrm{V}\rangle_\mathrm{A}\,|\mathrm{H}\rangle_\mathrm{B} - |\mathrm{H}\rangle_\mathrm{A}\,|\mathrm{V}\rangle_\mathrm{B}$.) Recalling from Section 6.3.3 of Chapter 6 that we only take inner products for the same particle, we rewrite this equation as

$$\begin{aligned}P_{++}(\alpha,\beta) = \tfrac{1}{2}\big|&\langle\mathrm{V}_\alpha|\mathrm{V}\rangle_\mathrm{A}\langle\mathrm{V}_\beta|\mathrm{H}\rangle_\mathrm{B}\\ &-\langle\mathrm{V}_\alpha|\mathrm{H}\rangle_\mathrm{A}\langle\mathrm{V}_\beta|\mathrm{V}\rangle_\mathrm{B}\big|^2,\end{aligned}$$

where we have restored the particle labels to the inner products. Using the expressions in Equations 7.12 for these inner products, we find

$$\begin{aligned}P_{++}(\alpha,\beta) &= \tfrac{1}{2}\,|\cos\alpha\sin\beta - \sin\alpha\cos\beta|^2\\ &= \tfrac{1}{2}\sin^2(\alpha-\beta).\end{aligned}$$

**Ex 7.9** Substituting the values for $\alpha_1 = 0°$, $\alpha_3 = 45°$, $\beta_1 = 22.5°$ and $\beta_3 = -22.5°$ into Equation 7.18 gives for the first term $C(\alpha_1,\beta_1) = -\cos(2(0-22.5°))$. Doing the same for the other terms gives

$$\begin{aligned}\Sigma &= -\cos(-45°) - \cos(45°)\\ &\quad -\cos(45°) + \cos(135°)\\ &= -2\sqrt{2}.\end{aligned}$$

**Ex 7.10** Following the model just given, we have

$$\begin{aligned}P_{+-}(\alpha,\beta) = \big|\langle\mathrm{V}_\alpha\mathrm{H}_\beta|\mathrm{VH}\rangle\big|^2 &= \big|\langle\mathrm{V}_\alpha|\mathrm{V}\rangle_\mathrm{A}\langle\mathrm{H}_\beta|\mathrm{H}\rangle_\mathrm{B}\big|^2\\ &= \cos^2\alpha\cos^2\beta,\end{aligned}$$

$$\begin{aligned}P_{-+}(\alpha,\beta) = \big|\langle\mathrm{H}_\alpha\mathrm{V}_\beta|\mathrm{VH}\rangle\big|^2 &= \big|\langle\mathrm{H}_\alpha|\mathrm{V}\rangle_\mathrm{A}\langle\mathrm{V}_\beta|\mathrm{H}\rangle_\mathrm{B}\big|^2\\ &= \sin^2\alpha\sin^2\beta.\end{aligned}$$

**Ex 7.11** From Equations 7.2 with $\theta = \pi/4$, we have

$$|\mathrm{V}_{\pi/4}\rangle = \frac{1}{\sqrt{2}}\Big(|\mathrm{V}\rangle + |\mathrm{H}\rangle\Big),$$

from which we see first that both amplitudes are real so that $\overline{\phi} = 0$, and secondly that $\cos(\overline{\theta}/2) = \sin(\overline{\theta}/2) = 1/\sqrt{2}$ so that $\overline{\theta}/2 = \pi/4$ and hence $\overline{\theta} = \pi/2$. Similarly,

$$|\mathrm{H}_{\pi/4}\rangle = \frac{1}{\sqrt{2}}\Big(-|\mathrm{V}\rangle + |\mathrm{H}\rangle\Big).$$

The pair of values $\overline{\theta} = \pi/2$ and $\overline{\phi} = \pi$ yields

$$\frac{\mathrm{i}}{\sqrt{2}}\Big(-|\mathrm{V}\rangle + |\mathrm{H}\rangle\Big)$$

which is the required form, noting that the overall factor of i is irrelevant to the specification of the state vector.

**Ex 7.12** From the third and fourth rows of Table 7.2 we have in the first case $\beta\,|V\rangle_3 + \alpha\,|H\rangle_3$, and in the second $-\beta\,|V\rangle_3 + \alpha\,|H\rangle_3$.

**Ex 7.13** The state vector after the transformation is found by multiplying the initial state vector by the transformation matrix:

$$\begin{bmatrix} 0 & 1 \\ -1 & 0 \end{bmatrix} \begin{bmatrix} \gamma \\ \delta \end{bmatrix} = \begin{bmatrix} \delta \\ -\gamma \end{bmatrix}.$$

But $|\delta|^2 + |-\gamma|^2 = |\gamma|^2 + |\delta|^2 = 1$, so the normalization has been preserved.

**Ex 7.14** Using the appropriate matrix multiplication,

$$\begin{bmatrix} 0 & 1 \\ 1 & 0 \end{bmatrix} \begin{bmatrix} \beta \\ \alpha \end{bmatrix} = \begin{bmatrix} \alpha \\ \beta \end{bmatrix},$$

and the right-hand side represents the amplitudes defining $|\psi\rangle_1$.

**Ex 7.15** The 'before' state is $|H\rangle\,|a\rangle$. We see from Equation 7.34 that the subsequent state is, in two alternative forms,

$$\frac{1}{\sqrt{2}}|H\rangle\Big(i\,|c\rangle + |d\rangle\Big) = \frac{1}{\sqrt{2}}\Big(i\,|H\rangle\,|c\rangle + |H\rangle\,|d\rangle\Big).$$

**Ex 7.16** The structure of Equation 7.40 tells us that if (a) the two photons are detected in the same detector, then the overall state vector $|\Psi_{\text{out}}\rangle$ will collapse onto one of the first three terms, so that the joint polarization state of photons 1 and 2 will be one of the three Bell states $|\Phi^{\pm}\rangle_{12}$ or $|\Psi^{+}\rangle_{12}$ defined in Equations 7.31. On the other hand, if (b) the photons are detected in different detectors, then the overall state vector $|\Psi_{\text{out}}\rangle$ will collapse onto the fourth term, and the joint polarization state of photons 1 and 2 will be the Bell state $|\Psi^{-}\rangle_{12}$.

**Ex 7.17** Points would include the following.

1. Why transfer of quantum state is non-trivial: the uncertainty principle, the no-cloning theorem, and information contained in a qubit.
2. Input photon 1 to Alice.
3. Create entangled pair, photons 2 and 3.
4. Photon 2 to Alice, photon 3 to Bob.
5. Alice makes Bell state measurement on photons 1 and 2.
6. This measurement projects the joint state of photons 1 and 2, which can be expanded as a sum over the four Bell states, onto one of the Bell states.
7. Each of the four terms in the overall state corresponds to a state of photon 3; this state could be transformed to the state of photon 1 by operating upon it by one of four transformations. But which one?
8. Alice reports the results of Bell state measurement to Bob using classical means.
9. Alice never learns the state of photon 1.
10. Bob makes a transformation of the state of his photon depending on which of the four Bell states Alice measures, as communicated by Alice by classical means.
11. The nature and limitations of simple Bell state measurement (include diagram like Figure 7.11), as in the implementation of Zeilinger and collaborators.
12. With the scheme of Zeilinger and collaborators, there is successful teleportation only 25% of the time.
13. What teleportation is and what it is not. (It is the transportation of states, not of particles; it does not permit cloning since the initial state of a particle is destroyed.)

**Ex 8.1** (a) $\mathbf{r}_2 - \mathbf{r}_1$ is the displacement vector from point 1 to point 2; (b) $|\mathbf{r}_2 - \mathbf{r}_1|$ is the distance between points 1 and 2 and (c) $(\mathbf{r}_2 + \mathbf{r}_1)/2$ is the position vector of the point that is midway between points 1 and 2, on the line between these two points.

**Ex 8.2** We have

$$\begin{aligned} 3\mathbf{a} + 2\mathbf{b} &= 3(\mathbf{e}_x + 3\mathbf{e}_y) + 2(5\mathbf{e}_x - 7\mathbf{e}_y) \\ &= (3 + 10)\mathbf{e}_x + (9 - 14)\mathbf{e}_y \\ &= 13\mathbf{e}_x - 5\mathbf{e}_y. \end{aligned}$$

**Ex 8.3** We have

$$\mathbf{a}\cdot\mathbf{a} = (0.6)^2 + (0.8)^2 = 1,$$

$$\mathbf{b}\cdot\mathbf{b} = (-0.8)^2 + (0.6)^2 = 1,$$

$$\mathbf{a}\cdot\mathbf{b} = (0.6)\times(-0.8) + (0.8)\times(0.6) = 0.$$

so $\mathbf{a}$ is normalized, $\mathbf{b}$ is normalized and $\mathbf{a}$ is orthogonal to $\mathbf{b}$. The Cauchy–Schwarz inequality is easily satisfied since $|0| \leq 1 \times 1 = 1$.

**Ex 8.4** From Equation 8.5 we have

$$ab\cos\theta = -ab.$$

Hence, $\cos\theta = -1$ and $\theta = \pi$; the vectors point in opposite directions.

**Ex 8.5** Using Equation 8.15,

$$\mathbf{a}\times\mathbf{b} = \begin{vmatrix} \mathbf{e}_x & \mathbf{e}_y & \mathbf{e}_z \\ 3 & 4 & 0 \\ -4 & 3 & 0 \end{vmatrix}$$

$$= \begin{vmatrix} 4 & 0 \\ 3 & 0 \end{vmatrix}\mathbf{e}_x - \begin{vmatrix} 3 & 0 \\ -4 & 0 \end{vmatrix}\mathbf{e}_y + \begin{vmatrix} 3 & 4 \\ -4 & 3 \end{vmatrix}\mathbf{e}_z$$

$$= 0\,\mathbf{e}_x + 0\,\mathbf{e}_y + 25\,\mathbf{e}_z = 25\,\mathbf{e}_z.$$

**Ex 8.6** Point your right hand horizontally to the South in such a way that its fingers can bend horizontally to the West. Your outstretched right thumb then points downwards; this is the direction of $\mathbf{a}\times\mathbf{b}$.

**Ex 8.7** We have

$$\langle f|g\rangle^* = \left(\int_{-\infty}^{\infty} f^*(x)g(x)\,\mathrm{d}x\right)^*$$

$$= \int_{-\infty}^{\infty} f(x)g^*(x)\,\mathrm{d}x$$

$$= \int_{-\infty}^{\infty} g^*(x)f(x)\,\mathrm{d}x = \langle g|f\rangle.$$

**Ex 8.8** Since $t$ is real, $e_1^* = e_1$ and so we have

$$\langle e_1|e_2\rangle = \int_{-1}^{1} \sqrt{\frac{3}{2}}\,t \times \sqrt{\frac{5}{2}}\,\frac{1}{2}(3t^2-1)\,\mathrm{d}t = 0$$

because the integrand is an odd function, and the integral is over a range centred on $t = 0$.

**Ex 8.9** We have $\langle a| = \begin{bmatrix} 1 & -\mathrm{i} \end{bmatrix}$, so

$$\langle a|b\rangle = \begin{bmatrix} 1 & -\mathrm{i} \end{bmatrix}\begin{bmatrix} \mathrm{i} \\ 1 \end{bmatrix} = \mathrm{i} - \mathrm{i} = 0.$$

**Ex 8.10** For $\theta = 90°$, the rotation matrix is

$$\mathrm{R}(90°) = \begin{bmatrix} \cos 90° & -\sin 90° \\ \sin 90° & \cos 90° \end{bmatrix} = \begin{bmatrix} 0 & -1 \\ 1 & 0 \end{bmatrix},$$

so $\begin{bmatrix} 1 \\ 1 \end{bmatrix}$ is rotated to $\begin{bmatrix} 0 & -1 \\ 1 & 0 \end{bmatrix}\begin{bmatrix} 1 \\ 1 \end{bmatrix} = \begin{bmatrix} -1 \\ 1 \end{bmatrix}.$

**Ex 8.11** Two successive rotations through $\theta$ have the same effect as a single rotation through $2\theta$, so we must have

$$\begin{bmatrix} \cos(2\theta) & -\sin(2\theta) \\ \sin(2\theta) & \cos(2\theta) \end{bmatrix} = \begin{bmatrix} \cos\theta & -\sin\theta \\ \sin\theta & \cos\theta \end{bmatrix}\begin{bmatrix} \cos\theta & -\sin\theta \\ \sin\theta & \cos\theta \end{bmatrix}$$

$$= \begin{bmatrix} \cos^2\theta - \sin^2\theta & -2\sin\theta\cos\theta \\ 2\sin\theta\cos\theta & \cos^2\theta - \sin^2\theta \end{bmatrix}.$$

Hence, equating corresponding matrix elements,

$$\cos(2\theta) = \cos^2\theta - \sin^2\theta \quad\text{and}\quad \sin(2\theta) = 2\sin\theta\cos\theta.$$

**Ex 8.12** The characteristic equation is

$$\det(\mathrm{A} - \lambda\mathrm{I}) = \begin{vmatrix} -\lambda & -\mathrm{i} \\ \mathrm{i} & -\lambda \end{vmatrix} = 0,$$

so $\lambda^2 - (-\mathrm{i})(\mathrm{i}) = 0$, giving $\lambda = \pm 1$.

For $\lambda = +1$, the eigenvalue equation gives

$$\begin{bmatrix} -1 & -\mathrm{i} \\ \mathrm{i} & -1 \end{bmatrix}\begin{bmatrix} x_1 \\ x_2 \end{bmatrix} = \begin{bmatrix} 0 \\ 0 \end{bmatrix}$$

so $x_1 = -\mathrm{i}x_2$ and a suitable eigenvector is $\dfrac{1}{\sqrt{2}}\begin{bmatrix} 1 \\ \mathrm{i} \end{bmatrix}$.

For $\lambda = -1$, the eigenvalue equation gives

$$\begin{bmatrix} 1 & -\mathrm{i} \\ \mathrm{i} & 1 \end{bmatrix}\begin{bmatrix} x_1 \\ x_2 \end{bmatrix} = \begin{bmatrix} 0 \\ 0 \end{bmatrix}$$

so $x_1 = \mathrm{i}x_2$ and a suitable eigenvector is $\dfrac{1}{\sqrt{2}}\begin{bmatrix} \mathrm{i} \\ 1 \end{bmatrix}$.

**Ex 8.13** The characteristic equation is

$$\begin{vmatrix} 1-\lambda & 0 \\ 1 & 1-\lambda \end{vmatrix} = (1-\lambda)^2 = 0,$$

so the only eigenvalue is $\lambda = 1$. The corresponding eigenvector has components $x_1$ and $x_2$ satisfying

$$\begin{bmatrix} 0 & 0 \\ 1 & 0 \end{bmatrix}\begin{bmatrix} x_1 \\ x_2 \end{bmatrix} = \begin{bmatrix} 0 \\ 0 \end{bmatrix},$$

which gives $x_1 = 0$. So the corresponding eigenvector is $\alpha\begin{bmatrix} 0 \\ 1 \end{bmatrix}$, where $\alpha$ can be chosen to be equal to 1 for normalization.

# Index

Items that appear in the Glossary have page numbers in **bold type**. Ordinary index items have page numbers in Roman type.

## Complex numbers

$z = x + \mathrm{i}y = r\mathrm{e}^{\mathrm{i}\theta}$ $\quad z^* = x - \mathrm{i}y = r\mathrm{e}^{-\mathrm{i}\theta}$ $\quad |z|^2 = zz^* = x^2 + y^2 = r^2$

$\mathrm{Re}(z) = \dfrac{z + z^*}{2}$ $\quad \mathrm{Im}(z) = \dfrac{z - z^*}{2\mathrm{i}}$ $\quad z^n = r^n \mathrm{e}^{\mathrm{i}n\theta}$

$\mathrm{e}^{\mathrm{i}\theta} = \cos\theta + \mathrm{i}\sin\theta$ $\quad \cos\theta = \dfrac{\mathrm{e}^{\mathrm{i}\theta} + \mathrm{e}^{-\mathrm{i}\theta}}{2}$ $\quad \sin\theta = \dfrac{\mathrm{e}^{\mathrm{i}\theta} - \mathrm{e}^{-\mathrm{i}\theta}}{2\mathrm{i}}$

$\mathrm{e}^{\pm\mathrm{i}\pi} = -1$ $\quad \mathrm{e}^{\mathrm{i}\pi/2} = \mathrm{i}$ $\quad \mathrm{e}^{-\mathrm{i}\pi/2} = -\mathrm{i}$

## Elementary functions $(a > 0, b > 0)$

$\mathrm{e}^x\mathrm{e}^y = \mathrm{e}^{x+y}$ $\quad \ln a + \ln b = \ln(ab)$ $\quad \mathrm{e}^{\ln a} = \ln(\mathrm{e}^a) = a$

$\mathrm{e}^x = \cosh x + \sinh x$ $\quad \cosh x = \dfrac{e^x + \mathrm{e}^{-x}}{2}$ $\quad \sinh x = \dfrac{e^x - \mathrm{e}^{-x}}{2}$

$\cos(\theta \pm \pi) = -\cos\theta$ $\quad \sin(\theta \pm \pi) = -\sin\theta$ $\quad \tan(\theta \pm \pi) = \tan\theta$

$\cos(\theta + \pi/2) = -\sin\theta$ $\quad \sin(\theta + \pi/2) = \cos\theta$ $\quad \tan(\theta + \pi/2) = -\cot\theta$

$\cos(\theta - \pi/2) = \sin\theta$ $\quad \sin(\theta - \pi/2) = -\cos\theta$ $\quad \tan(\theta - \pi/2) = -\cot\theta$

$\cos(2\theta) = \cos^2\theta - \sin^2\theta$ $\quad \sin(2\theta) = 2\sin\theta\cos\theta$ $\quad \tan(2\theta) = 2\tan\theta/(1 - \tan^2\theta)$

$\sin(A \pm B) = \sin A\cos B \pm \cos A\sin B$ $\quad \cos(A \pm B) = \cos A\cos B \mp \sin A\sin B$

$\sin A\sin B = \tfrac{1}{2}\big(\cos(A - B) - \cos(A + B)\big)$ $\quad \cos A\cos B = \tfrac{1}{2}\big(\cos(A - B) + \cos(A + B)\big)$

$\sin A\cos B = \tfrac{1}{2}\big(\sin(A - B) + \sin(A + B)\big)$ $\quad \cos^2 A + \sin^2 A = 1$

## Physical constants

| | | | | | |
|---|---|---|---|---|---|
| Planck's constant | $h$ | $6.63 \times 10^{-34}\,\mathrm{J\,s}$ | Planck's constant/$2\pi$ | $\hbar$ | $1.06 \times 10^{-34}\,\mathrm{J\,s}$ |
| vacuum speed of light | $c$ | $3.00 \times 10^{8}\,\mathrm{m\,s^{-1}}$ | Coulomb law constant | $\frac{1}{4\pi\varepsilon_0}$ | $8.99 \times 10^{9}\,\mathrm{m\,F^{-1}}$ |
| permittivity of free space | $\varepsilon_0$ | $8.85 \times 10^{-12}\,\mathrm{F\,m^{-1}}$ | permeability of free space | $\mu_0$ | $4\pi \times 10^{-7}\,\mathrm{H\,m^{-1}}$ |
| Boltzmann's constant | $k$ | $1.38 \times 10^{-23}\,\mathrm{J\,K^{-1}}$ | Avogadro's constant | $N_\mathrm{m}$ | $6.02 \times 10^{23}\,\mathrm{mol^{-1}}$ |
| electron charge | $-e$ | $-1.60 \times 10^{-19}\,\mathrm{C}$ | proton charge | $e$ | $1.60 \times 10^{-19}\,\mathrm{C}$ |
| electron mass | $m_\mathrm{e}$ | $9.11 \times 10^{-31}\,\mathrm{kg}$ | proton mass | $m_\mathrm{p}$ | $1.67 \times 10^{-27}\,\mathrm{kg}$ |
| Bohr radius | $a_0$ | $5.29 \times 10^{-11}\,\mathrm{m}$ | atomic mass unit | $u$ | $1.66 \times 10^{-27}\,\mathrm{kg}$ |